Calculus

*for Students of Business
and Management*

Third Printing, June 1969

Calculus

for Students of Business and Management

BEVAN K YOUSE

Department of Mathematics
Emory University

ASHFORD W. STALNAKER

School of Industrial Management
Georgia Institute of Technology

INTERNATIONAL TEXTBOOK COMPANY
Scranton, Pennsylvania

Preface

The rapid expansion of curricula in management science and quantitative analysis in undergraduate and graduate programs of schools of business administration and management has created a new and growing demand for education in the fundamentals of calculus. It is for students in these programs that this text is intended. The student who does not plan to specialize in quantitative techniques, econometrics, or statistics at the graduate level will find the material well-suited for a terminal course in calculus. It is our opinion that if anything is to be gained from requiring the business student to study calculus, his course work should be sufficiently concentrated to insure a thorough understanding of rudimentary techniques. Other necessary noncalculus topics such as linear algebra, difference equations, and probability should be treated separately; accordingly these are not part of the present text.

Topics selected for inclusion are primarily those commonly used in solution of deterministic models. Within practical limits, however, these topics have been supplemented to provide completeness of coverage—on the premise that even though the student is enrolled in a business or management curriculum he will likely receive his mathematical training either in a mathematics department or from a mathematician teaching in the business school. For the same reason, although numerous business type examples and exercises are included they are presented in such a way that extensive training in management science is not necessary.

Proofs are omitted if they do not contribute to an understanding of the basic techniques of calculus. When, on the other hand, some further understanding is to be gained, detailed proofs are included, although these may in most cases be skipped without loss of continuity.

Certain portions of the textual material and some exercises and examples have been starred thus ★. All starred items may be omitted without affecting completion of the text. For example, the portion of Chapter 8 concerned with the trigonometric functions may be by-passed, since all subsequent examples and exercises using such functions are also starred.

The material should be adequate for a two-semester or two-quarter sequence. However, if less time is available, if a more leisurely pace is desirable, or if only an understanding of the essentials of differential and integral calculus is desired, the course may terminate with Chapter 8. If used for a refresher course, the material can easily be completed in one semester or quarter.

BEVAN K YOUSE
ASHFORD W. STALNAKER

Atlanta, Georgia
June, 1967

Contents

1. **The Real Number System** 1
   1-1. Sets 1
   1-2. Real Numbers 4
   1-3. Order 7
   1-4. Absolute Value and Inequalities 9

2. **Relations and Functions** 15
   2-1. The Rectangular Coordinate System 15
   2-2. Relations and Their Graphs 18
   2-3. Inverse of a Function.................................... 26
   2-4. Constant and Linear Functions........................... 29
   2-5. Quadratic Functions 33
   2-6. Algebra of Functions.................................... 39

3. **Sequences and Series** 43
   3-1. Sequences.. 43
   3-2. Series 44
   3-3. Infinite Geometric Series................................ 54

4. **Introduction to the Derivative** 57
   4-1. Slope.. 57
   4-2. The Limit Concept 59
   4-3. The Derivative.. 66

5. **Techniques of Differentiation** 73
   5-1. Derivative of the Sum of Two Functions 73
   5-2. Derivative of the Product of Two Functions 76
   5-3. Derivative of the Quotient of Two Functions 78
   5-4. Composite Function Theorem 83
   5-5. Higher Derivatives and Implicit Differentiation 85

6. **Applications of the Derivative** 90
   6-1. Increasing and Decreasing Functions 90
   6-2. Concavity and Inflection Points 93
   6-3. Maxima and Minima.. 97
   6-4. Mean Value Theorem 109
   6-5. Antiderivatives 112
   6-6. Differentials 113
   6-7. Newton's Method of Root Approximation.................... 116
   6-8. Taylor's Polynomials..................................... 119

7. Functions of Several Variables **123**
    7-1. Functions of Two Variables............................... 123
    7-2. Partial Derivatives 130
    7-3. The Total Differential.................................... 132
    7-4. Maxima and Minima...................................... 135
    7-5. Maxima and Minima with Constraints..................... 144

8. Exponential, Logarithm, and Trigonometric Functions **153**
    8-1. Differentiation of the Inverse of a Function 153
    8-2. Exponential and Logarithm Functions...................... 156
    ★8-3. Trigonometric Functions 165
    ★8-4. A Special Limit.. 169
    ★8-5. Differentiation of the Trigonometric Functions.............. 171
    ★8-6. Applications.. 172

9. Introduction to the Definite Integral **176**
    9-1. Area 176
    9-2. The Riemann Integral...................................... 181
    9-3. Fundamental Theorem of Calculus......................... 185

10. Techniques of Integration **193**
    10-1. Substitution 193
    10-2. Integration by Parts 198
    10-3. Partial Fractions 202
    ★10-4. Inverse Tangent Function................................ 208

11. More on Limits **211**
    11-1. L'Hôpital's Rule 211
    11-2. Infinite Limits 213
    11-3. Improper Integrals 216

12. Differential Equations **221**
    12-1. Introduction... 221
    12-2. Separable Equations 224
    12-3. Homogeneous Equations 226
    12-4. Exact Equations... 230
    12-5. Linear Equations.. 232
    12-6. Applications of Differential Equations 234

Tables **243**

Answers to Odd-Numbered Exercises.................................... **253**

Index **269**

1

The Real Number System

1-1. SETS

A *set* is a collection of distinct objects, the objects being called *elements*, or *members*, of the set. For example, consider the set of even integers; 2, 4, 6, and 8 are four of the elements in this set. Since a factor of 6 is any *integer* x such that $6 \div x$ is an integer, the set of positive factors of 6 contains 1, 2, 3, and 6 as its elements. Letters are often used as names for sets. If we let P be the set of all positive integers that have exactly two different positive factors, then P is the set of *prime* numbers; P contains such elements as 2, 3, 5, 7, 11, 13, 17, 19, 23, etc.

Sets may be defined by two methods: (1) by enumerating, or listing, the elements in the set or (2) by stating specific properties possessed by each element in the set. When defining a set by listing its elements, we enclose the names of the objects in the set in braces { }. For example, $T = \{1, 2, 3, 4\}$ is the set T whose elements are 1, 2, 3, and 4. If M is the set of all positive multiples of 3, then we can define M by $M = \{x \mid x$ is a multiple of 3} which is read "M is the set of all x such that x is a multiple of 3." The latter method is commonly used for defining sets that do not have a finite number of elements. However, a partial list of the elements is sometimes given to define a set with infinitely many elements. For example, the set M of positive multiples of 3 can also be defined by $M = \{3, 6, 9, 12, 15, 18, 21, 24, 27, \ldots\}$.

Two sets S and T are said to be *equal* if and only if they contain exactly the same elements. If sets S and T are equal, we write $S = T$. For example, if $S = \{1, 2, 4, 8\}$ and $T = \{x \mid x$ is a positive factor of 8}, then $S = T$. If two sets A and B do not contain the same elements, they are said to be *unequal* and this fact is denoted by $A \neq B$. It should be noted that a set is uniquely determined by its membership; thus, the order in which its elements are listed is immaterial. Consequently, $\{1, 2, 3, 6\} = \{3, 6, 2, 1\}$.

If E is the set of even integers, then 2 is an element of E. To indicate this membership, we write $2 \in E$, read "2 is in E," or "2 is an element in E." Since 7 is not an even integer, 7 is not in E; this fact is stated by $7 \notin E$. A symbol, usually a letter, used to represent any element of a set is called a *variable* on the set. If t represents any even integer, then t is a variable on the set E.

If $S = \{3, 5, 7, 9\}$ and $T = \{7, 9, 11, 13, 15\}$, then the set $W = \{3, 5, 7, 9, 11, 13, 15\}$ consisting of all the elements in S, in T, or in both S and T is called the *union* of S and T. The union of S and T is denoted by $S \cup T$, read "S union T"; symbolically, $W = S \cup T$. More generally, if S and T are any sets, $S \cup T$ is defined as

$$S \cup T = \{x \mid x \in S \quad \text{or} \quad x \in T\}.$$

(Note that "or" is used in the inclusive sense and not exclusive sense.) If E is the set of even integers and F is the set of odd integers, $E \cup F$ is the set of all integers.

The collection of all elements which are common to two sets S and T is called the *intersection* of S and T; it is denoted by "$S \cap T$," read "S intersection T." For example, if $S = \{3, 5, 7, 9\}$ and $T = \{7, 9, 11, 13\}$, then $S \cap T = \{7, 9\}$. In general, if S and T are any sets

$$S \cap T = \{x \mid x \in S \quad \text{and} \quad x \in T\}.$$

Since union and intersection can be considered as methods for constructing sets from two given sets, they are often called *set operations*.

We postulate the existence of a set with no elements called an *empty set* and represented by the symbol ϕ. Two sets are said to be *disjoint* if they have no elements in common. Thus if S and T are disjoint sets, $S \cap T = \phi$. For example, if E is the set of even integers and F is the set of odd integers, $E \cap F = \phi$.

If $S = \{2, 3\}$ and $T = \{1, 2, 3, 4, 5\}$, then S and T not only have elements in common but every element in S is in T. In this case, we say that S is a *subset* of T and denote this fact by $S \subseteq T$. More generally, $S \subseteq T$ if and only if $x \in S$ implies $x \in T$. Notice that every element in a set T is in T; thus, T is a subset of T by definition. If S is a subset of T and if T contains at least one element not in S, then S is called a *proper subset* of T; symbolically, $S \subset T$. In other words, $S \subset T$ if and only if $S \subseteq T$ and $S \neq T$. Since the empty set ϕ contains no elements, it is vacuously true that every element in ϕ is in any given set S; thus, ϕ is a subset of any set S.

Usually, throughout a given discussion one only considers sets that are subsets of some given set; this given set is called the *universal* set. For example, since we have discussed only subsets of the set of positive integers in this section, it would be considered the universal set for our discussion.

If I is a universal set, there is a convenient way to picture operations on subsets of I. We draw a rectangle and let the interior of the rectangle represent the universal set. Within the rectangle, we draw circles and let the interiors and exteriors of these circles represent subsets of I. We hachure (shade) the regions in the rectangle that represent the subsets being considered. For example, if A and B are subsets of I, then we draw intersecting circles in the interior of the rectangle to represent these sets. The subset $A \cap B$ is represented by the points in the rectangle that are in the interior of both circle A and circle B. (See Fig. 1-1.) Such pictorial representations of subsets of a universal set I are called *Venn diagrams*.

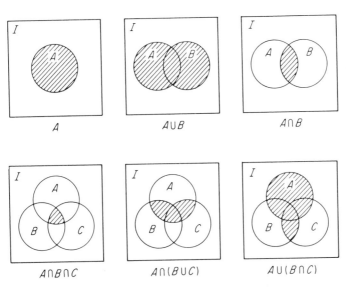

FIG. 1-1. Venn diagrams.

EXERCISES

Let $A = \{1, 2, 3, 4, 5, 6\}$; $B = \{x \mid x$ is a positive factor of 6$\}$; $C = \{3, 7, 11\}$; and $D = \{x \mid x$ is a positive multiple of 5$\}$.

1. List the elements of set B.
2. List all the subsets of set C.
3. Describe each of the following sets.
   (a) $A \cup B$ (b) $A \cap B$ (c) $D \cup C$
   (d) $D \cap C$ (e) $A \cup C$ (f) $A \cap C$.
4. Which of the following are true?
   (a) $B \subseteq A$ (b) $B \subset A$ (c) $5 \in C$
   (d) $3 \notin B$ (e) $\phi \subset A$ (f) $3 \subseteq (A \cap B)$.
5. Give the number of subsets of each of the following sets.
   (a) $\{1\}$ (b) $\{1, 2\}$ (c) $\{1, 2, 3\}$ (d) $\{1, 2, 3, 4\}$
   (e) $\{1, 2, 3, 4, 5, 6, \ldots, n\}$, where n is a positive integer.

Let E be the set of positive even integers; F be the set of positive odd integers; $S = \{2, 4, 6\}$; $T = \{3, 5, 7\}$; and $W = \{1, 2, 3\}$.

6. List all the subsets of S.

7. Describe each of the following sets.
   (a) $S \cap W$ (b) $S \cap T$ (c) $T \cap W$ (d) $S \cup W$
   (e) $T \cup W$.

8. Describe each of the following sets.
   (a) $S \cap E$ (b) $T \cap F$ (c) $S \cap F$ (d) $W \cap F$
   (e) $S \cup E$ (f) $T \cup F$.

9. Which of the following are true?
   (a) $S \subset T$ (b) $S \subset E$ (c) $S \subset F$ (d) $\phi \subset W$
   (e) $T \subset S$ (f) $E \cap F = \phi$.

10. A firm plans to make a color solution from four color dyes. If each color solution is to contain equal amounts of the color dyes used in that solution, how many different color solutions can be obtained?

11. Let S and T be sets with a finite number of elements. If $n(S) = a$ and $n(T) = b$ are the number of elements in S and T, respectively, and if $n(S \cap T) = c$ is the number of elements in the intersection of S and T, how many elements are there in $(S \cup T)$?

12. In a sample group of 500 persons it was found that each used one or both of Product A and Product B. Furthermore, it was found that 376 used Product A and 412 used Product B. How many used both? (See Exercise 11.)

13. A dairy manufactures several flavors of ice cream. It has found that 87 percent of its customers buy vanilla or chocolate, 58 percent prefer vanilla only, and 62 percent prefer chocolate. What percentage of customers liked both ice-cream flavors? (See Exercises 11 and 12.)

14. Let R, S, and T be sets. Show that

$$n(R \cup S \cup T) = n(R) + n(S) + n(T) - n(R \cap S)$$
$$- n(R \cap T) - n(S \cap T) + n(R \cap S \cap T).$$

HINT: Use a Venn diagram.

15. Suppose 462 families own at least one of three different makes of automobiles and no family owns as many as two cars of the same make. If 228 families own an "A" make, 258 own a "B" make, 332 own a "C" make, and 310 families own at least two of the makes, (a) how many of these 462 families own all three kinds of cars? (See Exercise 14.) (b) How many own only two cars? (c) How many own only one car?

1-2. REAL NUMBERS

The mathematical structure of calculus has as its foundation the set of real numbers. In elementary and secondary schools, a considerable amount of time is spent in the study of various subsets of the set of real numbers and learning to perform basic arithmetic operations on the members of these subsets. The subsets of the set of real numbers of major interest are the set of positive integers, the set of integers, the set of rationals, the set of irrationals, and, of course, the set of reals.

One of the important subsets of the set of real numbers is the set of positive integers, $\{1, 2, 3, 4, 5, 6, 7, \ldots\}$. (NOTE: Although zero is an integer, it is not considered to be positive or negative.) We are familiar with the fact that the sum and product of two positive integers is itself a positive integer; we express this by saying that the set of positive integers is *closed* with respect to both addition and multiplication. In general, for any set S and a given operation, S is said to be *closed* with respect to the given operation if another element in the set is obtained by performing the operation on any two elements in the set. For example, since the sum or product of any two even integers is an even integer, the set of even integers is closed with respect to both addition and multiplication. The set of prime numbers is not closed with respect to addition, since there are at least two prime numbers whose sum is not a prime number; for example, $3 + 7 = 10$, but 10 is not a prime number.

The positive integers can be associated with points on a line. Let P be a fixed point on a given horizontal line. The points obtained by marking off equal segments to the right of P are associated with the positive integers: 1 is associated with the right-hand end point of the first segment, 2 with the right-hand end point of the second segment, etc. The number associated with a point on a line is called the *coordinate* of the point.

The integer 0 is assigned as the coordinate of point P, the fixed point on the number line which is called the *origin* of the *coordinate* system. The numbers $-1, -2, -3, -4, \ldots$ are negative integers. If equal segments to the left of the origin are marked off as in Fig. 1-2, then -1 is associated with the left-hand end point of the first segment to the left of 0, -2 is associated with the left-hand end point of the second segment to the left of 0, etc. The set consisting of the positive integers, negative integers, and zero is the set of *integers*. A main distinction between the set of positive and the set of negative integers is the fact that the set of positive integers is closed with respect to multiplication but the set of negative integers is not closed with respect to multiplication.

The operations of subtraction and division are defined in terms of addition and multiplication. If for any two numbers a and b in a set there exists one and only one number c in the set such that $a + c = b$, then c is called the *difference* of b subtract a; symbolically, $b - a = c$. For example, since $2 + 7 = 9$, we conclude that $9 - 2 = 7$.

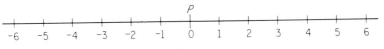

FIG. 1-2. The number line.

If for any two numbers a and b in a set there exists one and only one number c in the set such that $ac = b$, then c is called the *quotient* of b divided by a; symbolically, $b \div a = c$. Since $2 \times 13 = 26$, we conclude that $26 \div 2 = 13$. Furthermore, since $6 \times 0 = 0$, $0 \div 6 = 0$. In fact, if $a \neq 0$ then $0 \div a = 0$. As a consequence of the fact that any number multiplied by zero is zero, there is no number c such that $0 \times c = 6$; thus, $6 \div 0$ is undefined. In general, if $a \neq 0$ then $a \div 0$ is undefined. Furthermore, since *any* number multiplied by zero is zero, there is more than one number c such that $0 \times c = 0$; hence, $0 \div 0$ is also undefined. In summary, *division by zero is an excluded operation as a consequence of the definition of division.*

Another important subset of the set of real numbers is the set of *rational numbers.* This set consists of numbers that can be expressed as the ratio of two integers p and q where $q \neq 0$. The notation p/q is the *fractional notation* for rational numbers; the reader should be familiar with other notations for rational numbers such as the mixed numeral notation and the decimal notation. For example, $5/4 = 1\frac{1}{4} = 1.25$. Rational numbers can also be associated with points on a line. For example, to find the point associated with $18/7$, we divide the unit segments into 7 equal parts and associate the number $18/7$ with the right-hand end point of the 18th such segment to the right of zero. A point on the number line with a rational number as coordinate is called a *rational point.* (See Fig. 1-3.)

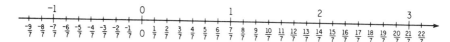

FIG. 1-3. Rational points.

The operations of addition, subtraction, multiplication, and division are called the *rational operations.* The set of rational numbers is closed with respect to all of the rational operations, except division by zero.

There are points on the number line that are not rational points. If x represents the length of the hypotenuse of a right triangle with sides each one unit in length, by the Pythagorean theorem $x^2 = 1^2 + 1^2 = 2$. (See Fig. 1-4.) It is not too difficult to prove that no rational number p/q exists such that $(p/q)^2 = 2$. The positive real number whose square is 2 is called an *irrational number* and is denoted by $\sqrt{2}$. There are infinitely many irrational numbers. For example, $\sqrt{7}$, $\sqrt[15]{11}$, $1 + \sqrt{3}$, $\sqrt[4]{6}$ and π are irrational numbers.

The set of *real numbers* is the union of the set of rational and the set of irrational numbers, and we assume that the set of real numbers is in one-to-one correspondence with the points on the coordinate line. In other words, exactly one real number is associated with each point on

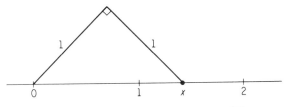

FIG. 1-4. $x^2 = 1^2 + 1^2 = 2$ and $x = \sqrt{2}.$

the number line and exactly one point on the number line is associated with each real number. Because of this complete identification of real numbers with points on the line, we often say "consider the point 7" instead of saying "consider the point with 7 as its coordinate."

The set of real numbers satisfies certain basic properties with respect to addition and multiplication which are called *field properties*. We complete this section by listing these properties.

1. *Closure property of addition.* A real number $x + y$ called the *sum* is uniquely determined for every pair of real numbers x, y.

2. *Commutative property of addition.* For every pair of real numbers x and y, $x + y = y + x$.

3. *Associative property of addition.* For all real numbers x, y, and z, $x + (y + z) = (x + y) + z$.

4. *Additive identity.* There exists a real number denoted by 0 called the additive identity such that $x + 0 = x$ for every real number x.

5. *Additive inverses.* For every real number x, there exists a real number called the additive inverse of x and denoted by $-x$ such that $x + (-x) = 0$.

6. *Closure property of multiplication.* A real number xy called the *product* is uniquely determined for every pair of real numbers x, y.

7. *Commutative property of multiplication.* For every pair of real numbers x and y, $xy = yx$.

8. *Associative property of multiplication.* For all real numbers x, y, and z, $x(yz) = (xy)z$.

9. *Multiplicative identity.* There exists a real number different from 0 denoted by 1, called the multiplicative identity, such that $x \cdot 1 = x$.

10. *Multiplicative inverses.* For every real number $x \neq 0$, there exists a real number called the multiplicative inverse of x and denoted by x^{-1} (or $1/x$) such that $x \cdot x^{-1} = 1$.

11. *Distributive property.* For all real numbers x, y, and z, $x(y + z) = xy + xz$.

1-3. ORDER

Let a and b be real numbers. If there exists a positive number x such that $a + x = b$, then a is said to be *less than* b, denoted by $a < b$. For example, $2 < 7$, $0 < \pi$, and $-25 < -3$. Geometrically, if P and Q are two points on the number line with coordinates a and b, respectively, then $a < b$ if and only if P is to the left of Q. We say that b is *greater than a*, denoted by $b > a$, if and only if $a < b$. Furthermore, $a \leq b$ if and only if $a < b$ or $a = b$, and $a \geq b$ if and only if $a > b$ or $a = b$. The relations $a < b$, $a > b$, $a \leq b$, and $a \geq b$ are called *inequalities*.

If a firm manufactures a single product that requires exactly 2 lb of a scarce raw material of which only 2,000 lb are available for the next production period, the number of units of the product which may be manufactured (which we shall denote by x) must satisfy the inequalities $x \geq 0$ and $2x \leq 2,000$.

If an investment is believed to have a potential rate of return of at least 6 percent but no more than 15 percent, then the rate of return R must satisfy both of the inequalities $6 \leq R$ and $R \leq 15$.

If a and b are real numbers, then one and only one of the following is true: $a < b$, $a = b$, or $a > b$. This is called the *trichotomy* property and it states geometrically that a is to the left of b, a is the same point as b, or a is to the right of b.

Another important property is that if $a < b$ and $b < c$, then $a < c$. This is called the *transitive property* and it states geometrically that on the number line if a is to the left of b and b is to the left of c, then a is to the left of c. We give a proof of this property.

If $a < b$, then there is a number $x > 0$ such that

$$a + x = b. \tag{1}$$

If $b < c$, then there is a number $y > 0$ such that

$$b + y = c. \tag{2}$$

(Note that the number y need not be different from x, but since it could be it is necessary to use different letters.)

Substituting Eq. 1 in Eq. 2,

$$(a + x) + y = c$$

and

$$a + (x + y) = c$$

by the associative property of addition. Since the sum $(x + y)$ of two positive numbers is a positive number, $a < c$ as a consequence of the definition of "less than."

Let S be any subset of the set of real numbers. Suppose there exists a number t such that $x \leq t$ for every x in S; then, the number t is called an *upper bound* for the set S. For example, if S is the set $\{2, 11, 19\}$, then, since every number in S is less than 40, we conclude that 40 is an upper bound of S. Of course, 100, 75, and 19 are also upper bounds of S. If T is the set of real numbers x such that $x < 5$, then any real number greater than or equal to 5 is an upper bound of T. If $W = \{x \mid x \leq 5\}$, then any real number greater than or equal to 5 is an upper bound of W. Note that the set of upper bounds for the two different sets T and W is the same.

Let S be an ordered set. If there exists an element t in S such that $t \leq x$ for every x in S, then t is called the *least* element in S. If the set of upper bounds of a set S has a least number z, then z is said to be the *least upper bound* of S. For the three preceding examples, the least upper bound of S is 19, the least upper bound of T is 5, and the least upper bound of W is 5. It should be noted that the least upper bound of a given set may or may not be an element in the set.

A set of numbers need not have an upper bound. For example, consider the set of positive integers, the set of rational numbers, the set of real numbers, or the set of even integers; none of these sets has an upper bound. However, *if a set of real numbers has an upper bound, then the set has a least upper bound.* This is called the *completeness property* for the real number system. The completeness property is the main distinguishing feature between the set of rational and set of real numbers. For example, it can be proved that although the set of positive rational numbers x such that $x^2 < 2$ has an upper bound, this set does not have a *rational* least upper bound. However, the set of positive real numbers x such that $x^2 < 2$ does have a real least upper bound; it is $\sqrt{2}$.

EXERCISES

1. Explain why division by zero is an excluded operation.
2. Which of the following are true statements?
   (a) $2 < 17$ (b) $-47 > -0.13$ (c) $19/27 < 200/297$
   (d) $23/164 < 29/205$.
3. What is the additive inverse of each of the following real numbers?
   (a) 13   (b) $-2/3$ (c) $-\sqrt{3}$ (d) 0.
4. What is the multiplicative inverse of each of the following real numbers?
   (a) 13   (b) $-2/3$ (c) $-\sqrt{3}$ (d) 0.1
   (e) Does 0 have a multiplicative inverse?
5. State the least upper bound of each of the following sets of real numbers.
   (a) $\{1, -15, 4/63, 11\}$
   (b) $\{x \mid x$ is a real number and $x < 1\}$
   (c) $\{y \mid y$ is a real number and $y \leq 1\}$
   (d) $\{t \mid t$ is an integer and $t < 1\}$
   (e) $\{x \mid x$ is a real number, $0 < x$, and $x^2 < 3\}$.

1-4. ABSOLUTE VALUE AND INEQUALITIES

If P and Q are points on the real line with coordinates a and b, respectively, such that $a \leq b$, then the nonnegative number $b - a$ is the

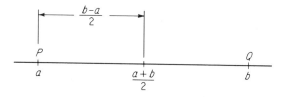

Fɪɢ. 1-5. Midpoint.

distance between P and Q. If P is to the left of Q, then $b - a$ is positive and $(b - a)/2$ is half the distance from P to Q. Hence, the sum $a + \dfrac{b - a}{2} = \dfrac{a + b}{2}$ is the coordinate of the *midpoint* between P and Q.

If P and Q have coordinates 2 and 7, respectively, the distance between P and Q is $7 - 2 = 5$ and the coordinate of the midpoint between P and Q is $(2 + 7)/2 = 9/2$. (See Fig. 1-5.)

If x is a real number such that $x > a$ and $x < b$, then x is between a and b and this is denoted by $a < x < b$. If $S = \{x \mid a < x < b\}$, then S is called an *open interval*; it is often denoted by (a, b). The set T defined by $T = \{x \mid a \leq x \leq b\}$ contains a and b in addition to the numbers in S and is called a *closed interval*; it is often denoted by $[a, b]$. The set $\{x \mid a \leq x < b\}$ (or $\{x \mid a < x \leq b\}$) is an interval but it is neither open nor closed. The set $\{x \mid x < a \text{ or } x > b\}$ is not an interval. If W is a set of real numbers, the points on the coordinate line with the real numbers as coordinates is called the *graph* of W. (See Fig. 1-6.)

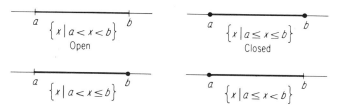

Fɪɢ. 1-6. Intervals.

Let P be a point with x as coordinate. If $x \geq 0$, then $x - 0 = x$ is the distance of P from the origin. If $x < 0$, then $0 - x = -x$ is the distance of P from the origin. (Notice that if $x < 0$ then $-x$ is positive.) The distance of P from the origin is called the *absolute value* of the real number x and is denoted by $|x|$. More precisely,

$$|x| = x \quad \text{if} \quad x \geq 0$$

and

$$|x| = -x \quad \text{if} \quad x < 0.$$

Hence

$$|6| = 6, \ |-17| = -(-17) = 17, \text{ and } |1 - \sqrt{3}| = \sqrt{3} - 1.$$

If $S = \{x \mid |x| = 6\}$, then S is the set of real numbers whose distances from the origin is 6. Thus $S = \{6, -6\}$. If $T = \{x \mid |x| < 6\}$, then T is the set of points whose distances from the origin is less than 6. Thus, T is the set of real numbers x such that

$$-6 < x < 6.$$

Geometrically, $|x - 4|$ is the distance between the points with x and 4 as coordinates. Thus, the real numbers satisfying $|x - 4| < 3$ are the coordinates of the points whose distances from 4 are less than 3; that is, $x < 7$ and $x > 1$. The real numbers x satisfying $|x + 5| > 2$ also satisfy $|x - (-5)| > 2$. This is the set of coordinates of the points whose distances from (-5) are greater than 2; that is, $x > -3$ or $x < -7$. Algebraically, $|x + 5| > 2$ if and only if

$$x + 5 > 2 \quad \text{or} \quad x + 5 < -2,$$
$$x > -3 \quad \text{or} \quad x < -7.$$

Since $|x| = -x$ if $x < 0$ and $|x| = x$ if $x \geq 0$, it follows that $-|x| = x$ if $x < 0$ and $|x| = x$ if $x \geq 0$. Hence we conclude

$$-|x| \leq x \leq |x|$$

for any real number x. Similarly, for any real number y we conclude

$$-|y| \leq y \leq |y|.$$

Consequently,

$$-(|x| + |y|) \leq x + y \leq |x| + |y|.$$

This is equivalent to what is called the *triangular inequality*:

$$|x + y| \leq |x| + |y|.$$

In algebra, we learn that the *solution set* of a quadratic equation such as $x^2 - x - 6 = 0$ is the set of real numbers x which makes the equality a true statement. For this example the solution set is $\{3, -2\}$. The solution set of the quadratic inequality $x^2 - x - 6 < 0$ is the set of all real numbers which make the inequality a true statement. We use the quadratic formula to solve quadratic equations; we now discuss methods to solve linear, quadratic, and other inequalities.

To solve an equation such as $2x + 6 = 20$, we subtract 6 from both sides of the equality and then divide both sides by 2. To solve the inequality $2x + 6 < 20$, we actually do the same thing; that is,

$$2x < 14$$
$$x < 7.$$

The solution set is $\{x \mid x < 7\}$. Not all operations defined for equalities are valid for inequalities; thus, before pursuing the methods for solving more general inequalities we state the important properties pertinent to the solution of inequalities. These properties can be proved from the definition of the less-than relation and the properties of real numbers in much the same way used to prove the transitive property of inequality. The proofs are left as exercises.

    Property 1. If $a < b$, then $a + c < b + c$. (You can add the same number to both sides of an inequality without changing the sense of the inequality.)

    Property 2. If $a < b$, then $a - c < b - c$. (You can subtract the same number from both sides of an inequality without changing the sense of the inequality.)

    Property 3. If $a < b$ and $c > 0$, then $ac < bc$. (You can multiply both sides of an inequality by the same positive number without changing the sense of the inequality.)

    Property 4. If $a < b$ and $c < 0$, then $ac > bc$. (You change the sense of an inequality if you multiply both sides by a negative number.)

    Property 5. If $a < b$ and $c < d$, then $a + c < b + d$.

    Property 6. If $a < b$ and $ab > 0$, then $1/a > 1/b$. (If both sides of an inequality have the same sign, you change the sense of the inequality when you take the reciprocal of each side.)

    Consider the inequality $3x + 5 < 10x + 11$. If there are real numbers x satisfying

$$3x + 5 < 10x + 11,$$

then

$$3x - 10x < 11 - 5 \text{ by Property 2.}$$

Also,

$$-7x < 6 \text{ and } x > -6/7 \text{ by Property 4.}$$

We have shown that if there are any real numbers satisfying the inequality then they are greater than $-6/7$. Since all the "steps" are reversible, we can assert that all numbers greater than $-6/7$ satisfy the inequality; hence, $\{x \mid x > -6/7\}$ is the solution set. The graph of this solution set is all points on the real number line to the right of the point with $-6/7$ as coordinate.

    Example 1. Solve $\dfrac{7x + 5}{x - 3} < 2$.

    First Solution: If $x - 3 > 0$, then $(7x + 5) < 2(x - 3)$ by Property 3. Thus

$$7x + 5 < 2x - 6$$
$$5x < -11$$
$$x < -11/5.$$

    Hence, the solution set would consist of real numbers x such that $x - 3 > 0$ (or $x > 3$) and $x < -11/5$. Since no real numbers satisfy both of these inequalities, there are no solutions where $x - 3 > 0$.

Obviously, there are no solutions where $x - 3 = 0$. If $x - 3 < 0$ (or $x < 3$), then $(7x + 5) > 2(x - 3)$ by Property 4. Also,

$$7x + 5 > 2x - 6$$
$$5x > -11$$
$$x > -11/5.$$

The real numbers that are less than 3 and greater than $-11/5$ make the inequality a true statement. Thus, the solution set is $\{x \mid -11/5 < x < 3\}$.

Second Solution: If $\dfrac{7x + 5}{x - 3} < 2$, then $\dfrac{7x + 5}{x - 3} - 2 < 0$.

$$\frac{7x + 5 - 2x + 6}{x - 3} < 0$$

$$\frac{5x + 11}{x - 3} < 0.$$

For the quotient to be negative (< 0), then either

$5x + 11 < 0$ and $x - 3 > 0$ or	$5x + 11 > 0$ and $x - 3 < 0$
$5x < -11$ and $x > 3$	$5x > -11$ and $x < 3$
$x < -11/5$ and $x > 3$	$x > -11/5$ and $x < 3$
(No solutions.)	Thus, $-11/5 < x < 3$.

Example 2. Suppose the total cost of two different mowers A and B is \$372. If it is known that the total cost of 3 of the A mowers and 7 of the B mowers is no more than \$2,204, what is the minimum cost of mower A?

Solution: Let x be the cost of mower A. Thus, the cost of B is $372 - x$. Now

$$3x + 7(372 - x) \leq 2,204$$
$$3x + 2,604 - 7x \leq 2,204$$
$$-4x \leq -400$$
$$x \geq 100.$$

Thus A must cost at least \$100.

EXERCISES

For Exercises 1 through 14 find the solution set.

1. $3x + 5 < 2x + 17$.

2. $7x - 23 < 22x - 15$.

3. $(x + 3)(2x - 3) < 0$.

4. $(2x + 1)(3x - 5) > 0$.

5. $\dfrac{2x + 1}{3x - 7} < 0$.

6. $\dfrac{2x + 1}{3x - 11} > 15$.

7. $\dfrac{2x + 16}{4x + 5} < \dfrac{5x + 13}{10x + 2}$.

8. $|3x - 1| < 5$.

9. $|7x + 12| < 6.$

10. $\dfrac{3x + 11}{2x + 7} < 0.$

11. $|x^2 + 3| + |x^2 - 1| > 0.$ **12.** $|5x + 6| \geq 5.$

13. $x^2 < x.$ **14.** $(2x - 1)(3x + 2)(5x + 10) > 0.$

15. A manufacturer has available exactly 20,000 lb of a raw material required in the manufacture of two different Products A and B. Let x and y be the number of units produced of each, respectively. If Product A requires 7 lb of the raw material and Product B requires 12 lb, find the inequality which expresses the upper bound on total production.

16. Assume that the total cost of two watches, A and B, is $100. If it is known that 5 watches of type A and 3 watches of type B can be bought for $424 or less, what is the maximum cost of the type A watch?

17. Two trucks must make deliveries totaling 100 miles. Truck A gets 15 miles per gallon of fuel and Truck B gets 10 miles per gallon. If total fuel consumption is to be no more than 8 gal, what is the minimum number of miles Truck A must travel?

★18. Let S be a set of real numbers. Assume there is a real number t such that $x \geq t$ for every x in S; the number t is called a *lower bound* of S. If T is the set of all lower bounds of S and if T contains a greatest number w, then w is called the *greatest lower bound* of S. Prove that a nonempty set of real numbers S with a lower bound has a greatest lower bound. HINT: Let $R = \{-x \mid x \in S\}$ and prove that if t is a lower bound of S then it is an upper bound of R. Use the completeness property.

★19. Prove that $|x|^2 = x^2$.

★20. Prove Property 1 for inequalities.

★21. Prove Property 2 for inequalities.

★22. Prove Property 3 for inequalities.

★23. Prove Property 4 for inequalities.

★24. Prove Property 5 for inequalities.

★25. Prove Property 6 for inequalities.

2

Relations and Functions

2-1. THE RECTANGULAR COORDINATE SYSTEM

An *ordered pair* of real numbers is denoted by (x, y).* The number x is called the *first coordinate*, or *first element*, and the number y is called the *second coordinate*, or *second element*. Two ordered pairs (x, y) and (u, v) are equal if and only if $x = u$ and $y = v$.

A method has already been discussed for associating real numbers with points on a line. Now we consider a method for associating ordered pairs of real numbers with points in a plane.

Draw two number lines in a plane, one horizontal and one vertical, intersecting at right angles at their origins. The standard orientation is to have the positive direction to the right for the horizontal number line and the positive direction upward for the vertical number line. (See Fig. 2-1.) The two number lines are called *coordinate axes*. The horizontal coordinate axis is the *x-axis*, or *first coordinate axis*, and the vertical coordinate axis is the *y-axis*, or *second coordinate axis*.

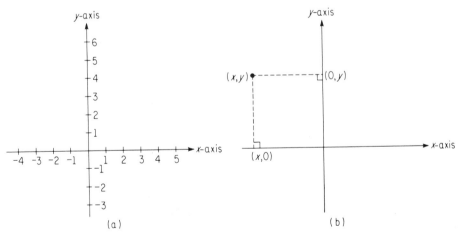

FIG. 2-1. (a) Rectangular coordinate system. (b) Coordinates of points in the plane.

*Although the same notation is also used to denote an open interval, it should be clear in context which is intended.

If x is the real number associated with a given point on the x-axis (the horizontal number line), then the ordered pair $(x, 0)$ is associated with this point in the plane. If y is the real number associated with a given point on the y-axis, then the ordered pair $(0, y)$ is associated with this point. If P is any point in the plane not on either of the coordinate axes, if $(x, 0)$ represents the point at the foot of the perpendicular drawn from P to the x-axis, and if $(0, y)$ represents the point at the foot of the perpendicular drawn from P to the y-axis, then the ordered pair (x, y) is associated with the point P. This gives us a method for corresponding in a one-to-one fashion the set of points in the plane and the set of all ordered pairs of real numbers; that is, exactly one ordered pair of real numbers is associated with a particular point in the plane and exactly one point in the plane is associated with an ordered pair of real numbers.

The coordinate system for the plane just described was developed by the French mathematician René Descartes (1596–1650) and is called the *rectangular coordinate system* or the *cartesian coordinate system*.

Let P and Q be two different points in the plane with cartesian co-ordinates (a, b) and (c, d), respectively. (See Fig. 2-2.) The distance between P and R is $|c - a|$ and the distance between R and Q is $|d - b|$. Since PQ is the hypotenuse of a right triangle, it follows from the Pythagorean theorem that the distance between P and Q is

$$|PQ| = \sqrt{(c - a)^2 + (d - b)^2}.$$

To form the right triangle in Fig. 2-2, it is necessary to assume that the line containing P and Q is not parallel to either axis. If $b = d$, the line containing P and Q is parallel to the x-axis and the distance between (a, b) and (c, b) is obviously $|c - a|$. Since $\sqrt{(c - a)^2} = |c - a|$,

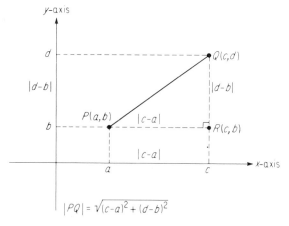

FIG. 2-2. Length of line segment.

the distance formula is valid when $b = d$. Similarly, the formula is valid when $a = c$. If P and Q are not two different points, the distance is defined to be 0; in this case, $a = c$ and $b = d$ and the distance formula gives the desired result.

Let (a, b) and (c, d) be two points in the plane such that $a \neq c$ and $b \neq d$. (See Fig. 2-3.) Let (x, y) be the coordinates of the midpoint of the

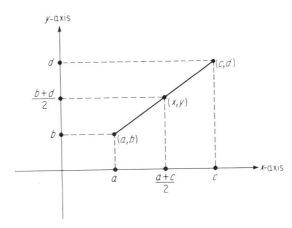

FIG. 2-3. Midpoint of line segment.

line segment joining the two points. The orthogonal projection of the point (x, y) onto the x-axis is the midpoint of the line segment on the x-axis with a and c as coordinates. Hence

$$x = \frac{a + c}{2}.$$

Similarly,

$$y = \frac{b + d}{2}.$$

Thus

$$\left(\frac{a + c}{2}, \frac{b + d}{2} \right)$$

are the coordinates of the midpoint of the segment joining (a, b) and (c, d). If $a = c$ or $b = d$, it is easy to verify that the midpoint formula is still valid.

EXERCISES

1. Graph the following ordered pairs of real numbers in the rectangular coordinate plane: $(2, 3)$, $(-7, -4)$, $(\sqrt{3}, 0)$, $(-1, -1)$, $(-3, 3)$, $(-1/2, 11/3)$.

2. Let (a, b) be some point in the coordinate plane different from the origin $(0,0)$. Show that $(0,0)$, (a, b), $(c,0)$, and $(a + c, b)$ are vertices of a parallelogram in the coordinate plane if $c \neq a$ and $c \neq 0$. Prove that the diagonals bisect each other by finding the midpoint of each diagonal.

3. (a) Use the distance formula to find the lengths of the sides of the triangle with $(-3, -1)$, $(2, 5)$, and $(5, 5/2)$ as vertices. (b) Use the Pythagorean theorem to prove that the triangle is a right triangle. (c) Find the area of the triangle.

4. (a) Find the midpoint of the line segment joining $(3,7)$ and $(8,15)$. (b) Use the distance formula to prove that the midpoint is equidistant from the two given points.

5. Let A, B, and C be points with coordinates $(-3, -4)$, $(3,0)$, and $(12,6)$ respectively. Prove that the sum of the distances from A to B and B to C is the distance from A to C. Interpret geometrically.

6. Prove that the point $(-3,10)$ is on the perpendicular bisector of the line segment whose end points are $(1, -3)$ and $(8, 2)$.

7. (a) Using the distance formula and the Pythagorean theorem, prove that the points $(3,0)$, $(5,6)$, and $(6, -1)$ are vertices of a right triangle. (b) Find the area of the triangle.

8. In developing the wiring design for a new computer, a manufacturer specifies that each of three components is to be the same distance from the power source. When a rectangular coordinate system is imposed on the connection panel it is found the three components are located at $(-4, 3)$, $(2, -1)$ and $(3, 4)$; where should the power terminal be placed?

2-2.   RELATIONS AND THEIR GRAPHS

We now consider sets whose elements are ordered pairs of real numbers; such a set is called a *relation.* The set of all first coordinates in a relation is called the *domain* of the relation, and the set of all second coordinates is called its *range.* For example, if $F = \{(2, 3), (\sqrt{3}, -6),$ or $(0, 3)\}$, then the set F is a relation. The domain of F is $\{2, \sqrt{3}, 0\}$ and the range is $\{3, -6\}$.

Since a relation is a set, there are two general methods for defining relations: (1) by listing the ordered pairs in the set and (2) by stating properties that determine the ordered pairs in the set. If $S = \{(x, y) \mid x$ is a real number and $y = 3x + 1\}$ (read "S is the set of all ordered pairs x, y such that x is a real number and $y = 3x + 1$") then S is a relation. Since $4 = 3(1) + 1$, we conclude that $(1, 4) \in S$. In fact, the relation S has infinitely many elements; some of them are $(-2, -5)$, $(\sqrt{3}, 3\sqrt{3} + 1)$, $(0, 1)$, $(2, 7)$, and $(-1/3, 0)$. Since $7 \neq 3(11) + 1$, $(11, 7) \notin S$.

The set of all points in the coordinate system determined by the ordered pairs of real numbers in a relation F is called the *graph* of the relation.

As we have indicated earlier, the letters used to define a relation (set) are immaterial. If $T = \{(s, t) \mid t = 3s + 1\}$ and $S = \{(x, y) \mid y = 3x + 1\}$, then $S = T$. Of course in graphing T, the first coordinate axis, or horizontal axis, would be the s-axis and the second coordinate axis, or vertical axis, would be the t-axis. (See Fig. 2-4.) A symbol, such as s, used to

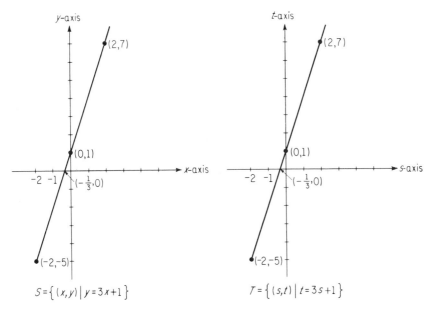

Fig. 2-4. $S = T$.

denote numbers in the domain of a function is called the *independent variable*, and a symbol, such as t, used to denote numbers in the range of a function is called the *dependent variable*. The variable t "depends" on s in the sense that a given number in the domain uniquely determines a number in the range.

Throughout this text, we focus our study on a very special class of relations called *real functions*. A *function* F is a relation such that no two different pairs in the relation have the same first coordinates. Functions whose domains and ranges are subsets of real numbers are called *real functions*. As a consequence of the agreement to discuss only real functions, we observe the common practice of using "function" for "real function."

There is a simple geometric method to determine if a relation is a function. A set of points in the rectangular coordinate plane such that no two points are on a line parallel to the y-axis (range axis) is the graph of a function. In other words, any line parallel to the y-axis intersects the graph of a function in *at most* one point. Although a function associates with each real number in the domain one and only one number in the range, it is not necessary for two ordered pairs in a function to have distinct second coordinates. We cannot assert that every function associates with each number in the range one and only one number in the domain. Geometrically, although lines parallel to the *y*-axis intersect the graph of a function in at most one point, lines parallel to the *x*-axis may intersect the graph of a function in more than one point.

Let *f* be the function defined as follows: $f = \{(x, x^2) \mid x$ is a real number$\}$. The domain of *f* is the set of all real numbers and the range is the set of nonnegative real numbers. (See Fig. 2-5.) We use the notation

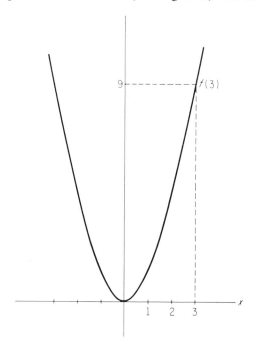

FIG. 2-5. $f(x) = x^2$.

$f(x)$ (read "*f* of *x*," or "the value of *f* at *x*") to denote the number in the range of *f* paired with *x* in the domain. For example, since $(3, 9) \in f$, $f(3) = 9$. This is a very useful notation since it gives us a simpler method to define many functions. For example, we use the equation $f(x) = x^2$ to define *f*; it is understood that the domain is any real number *x* for which $f(x)$ is a real number. Of course, the equation $y = x^2$ could also be used to determine the ordered pairs in *f*.

When we say "Let *g* be defined by $g(x) = \sqrt{3x + 1}$," it is understood that the domain is $\{x \mid x \geq -1/3\}$ since if $x < -1/3$ then $3x + 1 < 0$ and $\sqrt{3x + 1}$ is not a real number. If $x \geq -1/3$, then $\sqrt{3x + 1}$ is a real number.

A function can be thought of as a method for associating a number in its range with a number in its domain. In this context, it is often called a *mapping*. If f is the function defined by $f(x) = x^2$, then f is also called a mapping of the set of real numbers (domain) into the set of nonnegative real numbers (range). Sometimes, one writes "$f: x \rightarrow x^2$," read "f maps x into x^2." Although we shall avoid this added terminology and notation, the student should be familiar with it since he may encounter it in his other reading.

In the application of mathematics to business decision problems the first coordinate is frequently referred to as a *real decision variable* and the second is called the *value of the decision*. For example, if the operating costs of a factory are given by

$$T(x) = \$10,000 + \$50x,$$

where x represents the level of production in units, x would be a real decision variable. The choice of a specific value of x, say 100, yields a decision value of $15,000.

Much business data can be looked upon as a real-valued function with time increments for its domain and subsets of the real numbers as its range. However, the rule which assigns to a point in the domain the corresponding value in the range may be exceedingly complex or may not be determinable. For example, the monthly sales data of a large department store might be expressed as a function as follows.

SALES
(Millions of Dollars)

x	Jan.	Feb.	Mar.	Apr.	May	June	July	Aug.	Sept.	Oct.	Nov.	Dec.
$f(x)$	9.1	8.3	12.2	7.8	9.6	11.4	5.5	5.6	6.0	7.9	10.6	13.7

Each ordered pair consists of a month and the sales for that month. It should be noted that January, February, etc. are not members of the real number system but instead are nonnumeric representations of time increments, where the increments are each one month long. Thus a subset of the set of positive integers can be taken as the domain of the function.

It should be evident that a function called *monthly sales* is discrete in the sense that it possesses values only at the points on the real line where the first members of the ordered pairs are integers. The graph of this function is shown in Fig. 2-6.

Frequently the graph of such a function is shown as a *bar graph* in

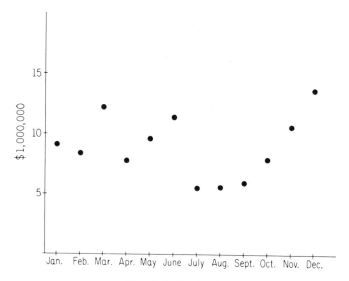

Fig. 2-6. Graph of f.

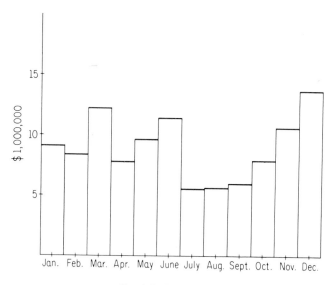

Fig. 2-7. Bar graph.

order to improve comprehension. (See Fig. 2-7.) However, it must be remembered that values for f exist only at the integer points of the scale, which are the centers of the base of the bars. To further improve comprehension and to facilitate comparisons to earlier time periods the discrete points of the graph are often joined by line segments, such as is shown in

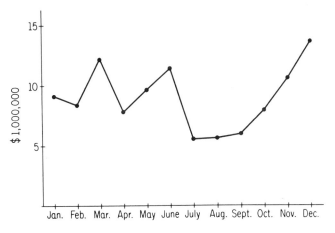

Fig. 2-8. Line graph.

Fig. 2-8. This is called a *line graph*. One should not mistakenly assume from this line drawing that if we go half the distance between the January and February coordinates and then up to the graph that sales for the first half of February were 8.7 millions. There is no point with 1.5 in the domain of the function and therefore $f(1.5)$ does not exist.

An example of another function using the same data is the cumulative sales function g, where $g(x)$ is the total sales for the year up to and including the month x.

x	Jan.	Feb.	Mar.	Apr.	May	June	July	Aug.	Sept.	Oct.	Nov.	Dec.
$g(x)$	9.1	17.4	29.6	37.4	47.0	58.4	63.9	69.5	75.5	83.4	94.0	107.7

The graph of this function might be shown as a modified bar graph or by a line graph, both of which are shown in Fig. 2-9.

We have only discussed functions where the first coordinate in each ordered pair is a real number. A function f could be a set of ordered pairs where the first coordinates are themselves ordered pairs of real numbers. For example, $\{((x,y),t) \mid t = x^2 + 5y^2$ where x and y are integers$\}$ is a function. The domain of f is a set of ordered pairs of integers and the range of f is a set of nonnegative integers. This is an example of what is called a *function of two variables*. A discussion of such functions is given in Chapter 7. Unless otherwise stated, the term "function" will refer only to a real function whose first and second coordinates are real numbers; such functions are sometimes called *real functions of one variable*.

Functions that have particular significance in the development of mathematics are given special names to distinguish them. One such func-

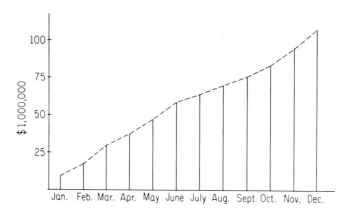

FIG. 2-9. Line graph of *g*.

tion is the *identity function I*; it is defined by $I(x) = x$. The graph of the identity function is the straight line containing the origin and the point $(1, 1)$. (See Fig. 2-10.)

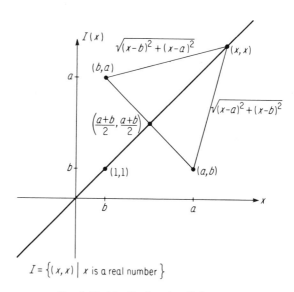

$$I = \left\{ (x, x) \mid x \text{ is a real number} \right\}$$

FIG. 2-10. Identity function $I(x) = x$.

If (a, b) is any point in the coordinate plane not on the graph of the identity function (that is, $a \neq b$), then let us consider a geometric method to locate the point (b, a). The distance of any point (x, x) on the graph of the identity function from (a, b) is

$$\sqrt{(x - a)^2 + (x - b)^2}.$$

Similarly, the distance between (x, x) and (b, a) is
$$\sqrt{(x - b)^2 + (x - a)^2}.$$
Since $\sqrt{(x - a)^2 + (x - b)^2} = \sqrt{(x - b)^2 + (x - a)^2}$, every point on the graph of the identity function is equidistant from (a, b) and (b, a). In other words, the graph of the identity function is the perpendicular bisector of the line segment joining (a, b) and (b, a). Hence (a, b) and (b, a) are symmetrically placed with respect to the graph of the identity function.

EXERCISES

In Exercises 1 through 10, answer each of the following questions: (a) Is the relation a function? (b) What is the domain of the relation? (c) What is the range of the relation?

1. $f = \{(2, 7), (3, 8), (4, 2)\}$.

2. $g = \{(3, 1), (5, 1), (-3, 17)\}$.

3. $H = \{(3, y) \mid y \text{ is a real number}\}$.

4. $G = \{(x, y) \mid x \text{ is an integer and } x^2 + y^2 = 25\}$.

5. $f = \{(x, x^2 + 4) \mid x \text{ is a real number}\}$.

6. $f = \{(x, 5) \mid x \text{ is a real number}\}$.

7. f is defined by $f(x) = \sqrt{3x + 11}$.

8. f is defined by $f(x) = \sqrt{2x - 3}$.

9. f is defined by $f(x) = \sqrt{\dfrac{2x + 1}{3x - 5}}$.

10. f is defined by $f(x) = \sqrt{x^2 - 9}$.

11. If f and g are functions defined by $f(x) = x^2 + 5x$ and $g(x) = 2x - 7$, find each of the following.

    (a) $f(3) + g(-2)$ (b) $f(1/3) \div g(5)$

    (c) $f(t) - f(2)$ (d) $\dfrac{f(t) - f(2)}{t - 2}, t \neq 2$.

12. (a) A function f is called an *even function* if whenever x is in the domain, $-x$ is in the domain and $f(-x) = f(x)$. What can be said about the graph of an even function? (b) A function f is called an *odd function* if whenever x is in the domain, $-x$ is in the domain and $f(-x) = -f(x)$. What can be said about the graph of an odd function? (c) Give an example of an even function. (d) Give an example of an odd function. (e) Give an example of a function that is neither even nor odd.

13. Let f and g be functions defined by $f(x) = 3x + 7$ and $g(x) = 5x + 13$. (a) For what real number x is $f(x) = g(x)$? (b) For what real numbers is $f(x) < g(x)$?

14. A firm manufactures and sells a single product. Let the maximum production be K units per time period, let the total manufacturing and marketing cost be c dollars per unit, and let each unit be sold for p dollars.

Assuming the firm can sell its total production, state the relation which gives the firm's total profit per time period. State the domain and range of this relation. Is it a function?

2-3. INVERSE OF A FUNCTION

Let f be a function. The relation defined by

$$g = \{(b, a) \mid (a, b) \in f\}$$

is called the *inverse relation* of f. If no two different ordered pairs of f have the same second coordinates, then the inverse relation g is a function. This function g is called the *inverse function of f* and is usually denoted by f^{-1}. (NOTE: "-1" is not an exponent and f^{-1} does not mean $1/f$.) Geometrically, the graphs of a function f and its inverse function f^{-1} are mirror images with respect to the graph of the identity functions. (See Fig. 2-11.)

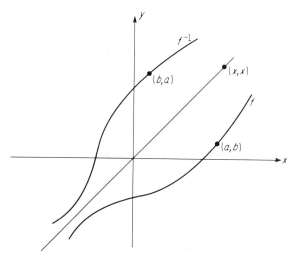

FIG. 2-11. Graphs of f and f^{-1} are symmetric to graph of the identity function.

Let f be a function with an inverse function f^{-1}. If $(a, b) \in f$, then $b = f(a)$; furthermore, $(b, a) \in f^{-1}$ and $f^{-1}(b) = a$. It is important to remember for inverse functions f and f^{-1} that $f(a) = b$ if and only if $f^{-1}(b) = a$.

Obviously, the inverse relation of a function need not be a function. If F is defined by $F(x) = x^2$, then $(2, 4)$ and $(-2, 4)$ are two elements in F with the same second coordinates; thus the inverse of F is not a function. However, if we restrict the domain of F and define a different function f by $f(x) = x^2$, where x is any nonnegative real number, then the inverse

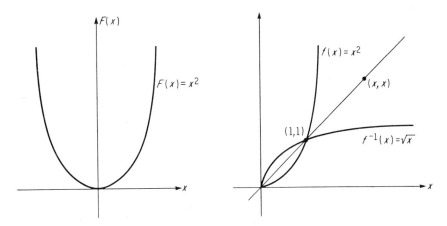

Fig. 2-12. Graphs of f and f^{-1}.

of f is a function. (See Fig. 2-12.) We call the inverse of f the *square root function* and use $\sqrt{x}$ to represent the number in the range of f^{-1} paired with x in the domain; thus, $f^{-1}(x) = \sqrt{x}$. (NOTE: $\sqrt{x} \geq 0$.)

Let g be the function defined by $g(x) = 3x + 7$. If $g(a) = g(b)$, then $3a + 7 = 3b + 7$ and $a = b$. Thus the function g cannot have two different ordered pairs with the second coordinates equal; the inverse of g is a function. We would like a formula, if one exists, for finding $g^{-1}(x)$ for each x in the domain of g^{-1}. Such a formula can be found by substituting x for $g(x)$ and $g^{-1}(x)$ for x in the equation $g(x) = 3x + 7$ and then solving for $g^{-1}(x)$. That is,

$$x = 3g^{-1}(x) + 7,$$
$$3g^{-1}(x) = x - 7.$$

Hence

$$g^{-1}(x) = \frac{x - 7}{3}.$$

Notice that $g(2) = 13$ and $g^{-1}(13) = 2$; in general, if $g(a) = b$, then $g^{-1}(b) = a$.

Example 1. The "break-even point" is defined as the level of sales at which the total profit is zero. If costs are considered to consist only of a fixed cost which does not vary with the level of production and of a constant cost for production of each unit, usually called *variable cost*, the total cost of production may be expressed as

Total production cost =

　　　fixed cost + (variable cost)(number units produced)

Profit is defined as total revenue minus total production cost where total revenue is sales price per unit multiplied by the number of units sold.

Letting FC be the fixed cost, VC the variable cost, p the sales price per unit and x the number of units sold, the total cost function C and revenue function R are defined by

$$C(x) = FC + (VC)(x)$$
$$R(x) = p \cdot x.$$

Since profit is defined as $R(x) - C(x)$ and the break-even point is that level of sales at which profit is zero, we find the break-even point by letting

$$R(x) - C(x) = 0.$$

That is,

$$p \cdot x - (FC + VC \cdot x) = 0,$$

$$x = \frac{FC}{p - VC}.$$

The last equation defines x as a function of p; that is,

$$x = f(p) = \frac{FC}{p - VC}.$$

The difference $p - VC$ is called the *incremental return per unit of sales*. Thus the quotient $\dfrac{FC}{p - VC}$ states how many times this increment must be earned in order to pay the fixed costs.

If, rather than computing the sales break-even point, we wish to determine the break-even sales price if the production quantity is at some fixed level we compute the inverse function f^{-1}. Solving $x = \dfrac{FC}{p - VC}$ for p, we obtain

$$p = \frac{FC + (VC)(x)}{x}.$$

Thus

$$f^{-1}(x) = \frac{FC + (VC)(x)}{x}.$$

EXERCISES

For each of the functions in Exercises 1 through 12, answer the following questions: Is the inverse relation a function? If so, define the inverse function f^{-1} by listing its elements or by giving a formula for $f^{-1}(x)$.

1. $f = \{(3,7), (5,8), (11,2)\}$.
2. $f = \{(3,5), (7,5), (-3,17)\}$.
3. f is defined by $f(x) = x$.
4. f is defined by $f(x) = 5x - 7$.

5. f is defined by $f(x) = 6x + 11$.
6. f is defined by $f(x) = x^4$.
7. f is defined by $f(x) = x^2 + 4$.
8. f is defined by $f(x) = \sqrt{3x + 11}$.
9. f is defined by $f(x) = \sqrt{2x - 3}$.

10. f is defined by $f(x) = \dfrac{3x + 6}{2x - 3}$.

11. f is defined by $f(x) = \dfrac{x + 1}{x}$ for $x \neq 0$ and $f(0) = 1$.

12. f is defined by $f(x) = \dfrac{7x + 11}{4x - 7}$.

13. (a) Let f be a function defined by $f(x) = \dfrac{ax + b}{cx - a}$. Prove that the inverse of f is a function and $f^{-1} = f$. (b) What can be concluded about the graph of a function f where $f^{-1} = f$?

★14. In each of the following, give an example of a function satisfying the equality for every pair of numbers in its domain.

(a) $f(x + y) = f(x) + f(y)$ (b) $g(xy) = g(x) \cdot g(y)$
(c) $F(x + y) = F(x) \cdot F(y)$ (d) $G(xy) = G(x) + G(y)$.

★15. (a) If f is a function with the set of all real numbers as its domain and if $f(xy) = f(x) + f(y)$ for every pair x and y in the domain, prove that f is the constant function with $\{0\}$ as its range. (b) Prove that even if zero is not in the domain of f that $f(1) = 0$ and $f(-1) = 0$. (c) Prove that even if zero is not in the domain of f the function is an even function. (d) If zero is not in the domain of f prove that $f(1/x) = -f(x)$ for every x in the domain.

2-4. CONSTANT AND LINEAR FUNCTIONS

Let c be a real number. The function f defined by $f(x) = c$ is called a *constant function*. For example, if $f(x) = 2$, then f is the constant function whose range is $\{2\}$ and whose graph is the set of all points in the coordinate plane with 2 as second coordinate. (See Fig. 2-13.) The graph of a constant function is continuous in the sense that there are no "gaps" in the line. A precise and nongeometric definition of continuity of functions is given in Sec. 4-2; however, for our purposes this geometric and intuitive idea of continuity will suffice at this time.

Consider the line determined by the points Q and R with coordinates $(2, 3)$ and $(8, 5)$, respectively. (See Fig. 2-13.) Let (x, y) be the coordinates of any point P on the line distinct from Q and R. The right triangles PQT and RQS obtained by drawing lines through P, Q, and R parallel to the coordinate axes are similar; hence the lengths of the corresponding sides

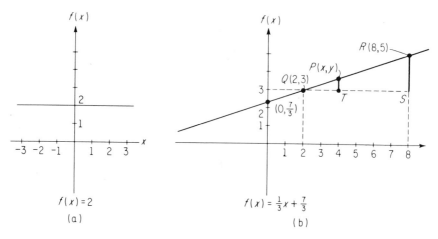

FIG. 2-13. (a) Constant function. (b) Linear function.

of the triangles are proportional. Thus

$$\frac{|RS|}{|QS|} = \frac{|PT|}{|QT|}.$$

Now

$$|RS| = 5 - 3 = 2,$$
$$|QS| = 8 - 2 = 6,$$
$$|PT| = y - 3,$$

and

$$|QT| = x - 2.$$

Consequently

$$\frac{2}{6} = \frac{y-3}{x-2}. *$$

Simplifying,

$$x - 2 = 3(y - 3),$$
$$x - 3y = -7$$

or

$$y = \frac{1}{3}x + \frac{7}{3}.$$

We have proved that the coordinates (x, y) of any point P, different from Q and R, which is on the line containing $(2,3)$ and $(8,5)$ satisfy the equation $y = \frac{1}{3}x + \frac{7}{3}$. By direct substitution, it is evident that $(2,3)$ and

*If (x, y) is on the other side of $(2, 3)$, $|PT| = 3 - y$ and $|QT| = 2 - x$. But since $\frac{3-y}{2-x} = \frac{y-3}{x-2}$, this equation is true provided (x, y) is different from $(2, 3)$.

(8, 5) satisfy this equation; thus, the coordinates of *any* point on the line satisfy the equation. We leave as an exercise for the reader to prove that if a point (a, b) is not on the line, then $b \neq \frac{1}{3}a + \frac{7}{3}$; that is, the coordinates do not satisfy the equation. We conclude that the line containing $(2, 3)$ and $(8, 5)$ is the graph of the function f defined by

$$f = \left\{ (x, y) \mid y = \frac{1}{3}x + \frac{7}{3} \right\}.$$

If L is any nonvertical line in the coordinate plane and if P and Q are two points on the line with coordinates (a, b) and (c, d), respectively, then the number

$$\frac{d - b}{c - a}$$

is uniquely determined; that is, the number is independent of the points chosen on L. (The proof of this fact is left as an exercise for the reader.) The ratio $\frac{d - b}{c - a}$ is called the *slope* of the line L and is usually denoted by m. (See Fig. 2-14.) Although any nonvertical line possesses a unique slope, a given slope does not determine a unique line, since all parallel lines have the same slope—another fact for the reader to verify. The slope

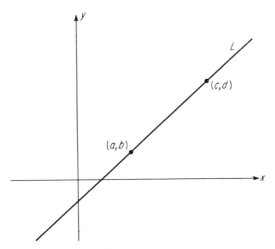

FIG. 2-14. Slope of line L: $m = (d - b)/(c - a)$.

of a line parallel to the x-axis is zero, lines "leaning to the right" have positive slope, and lines "leaning to the left" have negative slope. For a line parallel to the y-axis, the slope is not defined.

If a function f is defined by $y = mx + b$, or $f(x) = mx + b$, where

m and b are real numbers and $m \neq 0$, then f is called a *linear function*. The graph of this function is a straight line. If s and t are any two distinct numbers in the domain of f, then $f(s) = ms + b$ and $f(t) = mt + b$. Furthermore, $(s, ms + b)$ and $(t, mt + b)$ are distinct points on the graph of f. Since

$$\frac{(ms + b) - (mt + b)}{s - t} = \frac{m(s - t)}{s - t} = m,$$

the slope of the graph of f is m. Also, since $f(0) = b$, $(0, b)$ is a point on the graph of f. Consequently, the graph of the linear function f defined by $f(x) = mx + b$ is the straight line with slope m that crosses the y-axis at $(0, b)$. It is often said that the line has b as its *y-intercept*.

Suppose we buy 3 copies of the same book for \$18. If there is no discount or reduction in price for buying in quantity, the sale price of each book is $18/3 = \$6$. If we buy 6 books, the cost would be \$36; that is, if we double the number of books bought, then the total cost is doubled. If T is the total cost of x number of books purchased, then $T/x = 6$, or $T = 6x$. We say that the total cost is *directly proportional* to the number bought. (Direct proportionality implies that they are not "cheaper by the dozen.") In general, if $y = mx$, we say that y is directly proportional to x and that m is the *constant of proportionality*. Geometrically, if y is directly proportional to x, the graph of the function defined is a straight line through the origin having the constant of proportionality as its slope.

EXERCISES

1. Let f be the function defined by $f(x) = 7$. (a) Graph f. (b) What is the slope of the graph of f?

2. Let G be a function defined by $G(x) = 4x - 7$. (a) What is the slope of the graph of G? (b) What is the y-intercept of the graph? (c) Is the point $(5, -4)$ on the graph of G? (d) If $(a, 7)$ is a point on the graph of G, what is a? (e) If $(-3, b)$ is a point on the graph of G, what is b?

3. Graph each function f defined as follows.

    (a) $f(x) = 5x - 3$ (b) $f(x) = -3x + 2$

    (c) $f(x) = \frac{2}{3}x + 4$ (d) $f(x) = -\frac{4}{3}x - 11$.

4. Define the linear function f having the straight line containing $(5, 3)$ and $(-7, 5)$ as its graph.

5. Graph the straight line having y-intercept 6 and slope $-2/5$. Define the linear function having this line as its graph.

6. Graph the straight line containing the point $(-3, 7)$ and having $7/3$ as its slope. Define the linear function having this line as its graph.

7. Let f and g be two functions defined by $f(x) = 4x + 7$ and $g(x) = 3x - 11$. (a) Find the real number t such that $f(t) = g(t)$.

(b) Since f and g are sets, list the elements common to both sets and interpret geometrically.

8. Prove that if the point (a, b) is not on the line containing the points $(2, 3)$ and $(8, 5)$, then $b \neq \frac{1}{3}a + \frac{7}{3}$.

9. Prove that nonvertical parallel lines have the same slope.

10. Let (a, b) and (c, d) be any two points on a nonvertical line in the coordinate plane. Prove that the number $\frac{d - b}{c - a}$ is independent of the points chosen on the line.

11. Graph each of the following on the same coordinate system.
   (a) $f = \{(x, y) \mid 3x - 2y - 7 = 0\}$
   (b) $g = \{(x, y) \mid 2x + 3y - 6 = 0\}$
   (c) $\{(x, y) \mid (3x - 2y - 7) + t(2x + 3y - 6) = 0\}$ where $t = 1, t = 1/2, t = -1/2, t = 3, t = -4,$ and $t = -2$.

12. Assume the total cost of a manufacturing process follows a linear relation $f(x) = F + Vx$, where F is the fixed cost of providing the production facility and is independent of the level of production; V is the variable or unit cost of producing one item; and x is the number of units produced. (a) If the fixed cost of the plant is $75,000 per month and each unit requires 2 man-hours at $2.25 per hour and raw materials valued at $3, find $f(x)$. (b) What is $f(15,000)$, the total cost of producing 15,000 units per month? (c) What is the unit cost of producing 15,000 units a month?

2-5. QUADRATIC FUNCTIONS

The techniques of calculus are very useful in analyzing the graphs of functions. However, before we turn our attention to these techniques and to the general study of functions, let us consider one more special function for which the techniques of algebra are sufficient to determine important features of its graph.

Let f be defined by $f(x) = ax^2 + bx + c$ where a, b, and c are real numbers and $a \neq 0$; f is called a *quadratic function.* The simplest quadratic function is one for which $a = 1, b = 0,$ and $c = 0$; that is, $f(x) = x^2$. The quadratic function $f(x) = x^2$ is an even function since $f(-x) = f(x)$; thus, its graph is symmetric to the y-axis. Furthermore, since $f(0) = 0$ and since $f(x) = x^2 > 0$ if $x \neq 0$, the least number in the range of f is 0. We call 0 the absolute minimum of the function.

Let F be any function. If there is a number u in the domain of F such that $F(u) \leq F(x)$ for every x in the domain of F, then $F(u)$ is called the *absolute minimum of F.* Although the function is said to have a minimum at u, the number u need not be unique; for example, the constant function $f(x) = c$ has c as its absolute minimum at *every* number in the domain. Similarly, if there exists a number v in the domain such that $F(v) \geq F(x)$ for every x, then $F(v)$ is called the *absolute maximum of F*. As for the absolute minimum, the number v that makes the function a maximum need not be unique. As we have indicated, if f is defined by $f(x) = x^2$ for all real x, then f has 0 as its absolute minimum at 0 but f has no absolute maximum.

Let f be any function having t in its domain. If there exists an interval in the domain of f containing t such that

$$f(x) < f(t) \text{ if } x < t$$

and

$$f(x) > f(t) \text{ if } x > t,$$

then f is said to be *increasing* at t. If $f(x) \leq f(t)$ for $x < t$ and $f(x) \geq f(t)$ for $x > t$, it is said that f is a *nondecreasing* function at t. For $f(x) = x^2$, if $t > 0$, then there exists an interval containing t (for example, $0 < t < 2t$) such that for every x in the interval

$$f(x) < f(t) \text{ if } x < t$$

and

$$f(x) > f(t) \text{ if } x > t.$$

Consequently, f is an increasing function at any number t such that $t > 0$. We often say that f increases on $\{x \mid x > 0\}$.

Let f be any function having t in its domain. If there exists an interval in the domain of f containing t such that

$$f(x) > f(t) \text{ if } x < t$$

and

$$f(x) < f(t) \text{ if } x > t,$$

then f is said to be *decreasing* at t. If $f(x) \geq f(t)$ for $x < t$ and $f(x) \leq f(t)$ for $x > t$, f is said to be a *nonincreasing* function at t. For $f(x) = x^2$, if $t < 0$, then there exists an interval containing t (for example, $2t < t < 0$) such that for every x in the interval

$$f(x) > f(t) \text{ if } x < t$$

and

$$f(x) < f(t) \text{ if } x > t.$$

Consequently, f is a decreasing function at any number t such that $t < 0$. We often say that f decreases on $\{x \mid x < 0\}$. It should be noted that $f(x) = x^2$ is neither increasing nor decreasing at $x = 0$.

If f is a function that is either increasing in a given interval or decreasing in the interval, then f is said to be *strictly monotonic* in the interval. If f is a function that is either nondecreasing in a given interval or nonincreasing in the interval, then f is said to be *monotonic* in the interval. For $f(x) = x^2$, the function is strictly monotonic on $\{x \mid x < 0\}$ and on $\{x \mid x > 0\}$. The constant function $f(x) = c$ is neither increasing nor decreasing at any number in its domain; however, it is a nonincreasing (and a nondecreasing) function at every number in its domain. Thus the constant function is a monotonic function in its domain.

Let us consider the quadratic function g defined by

$$g(x) = x^2 + 6x + 14.$$

Since

$$x^2 + 6x + 14 = (x^2 + 6x + 9) + 5 = (x + 3)^2 + 5,$$
$$g(x) = (x + 3)^2 + 5.$$

Since $(x + 3)^2 \geq 0$ for any real number x, it is evident that $g(x) \geq 5$ for every x in the domain of g. Since $g(-3) \leq g(x)$ for every x in the domain, the function has 5 as its absolute minimum at -3. The function is increasing on $\{x \mid x > -3\}$ and decreasing on $\{x \mid x < -3\}$. (See Fig. 2-15.)

Let us now consider the general quadratic function f defined by $f(x) = ax^2 + bx + c$ where $a > 0$. (We shall leave as an exercise the analysis of the graph of this function when $a < 0$.)

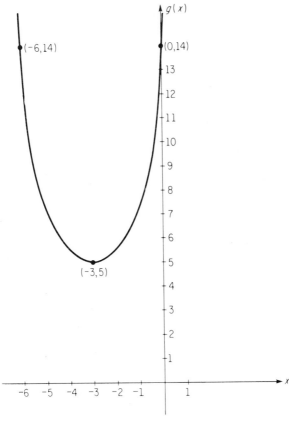

FIG. 2-15. Quadratic function: $g(x) = x^2 + 6x + 14.$

$$f(x) = a\left(x^2 + \frac{b}{a}x\right) + c$$

$$= a\left(x^2 + \frac{b}{a}x + \frac{b^2}{4a^2}\right) + c - \frac{b^2}{4a}$$

$$= a\left(x + \frac{b}{2a}\right)^2 + \frac{4ac - b^2}{4a}.$$

For every real number x,

$$\left(x + \frac{b}{2a}\right)^2 \geq 0.$$

Since $a > 0$,

$$a\left(x + \frac{b}{2a}\right)^2 \geq 0$$

and

$$a\left(x + \frac{b}{2a}\right)^2 + \frac{4ac - b^2}{4a} \geq \frac{4ac - b^2}{4a}.$$

Thus

$$f(x) \geq \frac{4ac - b^2}{4a}$$

for every x in the domain of f. Consequently, $\dfrac{4ac - b^2}{4a}$ is the absolute

minimum of f. Since $f(x) = \dfrac{4ac - b^2}{4a}$ if and only if $a\left(x + \dfrac{b}{2a}\right)^2 = 0$,

f has its absolute minimum at $x = -\dfrac{b}{2a}$.

  Assume

$$t > -\frac{b}{2a}.$$

If

$$-\frac{b}{2a} < x < t,$$

then

$$0 < x + \frac{b}{2a} < t + \frac{b}{2a},$$

$$\left(x + \frac{b}{2a}\right)^2 < \left(t + \frac{b}{2a}\right)^2,$$

$$a\left(x + \frac{b}{2a}\right)^2 < a\left(t + \frac{b}{2a}\right)^2,$$

and

$$a\left(x + \frac{b}{2a}\right)^2 + \frac{4ac - b^2}{4a} < a\left(t + \frac{b}{2a}\right)^2 + \frac{4ac - b^2}{4a}.$$

Thus

$$f(x) < f(t) \text{ if } x < t.$$

Similarly,

$$f(x) > f(t) \text{ if } x > t.$$

Consequently, f is increasing for any t in the domain of f such that $t > -\dfrac{b}{2a}$. We leave as an exercise the proof that f is decreasing at t if $t < -\dfrac{b}{2a}$. (See Fig. 2-16.)

As a further example, consider the quadratic function q defined by $q(x) = x^2 + 4x + 5$. By the earlier discussion, the absolute minimum of q is at $-\dfrac{b}{2a} = -\dfrac{4}{2} = -2$; the minimum is $q(-2) = 1$. However, since q is decreasing on $\{x \mid x < -2\}$ and increasing on $\{x \mid x > -2\}$, it possesses no absolute maximum. Now consider the quadratic function $h(x) = 9 - x^2$. Since h is increasing on $\{x \mid x < 0\}$ and decreasing on $\{x \mid x > 0\}$, it possesses an absolute maximum at $x = 0$; the maximum value is $h(0) = 9$. The problem we pose is that of finding the maximum of q on the restricted domain where $h(x) \geq 0$. The original domain of q was all real members but imposing the constraint $h(x) \geq 0$ restricts the

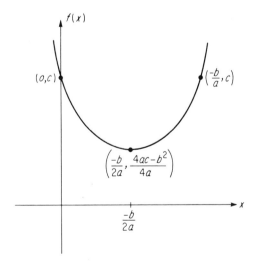

FIG. 2-16. $f(x) = ax^2 + bx + c$, where $a > 0$.

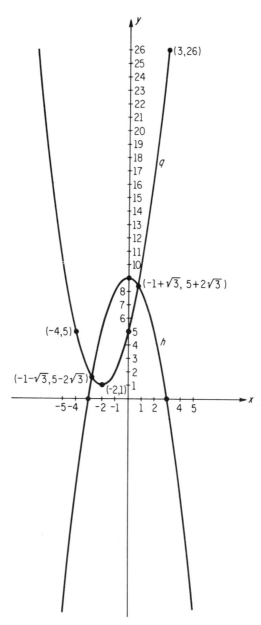

Fig. 2-17. $q(x) = x^2 + 4x + 5$ and $h(x) = 9 - x^2$.

domain of $q(x)$ to $\{x \mid -3 \leq x \leq 3\}$, because $h(x)$ is nonnegative only in this closed interval. To solve the problem we need only note that $q(x)$ is increasing in $\{x \mid -2 < x < 3\}$ and decreasing in $\{x \mid -3 < x < -2\}$; the maximum under the constraint must occur at either -3 or 3. Since $q(-3) = 2$ and $q(3) = 26$, the absolute maximum for q where $h(x) \geq 0$ is at $x = 3$; the absolute maximum is $q(3) = 26$. (See Fig. 2-17.)

2-6. ALGEBRA OF FUNCTIONS

Let us consider the methods for adding, subtracting, multiplying, and dividing functions. Suppose f and g are two functions defined by $f(x) = x^2$ and $g(x) = x^3$. The function s defined by

$$s(x) = x^2 + x^3$$

is called the *sum* of f and g. We write $s = f + g$ to indicate that s is the sum of f and g. It should be noted that $x^2 + x^3$ is the sum of real numbers x^2 and x^3, while $f + g$ is the sum of sets. That is,

$$f + g = \{(x, x^2 + x^3) \mid x \text{ is a real number}\}.$$

If f and g are functions, the sum $f(x) + g(x)$ is only defined when x is in the domain of both functions. For example, if

$$f = \{(2, 3), (-3, 0), (5, 1), (6, 8), (4, 7)\}$$

and

$$g = \{(2, 6), (-3, 4), (5, 6), (7, 1), (0, 2)\},$$

then $f(2) + g(2) = 3 + 6 = 9$; however, $f(6) + g(6)$ is not defined since 6 is not in the domain of g. The sum function $f + g$ has as its domain $\{2, -3, 5\}$, the intersection of the domains of f and g. Since

$$f(2) + g(2) = 3 + 6 = 9,$$
$$f(-3) + g(-3) = 0 + 4 = 4,$$

and

$$f(5) + g(5) = 1 + 6 = 7,$$
$$f + g = \{(2, 9), (-3, 4), (5, 7)\}.$$

In general, if f and g are two functions with domains D_f and D_g, respectively, then the sum function of f and g is defined as

$$f + g = \{(x, f(x) + g(x)) \mid x \in D_f \cap D_g\}.$$

The difference, product, and quotient of two functions f and g are defined as follows.

$$f - g = \{(x, f(x) - g(x)) \mid x \in D_f \cap D_g\}$$
$$f \times g = fg = \{(x, f(x)g(x)) \mid x \in D_f \cap D_g\}$$
$$f/g = \{(x, f(x)/g(x)) \mid x \in D_f \cap D_g \text{ and } g(x) \neq 0\}.$$

Let f and g be defined by $f(x) = x^2$ and $g(x) = x^3$. The difference function $d = f - g$ is defined by

$$d(x) = x^2 - x^3$$

where the domain is all real numbers. The product function $p = fg$ is defined by

$$p(x) = x^2 \cdot x^3$$

or

$$p(x) = x^5,$$

where the domain is all real numbers. The quotient function $q = f/g$ is defined by

$$q(x) = x^2/x^3$$

or

$$q(x) = \frac{1}{x},$$

where x is any real number different from zero.

It is particularly important to note that the quotient function $F = g/f$ is defined by

$$F(x) = g(x)/f(x) = x^3/x^2$$

or

$$F(x) = x,$$

where x *is any real number different from zero.* F is not equal to the identity function with the set of all real numbers as domain since zero is not in the domain of F. In other words, it is true that $x^3/x^2 = x$ only if $x \neq 0$.

We have discussed the rational operations on functions. There is still one very important operation on functions to be considered; it is called *composition*.

To better understand the composition of functions, let us consider first the following hypothetical situation. Assume that 50 men, each of whom is wearing a topcoat, decide to go to a restaurant to eat. Also assume that when they go in the restaurant they check their coats individually. If we let S be the set of men and T be the set of coats, then the set of ordered pairs (x, y) where $x \in S$, $y \in T$, and y belongs to x is a function; call it g. If we let W be the set of coat hangers on which the coats are hung, then the set of ordered pairs (y, z) where $y \in T$, $z \in W$, and y hangs on z is a function; call it f. This method pairs each man x with a hanger z, the one on which his coat hangs; the man is probably informed of this pairing by being given a check with the number of his hanger. Thus, this defines a new function with ordered pairs (x, z); it is called the composition of g by f and is denoted by $f(g)$ or $f \circ g$, read "f of g." Since $y = g(x)$ and $f(y) = z$,

$$f(g(x)) = z.$$

In general, if f and g are functions with domains D_f and D_g, then $f(g)$ is called the composition of f of g and is defined by

$$f(g) = \{(x, f(g(x))) \mid x \in D_g \text{ and } g(x) \in D_f\}.$$

Notice that the domain of $f(g)$ is always a subset of the domain of g. It is the subset of D_g such that for each $x \in D_g$ we have $g(x) \in D_f$. In our restaurant situation, if some men did not check their coats, they would not be paired with a hanger and the (man, hanger) function would have as its domain only those men that checked their coats.

Let f and g be defined by $f(x) = x^{1/2}$ and $g(x) = 3x + 5$. If $h = f(g)$, then

$$h(x) = f(g(x)) = (3x + 5)^{1/2}.$$

The domain of h consists of all x such that $3x + 5 \geq 0$; that is, $x \geq -5/3$. If $t = g(f)$, then

$$t(x) = g(f(x)) = 3x^{1/2} + 5.$$

The domain of t consists of all x such that $x \geq 0$.

Let

$$f = \{(2, 3), (4, 8), (3, -2), (5, 1)\}$$

and

$$g = \{(3, 5), (8, 2), (5, 4), (7, 3)\}.$$

Then

$$f(g) = \{(3, 1), (8, 3), (5, 8), (7, -2)\}$$

and

$$g(f) = (2, 5), (4, 2)\}.$$

Notice since every number in the range of g is in the domain of f, the domain of $f(g)$ is the same as the domain of g.

EXERCISES

Graph the functions defined in Exercises 1 through 5. In each case, state the set on which the function is increasing and the set on which it is decreasing.

1. $f(x) = 3x^3 + 1$.   2. $f(x) = x^2 + 2$.
3. $f(x) = x^2 + 6x + 9$.   4. $f(x) = 4x^2 + 6x - 3$.
5. $f(x) = 6x^2 - 2x + 4$.
6. Give an analysis of the graph of f defined by $f(x) = ax^2 + bx + c$, where $a < 0$.
7. Consider h and q defined in Fig. 2-17. For what x is $h(x) = q(x)$? Interpret geometrically.
8. Let f and g be functions defined by $f(x) = 3x - 7$ and $g(x) = 5x + 2$. (a) Define $f + g$. State the domain. (b) Define $f \times g$. State the domain. (c) Define f/g. State the domain. (d) Define g/f. State the do-

main. (e) Define $f(g)$. State the domain. (f) Define $g(f)$. State the domain.

9. Let f and g be defined by $f(x) = 7x - 1$ and $g(x) = 3x + 8$. (a) Define $f + g$. State the domain. (b) Define $f \times g$. State the domain. (c) Define f/g. State the domain. (d) Define g/f. State the domain. (e) Define $f(g)$. State the domain. (f) Define $g(f)$. State the domain.

10. Let f and g be defined by $f(x) = 2x + 5$ and $g(x) = x^2 - x - 2$. (a) Define $f + g$. State the domain. (b) Define $f \times g$. State the domain. (c) Define f/g. State the domain. (d) Define g/f. State the domain. (e) Define $f(g)$. State the domain. (f) Define $g(f)$. State the domain.

11. Let f and g be defined by $f(x) = 3x - 1$ and $g(x) = x^2 + 2x + 1$. (a) Define $f + g$. State the domain. (b) Define $f \times g$. State the domain. (c) Define f/g. State the domain. (d) Define g/f. State the domain. (e) Define $f(g)$. State the domain. (f) Define $g(f)$. State the domain.

12. Let f and g be defined by $f = \{(3,1), (-2,4), (1,3), (2,6), (7,3)\}$ and $g = \{3, -4), (2,3), (1,7), (6, -2), (5,5)\}$. (a) Define $f + g$. State the domain. (b) Define f/g. State the domain. (c) Define $f(g)$. State the domain. (d) Define $g(f)$. State the domain.

3

Sequences and Series

3-1. SEQUENCES

A function whose domain is the set of positive integers is called an *infinite sequence*, or *sequence*. The function value of a sequence t at n is usually denoted by t_n instead of $t(n)$. Furthermore, t_n is called the nth *term of the sequence*. A sequence t is often denoted by $\{t_n\}$ instead of by $\{(n, t_n)\}$.

Example 1. Let $t = \{(n, 2n) \mid n$ a positive integer$\}$. Then, t is a sequence and $t_1 = 2$, $t_2 = 4$, $t_3 = 6$, $t_4 = 8$, $t_5 = 10$, etc. This is the sequence of even positive integers.

Example 2. Let t be defined by $t_n = (-1)^{n-1}$. Then $t_1 = 1$, $t_2 = -1$, $t_3 = 1$, $t_4 = -1$, $t_5 = 1$, $t_6 = -1$, etc. Notice that although the sequence has infinitely many terms, the range of the sequence is the finite set $\{1, -1\}$.

Example 3. Let $t = \{(n, 3n + 1)\}$. The first seven terms of the sequence are 4, 7, 10, 13, 16, 19, and 22.

Example 4. Let t be defined by $t_n = 2^{n-1}$. Then $t_1 = 1$, $t_2 = 2$, $t_3 = 4$, $t_4 = 8$, $t_5 = 16$, $t_6 = 32$, etc.

Example 5. Let t be defined by $t_n = 2n^3 - 1$ where $n = 1, 2, 3, 4$. This is called a *finite sequence* of four terms. $t_1 = 1$, $t_2 = 15$, $t_3 = 53$, and $t_4 = 127$.

Examples 1 and 3 are examples of a special type sequence called an *arithmetic sequence*. If $\{t_n\}$ is a sequence and there exists a number d such that $t_{n+1} - t_n = d$ for every positive integer n, then $\{t_n\}$ is an arithmetic sequence with *common difference* d. In Example 1, $d = 2$ and in Example 3, $d = 3$.

If $\{t_n\}$ is an arithmetic sequence with common difference d,

$$t_2 = t_1 + d$$
$$t_3 = t_2 + d = (t_1 + d) + d = t_1 + 2d$$
$$t_4 = t_3 + d = (t_1 + 2d) + d = t_1 + 3d$$
$$t_5 = t_4 + d = (t_1 + 3d) + d = t_1 + 4d$$

Thus $t_n = t_1 + (n - 1)d$ is the nth term of an arithmetic sequence.

43

Example 4 is an example of a *geometric sequence*. In an arithmetic sequence each term after the first is found by adding a given number to the preceding term; in a geometric sequence each term after the first is found by multiplying the preceding term by a given number. The number we multiply by is called the *common ratio*; it is generally denoted by r. Thus if $t_{n+1} = rt_n$ for every positive integer n, then $\{t_n\}$ is a geometric sequence. In Example 4, $r = 2$.

If $\{t_n\}$ is a geometric sequence with common ratio r,

$$t_2 = rt_1$$
$$t_3 = rt_2 = r(rt_1) = r^2t_1$$
$$t_4 = rt_3 = r(r^2t_1) = r^3t_1$$
$$t_5 = rt_4 = r(r^3t_1) = r^4t_1$$
$$\cdot \qquad \cdot \qquad \cdot \qquad \cdot \qquad \cdot$$

Thus $t_n = r^{n-1}t_1$ is the nth term of a geometric sequence.

EXERCISES

1. In each of the following sequences, state which are geometric and which are arithmetic. For the arithmetic sequences state the common difference d and for the geometric sequences state the common ratio r.

(a) $t = \{(n, n^2)\}$
(b) t is defined by $t_n = 7n - 2$
(c) t is defined by $t_n = 3^{n-1}$
(d) $t = \{(n, 3n + 5)\}$
(e) $t = \{(n, 2^n + 5)\}$
(f) t is defined by $t_n = 1/2^n$
(g) $t = \{3, 11, 19, 27, 35, \ldots\}$
(h) $t = \{6, 12, 24, 48, 96, \ldots\}$.
2. For each sequence in Exercise 1, what is t_1? t_{20}?
3. List the first ten terms of the sequence $\{t_n\}$ defined by $t_n = \dfrac{(-1)^n + 1}{2}$. What is t_{50}?

4. Let $t_n = 2n - 1$, and define $\{s_n\}$ as $s_n = t_1 + t_2 + t_3 + \cdots + t_n$.
(a) What is t_1? s_1? (b) What is t_2? s_2? (c) What is t_3? s_3? (d) What is t_4? s_4? (e) What is t_{50}?

3-2. SERIES

Let $\{t_n\}$ be a sequence and define a new sequence $\{s_n\}$ in the following manner.

$$s_1 = t_1$$
$$s_2 = t_1 + t_2$$

$$s_3 = t_1 + t_2 + t_3$$
$$s_4 = t_1 + t_2 + t_3 + t_4$$
$$. \quad . \quad . \quad . \quad .$$
$$s_n = t_1 + t_2 + t_3 + \cdots + t_{n-1} + t_n.$$

The sequence $\{s_n\}$ is called a *series* and s_n is called the *nth partial sum* of the series. Furthermore, t_n is called the *nth term of the series.*

If $t_n = 2n - 1$, then $t_1 = 1$, $t_2 = 3$, $t_3 = 5$, $t_4 = 7$, etc.

$$s_1 = 1$$
$$s_2 = 1 + 3 = 4$$
$$s_3 = 1 + 3 + 5 = 9$$
$$s_4 = 1 + 3 + 5 + 7 = 16$$
$$. \quad . \quad . \quad . \quad .$$
$$s_n = 1 + 3 + 5 + 7 + \cdots + (2n - 3) + (2n - 1).$$

This is an example of an arithmetic series. The second term is 3, and the 4th partial sum, or the sum of the first four terms, is 16. In general, if $\{t_n\}$ is an arithmetic sequence, $\{s_n\}$ is called an *arithmetic series*, and if $\{t_n\}$ is a geometric sequence, $\{s_n\}$ is called a *geometric series.*

Consider the arithmetic sequence $t_n = n$. Then the associated arithmetic series is

$$s_n = 1 \quad + \quad 2 \quad + \quad 3 \quad + \cdots + (n - 1) + \quad n.$$

Thus

$$s_n = n \quad + (n - 1) + (n - 2) + \cdots + \quad 2 \quad + \quad 1.$$

Adding,

$$2s_n = \underbrace{(n + 1) + (n + 1) + (n + 1) + \cdots + (n + 1) + (n + 1)}_{n \text{ terms}}$$

$$2s_n = n(n + 1)$$

$$s_n = \frac{n(n + 1)}{2}.$$

Hence the sum of the first n positive integers is $\dfrac{n(n + 1)}{2}$, a fact to be remembered.

Let $\{t_n\}$ be any arithmetic sequence. If $\{s_n\}$ is the associated arithmetic series,

$$s_n = t_1 + (t_1 + d) + (t_1 + 2d) + (t_1 + 3d) + \cdots + [t_1 + (n - 1)d].$$

Thus

$$s_n = \underbrace{[t_1 + t_1 + t_1 + \cdots + t_1]}_{n \text{ terms}} + \underbrace{[1 + 2 + 3 + \cdots + (n - 1)]d}_{\text{first } (n - 1) \text{ positive integers}}$$

$$= nt_1 + \left[\frac{(n - 1)n}{2} d \right]$$

$$= \frac{n}{2} [2t_1 + (n - 1)d].$$

Consequently, the sum of n terms of an arithmetic sequence is

$$\frac{n}{2}[2t_1 + (n-1)d],$$

where t_1 is the first term and d is the common difference.

Example 1. An incentive plan for executives permits individuals to purchase 100 shares of the company's stock when the executive first becomes eligible for participation in the plan. Thereafter, if he has exercised the initial option, the participating executive may purchase 110 shares at the end of the first year, 120 shares the next year, 130 the next, and 140 at the end of the fourth year, etc., until he has accumulated a maximum total of 1,000 shares. How many years will be required to reach the maximum?

Solution: Here $s_n = 1,000$, $t_1 = 100$, $d = 10$ and substituting

$$1,000 = \frac{n}{2}[2(100) + (n-1)10]$$

$$1,000 = 100n + 5n^2 - 5n$$

$$5n^2 + 95n - 1,000 = 0$$

or

$$n^2 + 19n - 200 = 0.$$

Solving by use of the quadratic formula,

$$n = \frac{-b \pm \sqrt{b^2 - 4ac}}{2a}$$

where $a = 1$, $b = 19$, and $c = -200$,

$$n = \frac{-19 \pm \sqrt{1161}}{2}.$$

Thus

$$n \approx 7.54 \qquad \text{or} \qquad n \approx -26.54.$$

Since a negative or noninteger solution is meaningless for this example, the maximum will be reached on the eighth purchase, or at the end of the seventh year. To determine how many shares may be purchased on the last option we calculate the sum of the first seven purchases:

$$s_7 = \frac{7}{2}[2(100) + (6)(10)] = 910.$$

Thus the last purchase is $1,000 - 910 = 90$ shares.

Example 2. (a) In an attempt to decrease his inventory a paint manufacturer offers to sell the first case for $12. If two cases are ordered, a discount of $0.50 is applied to the second case, and an additional $0.50 discount on each succeeding case. What is the total cost of an order for 20 cases?

Solution: For this example $n = 20$, $t_1 = 12$, $d = -0.50$, and

$$S_{20} = \frac{20}{2}[2(12) + (19)(-0.50)] = \$145,$$

the total cost of 20 cases. The price of the 20th case is

$$t_{20} = 12.00 + (19)(-0.5) = \$2.50.$$

(b) Obviously, the manufacturer should put an upper bound on the number of cases a customer can buy so that the buyer will not be able to claim "free cases." To find the limit on purchases that the manufacturer should set, we want to find the largest n such that $t_n > 0$. Thus

$$t_n = 12.00 + (n - 1)(-0.50) > 0$$
$$12.00 > (0.50)(n - 1)$$
$$1{,}200 > 50n - 50$$
$$50n < 1{,}250$$
$$n < 25.$$

A maximum of 24 cases should be sold to a customer.

Consider the geometric sequence $\{t_n\}$ defined by $t_n = 2^{n-1}$. Then the associated geometric series is

$$S_n = 1 + 2 + 2^2 + 2^3 + 2^4 + \cdots + 2^{n-2} + 2^{n-1}.$$

Multiplying both sides of the equality by 2,

$$2S_n = 2 + 2^2 + 2^3 + 2^4 + 2^5 + \cdots + 2^{n-1} + 2^n.$$

Subtracting S_n from $2S_n$,

$$S_n = 2^n - 1,$$

the sum of n terms of the series. The formula for the sum of n terms of a general geometric series is derived similarly.

Let $\{t_n\}$ be any geometric sequence. If $\{s_n\}$ is the associated geometric series,

$$S_n = t_1 + rt_1 + r^2 t_1 + r^3 t_1 + \cdots + r^{n-1} t_1$$
$$rs_n = rt_1 + r^2 t_1 + r^3 t_1 + r^4 t_1 + \cdots + r^n t_1.$$

Subtracting s_n from rs_n,

$$rs_n - s_n = r^n t_1 - t_1$$
$$(r - 1)s_n = r^n t_1 - t_1.$$

If $r \neq 1$,

$$S_n = \frac{r^n t_1 - t_1}{r - 1} = \frac{t_1 - r^n t_1}{1 - r}.$$

Thus, if $r \neq 1$, the sum of n terms of a geometric series is $\dfrac{t_1 - t_1 r^n}{1 - r}$, where t_1 is the first term and r is the common ratio. If $r = 1$, each term is t_1 and the sum s_n of n such terms is nt_1.

Example 3. Federal laws require banks subject to regulation by the government to maintain as a reserve a certain proportion of the bank's current deposits. Cash in excess of this reserve may be loaned to the bank's borrowers. Assuming the reserve rate is 25 percent and that the bank requires its borrowers to deposit the amount loaned, find the total amount made available for loans as a result of a $500 deposit.

Solution: From the original deposit, the bank may loan $(500)(0.75) = 375$. Assuming unlimited demand for loans, the bank may now loan $(375)(0.75) = [(500)(0.75)](0.75) = (500)(0.75)^2 = 281.25$, and then $(500)(0.75)^3 = 211.31$. This is clearly a geometric sequence. Since $(500) \cdot (0.75)^n \neq 0$ for any integer n, there is no upper bound of n. We note that the sequence is decreasing and can be made arbitrarily close to zero by choosing n large enough; thus, assuming that no loan will be made for less than $1, we find the number of loans required to reach this minimum by letting

$$r^{n-1} t_1 = 1.$$

Thus

$$(0.75)^{n-1}(500) = 1$$

and taking logarithms of both sides,

$$(n - 1) \log 0.75 + \log 500 = 0$$
$$(n - 1)(9.87506 - 10) = -2.69877$$
$$(n - 1)(-0.12494) = -2.69877$$
$$0.12494n = 2.82371$$
$$n \approx 22.6.$$

Since n must be an integer, we find the total amount available for loan for the first 22 repetitions of the cycle. The total amount available is

$$S_{22} = \frac{500 - 500(0.75)^{22}}{1 - 0.75}$$
$$= \frac{500[1 - (3/4)^{22}]}{1/4}$$
$$= 2,000[1 - (3/4)^{22}]$$
$$\approx 2,000.$$

The total amount is just under $2,000. It should be evident that since $(3/4)^n$ can be made arbitrarily "close" to 0 for "large" n the total amount could not exceed $2,000 even with an unlimited number of loans.

Example 4. Capital assets, such as a factory, which will be used for several years cannot be considered as an expense at the time they are purchased. Instead, periodic charges called *depreciation* are made for the use of such assets. Many methods are available for computing depreciation charges, the simplest being the *straight-line method*. If C is the total cost of a capital asset and a fixed integer n is the estimated life, in years, of the asset, the annual straight-line depreciation charge is C/n. Thus, the *total* depreciation charge at the end of the first year is $s_1 = C/n$, at the end of the second year is $s_2 = 2C/n$, and at the end of the nth year $s_n = nC/n = C$. The total depreciation is directly proportional to time and the constant of proportionality is C/n. The points on the graph of this arithmetic series $(1, C/n)$, $(2, 2C/n)$, $(3, 3C/n)$, ... lie on a line through the origin with slope C/n.

As an alternative, one may use a double-declining method. For this method, the annual rate of depreciation is taken as twice the straight-line rate on the remaining value of the assets, if certain conditions are met. Under this method, depreciation for the first year is $C\left(\dfrac{2}{n}\right)$; for the second,

$$\left[C - C\frac{2}{n}\right]\frac{2}{n} = C\left(\frac{2}{n}\right)\left(1 - \frac{2}{n}\right);$$

for the third,

$$\left[C - C\left(\frac{2}{n}\right) - C\left(\frac{2}{n}\right)\left(1 - \frac{2}{n}\right)\right]\frac{2}{n} = C\left[\left(1 - \frac{2}{n}\right) - \frac{2}{n}\left(1 - \frac{2}{n}\right)\right]\frac{2}{n}$$

$$= C\left(1 - \frac{2}{n}\right)^2 \frac{2}{n};$$

and for the kth year the allowable charge is $C\left(1 - \dfrac{2}{n}\right)^{k-1}\dfrac{2}{n}$. The series representing the total depreciation allowed for the first k years is

$$s_k = C\frac{2}{n} + C\left(1 - \frac{2}{n}\right)\frac{2}{n} + C\left(1 - \frac{2}{n}\right)^2\frac{2}{n} + \cdots + C\left(1 - \frac{2}{n}\right)^{k-1}\frac{2}{n},$$

a geometric series with common ratio $r = \left(1 - \dfrac{2}{n}\right)$ and $t_1 = C\left(\dfrac{2}{n}\right)$. Thus

$$s_k = \frac{C\dfrac{2}{n} - C\dfrac{2}{n}\left(1 - \dfrac{2}{n}\right)^k}{1 - \left(1 - \dfrac{2}{n}\right)} = C\left[1 - \left(1 - \frac{2}{n}\right)^k\right].$$

Example 5. If an amount of money k can be deposited in a savings account where interest at a rate i is paid annually, the investment will earn ki in interest at the end of the first year. If the original investment and interest are left on deposit, the interest earned at the end of the second year will be $(k + ki)i = k(1 + i)i$; for the third year, $[k + ki + k(i + 1)i]i = [k(1 + i) + k(1 + i)i]i = k(1 + i)^2 i$, and for the nth year, $k(1 + i)^{n-1}i$. The total amount K on deposit at the end of n years is the original amount k plus the sum of the interest earned; that is, $k + [ki + k(1 + i)i + k(1 + i)^2 i + \cdots + k(1 + i)^{n-1}i]$. This is k plus a geometric series with first term ki and common ratio $(1 + i)$. Thus

$$K = k + \frac{ki - ki(1 + i)^n}{1 - (1 + i)} = \frac{-ki + ki - ki(1 + i)^n}{-i}$$

$$= k(1 + i)^n.$$

K is usually referred to as the *future value of an investment*. If, on the other hand, we wish to find the price one should pay today for something that has a value K some n periods in the future with a given interest rate i, this amount would be called the *present value*. To determine the present value we reverse the compounding used in the first part of the example and apply what is called *discounting*. Thus, if the value is K at the end of the nth time period,

$$K = k(1 + i)^n$$

and

$$k = \frac{K}{(1 + i)^n}.$$

Thus the present value k of an amount K which is to be paid n time periods in the future is $\dfrac{K}{(1 + i)^n}$.

Example 6. A prospector offers to sell a proven uranium claim for $1,000,000. Under normal mining the claim should yield a profit of $500,000 per year for each of three years and then will be worthless. If the purchaser considers the rate of interest to be 10 percent, the present value of the investment is found by first considering the capital investment as a negative earning and discounting the earnings of each of the three years:

$$\text{Present value} = -1,000,000 + \frac{500,000}{(1 + i)} + \frac{500,000}{(1 + i)^2} + \frac{500,000}{(1 + i)^3},$$

which may be rewritten as

$$\text{P.V.} = -1,000,000 + 500,000 \left[\frac{1}{(1 + i)} + \frac{1}{(1 + i)^2} + \frac{1}{(1 + i)^3} \right].$$

The terms inside the brackets form a geometric series with $t_1 = \dfrac{1}{1 + i}$ and $r = (1 + i)^{-1}$. For a period of n years

$$S_n = \frac{(1 + i)^{-1} - (1 + i)^{-1}(1 + i)^{-n}}{1 - (1 + i)^{-1}} = \frac{1 - (1 + i)^{-n}}{i}.$$

Thus, for the example,

$$\text{P.V.} = -1,000,000 + 500,000 \left[\frac{1 - (1 + 0.10)^{-3}}{0.10} \right]$$

$$= -1,000,000 + 500,000 \left[\frac{1 - 0.751315}{0.10} \right]$$

$$= -1,000,000 + 1,243,425 = \$243,425.$$

As we have seen, the sum of the first ten terms of the arithmetic sequence $t_n = 3n$ can be expressed by

$$3 + 6 + 9 + 12 + 15 + 18 + 21 + 24 + 27 + 30$$

and the sum of the first one hundred terms by

$$3 + 6 + 9 + \cdots + 297 + 300.$$

To avoid such "addition strings" we can use what is called the *sigma notation,* or *summation notation.* Let $\{t_n\}$ be a sequence, let

$$\sum_{n=1}^{1} t_n = t_1$$

and let

$$\sum_{n=1}^{k+1} t_n = \left(\sum_{n=1}^{k} t_n \right) + t_{k+1},$$

where k is any positive integer. As a consequence of this definition,

$$\sum_{n=1}^{2} t_n = \left(\sum_{n=1}^{1} t_n \right) + t_2 = t_1 + t_2$$

$$\sum_{n=1}^{3} t_n = \left(\sum_{n=1}^{2} t_n \right) + t_3 = t_1 + t_2 + t_3.$$

Thus

$$\sum_{n=1}^{10} 3n = 3 + 6 + 9 + 12 + 15 + 18 + 21 + 24 + 27 + 30$$

and $\displaystyle\sum_{n=1}^{100} 3n$ represents the sum of the first one hundred terms of $t_n = 3n$.

Let us consider three important properties of the sigma notation.

I. Let $\{t_n\}$ be a sequence and c a real number:

$$\sum_{n=1}^{4} ct_n = ct_1 + ct_2 + ct_3 + ct_4$$

$$= c(t_1 + t_2 + t_3 + t_4)$$

$$= c \sum_{n=1}^{4} t_n.$$

In general, $\displaystyle\sum_{n=1}^{k} ct_n = c \sum_{n=1}^{k} t_n.$

II. Let $\{s_n\}$ and $\{t_n\}$ be two sequences.

$$\sum_{n=1}^{4} (s_n + t_n) = (s_1 + t_1) + (s_2 + t_2) + (s_3 + t_3) + (s_4 + t_4)$$

$$= (s_1 + s_2 + s_3 + s_4) + (t_1 + t_2 + t_3 + t_4)$$

$$= \sum_{n=1}^{4} s_n + \sum_{n=1}^{4} t_n.$$

In general,

$$\sum_{n=1}^{k} (s_n + t_n) = \sum_{n=1}^{k} s_n + \sum_{n=1}^{k} t_n.$$

III. Let $\{t_n\}$ be a sequence.

$$\sum_{n=1}^{4} (t_{n+1} - t_n) = (t_2 - t_1) + (t_3 - t_2) + (t_4 - t_3) + (t_5 - t_4)$$

$$= t_5 - t_1.$$

In general,

$$\sum_{n=1}^{k} (t_{n+1} - t_n) = t_{k+1} - t_1.$$

This is called the *telescoping property* for the summation notation.

Example 7. Since $(n + 1)^2 - n^2 = 2n + 1$ for every integer n,

$$\sum_{n=1}^{k} [(n + 1)^2 - n^2] = \sum_{n=1}^{k} (2n + 1).$$

By the telescoping property, where $t_n = n^2$,

$$(1) \quad \sum_{n=1}^{k} [(n + 1)^2 - n^2] = (k + 1)^2 - 1^2.$$

Furthermore,

$$\sum_{n=1}^{k} (2n + 1) = \sum_{n=1}^{k} 2n + \sum_{n=1}^{k} 1$$

Notice that if $\{t_n\}$ is a sequence of k ones then $\sum_{n=1}^{k} t_n = k$. Usually, we write $\sum_{n=1}^{k} 1$ for the sum of k ones. If an index of summation is desired, since $n^0 = 1$ we can write $\sum_{n=1}^{k} n^0$ instead of $\sum_{n=1}^{k} 1$.

$$(2) \quad \sum_{n=1}^{k} (2n + 1) = 2 \sum_{n=1}^{k} n + k.$$

Hence, setting (1) equal to (2),

$$(k + 1)^2 - 1 = 2 \sum_{n=1}^{k} n + k$$

and

$$2 \sum_{n=1}^{k} n = k^2 + k.$$

Thus

$$\sum_{n=1}^{k} n = \frac{k(k + 1)}{2}.$$

The foregoing is another proof of the fact that the sum of the first k positive integers is $\frac{k(k + 1)}{2}$.

Example 8.

$$\sum_{n=1}^{k} (2n - 1) = \sum_{n=1}^{k} 2n - \sum_{n=1}^{k} 1$$

$$= 2 \sum_{n=1}^{k} n - k$$

$$= 2 \frac{k(k + 1)}{2} - k$$

$$= k^2.$$

EXERCISES

1. If $t_n = 3n + 2$, find t_5 and $\sum_{n=1}^{8} t_n$.

2. If $t_n = 3^{n-1}$, find t_4 and $\sum_{n=1}^{5} t_n$.

3. If $t_n = 5n - 2$, find t_{30} and $\sum_{n=1}^{59} t_n$.

4. If $t_n = 1/2^{n-1}$, find t_6 and $\sum_{n=1}^{10} t_n$.

5. If $t_n = (1.6)^n$, find t_3 and $\sum_{n=1}^{12} t_n$.

6. If $t_n = 7n + 3 + 3(-2)^n$, find t_5 and $\sum_{n=1}^{9} t_n$.

7. Prove that $\sum_{n=1}^{k} n^2 = \frac{k(k + 1)(2k + 1)}{6}$. $\left\{ \text{HINT: } (n + 1)^3 - n^3 = \right.$

$3n^2 + 3n + 1$ and

$\left. \sum_{n=1}^{k} [(n + 1)^3 - n^3] = 3 \sum_{n=1}^{k} n^2 + 3 \sum_{n=1}^{k} n + k. \right\}$

8. A company purchases an automatic lathe for $125,000. The useful life of the lathe is estimated to be 10 years. Using the double-declining balance method of the example, calculate the depreciation charge for the

fourth and sixth years; the cumulative depreciation at the end of the eighth year; and the undepreciated balance at the end of the tenth year.

3-3. INFINITE GEOMETRIC SERIES

Consider the geometric series

$$\sum_{k=1}^{n} \frac{1}{2^{k-1}} = 1 + \frac{1}{2} + \left(\frac{1}{2}\right)^2 + \left(\frac{1}{2}\right)^3 + \left(\frac{1}{2}\right)^4 + \cdots + \left(\frac{1}{2}\right)^{n-1}.$$

Since $t_1 = 1, r = 1/2$, and the number of terms is n, the sum is given by

$$s_n = \sum_{k=1}^{n} \frac{1}{2^{k-1}}$$

$$= \frac{1 - (1/2)^n}{1 - 1/2}$$

$$= \frac{1 - 1/2^n}{1/2}.$$

Thus

$$s_n = 2 - 1/2^{n-1}.$$

By choosing n large enough, we can make $1/2^{n-1}$ as small as we wish and, hence, make $2 - 1/2^{n-1}$ arbitrarily close to 2. In fact, we can find a positive integer N such that N terms of this geometric series will differ from 2 by less than, say, one-millionth. Furthermore, since s_n differs from 2 by $1/2^{n-1}$, the sum of any number of terms greater than N will still differ from 2 by less than one-millionth.

Since the sum of the geometric series can be made as close to 2 as we wish by choosing N large enough, we say that 2 is the "sum" of the infinite geometric series denoted by $\displaystyle\sum_{k=1}^{\infty} \frac{1}{2^{k-1}}$, or by

$$1 + 1/2 + 1/2^2 + 1/2^3 + 1/2^4 + \cdots + 1/2^{n-1} \cdots.$$

For a geometric series of n terms,

$$s_n = \frac{t_1 - t_1 r^n}{1 - r} = \frac{t_1}{1 - r} - \frac{t_1 r^n}{1 - r}.$$

If r is between -1 and 1, r^n can be made as close to zero as we wish by choosing n large enough; thus the difference between s_n and $\dfrac{t_1}{1 - r}$ can be made arbitrarily small by choosing n large enough. Therefore, we make the following definition.

Definition. The *sum* S of the infinite geometric series

$$t_1 + t_1 r + t_1 r^2 + t_1 r^3 + \cdots + t_1 r^{n-1} + \cdots$$

where $-1 < r < 1$ is

$$S = \frac{t_1}{1 - r}.$$

Example 1. In the bank example on page 48 we determined the number of times the deposit-borrow cycle could be repeated by solving for n in the equation

$$r^{n-1} t_1 = 1.$$

Since in this example the total amount available for loan with an unlimited number of loans is an infinite geometric series where $-1 < r < 1$, we can find the maximum amount available by using our formula for the sum of an infinite geometric series where $t_1 = 500$ and $r = 0.75$. Then,

$$S = \frac{500}{1 - 0.75} = \$2,000.$$

We have defined the sum of infinite series in a very restricted sense. It is beyond the scope of this text to define the sum of infinite series that are not geometric.

EXERCISES

1. The double-declining balance method (DDB) of depreciation will never reduce the value of an asset to zero and thus Federal law allows the method of depreciation to be changed one time. At the time the change is made from DDB to straight-line (SL) the value of the asset is considered to be the undepreciated balance and the life of the asset the remaining life. Since the amount of depreciation allowed under DDB decreases annually, there will exist a point in time when the annual amount of depreciation allowed under straight-line depreciation will exceed that allowed under DDB. Find a general expression for the time at which the change should be made.

2. Find the sum of the first n even integers: $2, 4, 6, 8, \ldots$.

3. For the geometric series $81, -27, 9, -3, 1, \ldots$, find the tenth term, the sum of the first ten terms, and the sum of the infinite series.

4. Find the present value of \$1,000 to be paid 10 years in the future at an interest rate of 10 percent per annum. Compare the solution in the case where compounding is quarterly rather than annually.

5. A sinking fund is usually employed to accumulate the funds necessary to redeem corporate bonds. In this method of accumulating funds the corporation is required to deposit an amount x each year, where x is determined in such a way that at the end of n years there will be sufficient cash to pay all bondholders. If the firm can earn interest at a rate i per annum, develop a general formula for the amount x. Test your model for the case where the sinking fund is to liquidate a $1,000,000 bond issue 20 years from now and the firm can earn 10 percent interest per year.

6. An inventor has assigned the rights to a patent to the Zebra Company. His contract with Zebra calls for the payment of $1,000 at the end of each year for ten years. If the prevailing interest rate is 10 percent, what is the present value of the contract? First establish a general solution, then solve the problem.

4

Introduction to the Derivative

4-1. SLOPE

Earlier we developed a method to determine the slope of a line in the coordinate plane. We now consider the geometric problem of finding the slope of the tangent line at some point on the graph of any function f.

Let f be the function defined by $f(x) = x^2$. For the points $(2, f(2))$ and $(2.1, f(2.1))$, the slope m of the line containing these two points is

$$m = \frac{f(2.1) - f(2)}{2.1 - 2}$$

$$= \frac{(2.1)^2 - 2^2}{0.1}$$

$$= \frac{(2.1 - 2)(2.1 + 2)}{0.1}$$

$$= \frac{(4.1)(0.1)}{0.1}$$

$$= 4.1.$$

If we choose a point closer to $(2, f(2))$ on the graph of f, such as $(2.01, f(2.01))$, we obtain a better approximation of the slope of the tangent line at $(2, f(2))$. (See Fig. 4-1.) The slope of the line containing the points $(2, f(2))$ and $(2.01, f(2.01))$ is 4.01, as the reader may verify.

The slope of the line through the points $(2, f(2))$ and $(x, f(x))$ where x is any real number different from 2 is

$$m(x) = \frac{x^2 - 2^2}{x - 2}$$

$$= \frac{(x - 2)(x + 2)}{x - 2}$$

$$= x + 2,$$

provided $x \neq 2$.

Since the line through the two points becomes the tangent line as the two points become coincident, the slope of the tangent line at $(2, f(2))$ is approximated by $(x + 2)$, where x is a real number close to 2. As x "approaches" 2, $(x + 2)$ "approaches" 4 so the slope of the tangent line

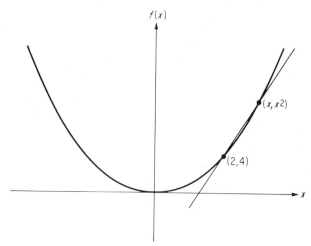

FIG. 4-1. $f(x) = x^2$ and $m = (x^2 - 4)/(x - 2) = x + 2$ if $x \neq 2$.

to the curve at $(2, f(2))$ is 4.   Note that if $m(x) = (x^2 - 4)/(x - 2)$, $m(2)$ is not defined.

Let $(t, f(t))$ be any point on the graph of $f(x) = x^2$. If $(x, f(x))$ is any point different from $(t, f(t))$, then the slope of the line containing the two points is

$$m = \frac{x^2 - t^2}{x - t}$$

$$= (x + t), \quad x \neq t.$$

By an argument similar to the one above, we conclude that the slope of the tangent line to the curve at $(t, f(t))$ is $2t$.

Let f be a function with the real number t in its domain. If there is an open interval in the domain of f containing t, consider the quotient

$$\frac{f(x) - f(t)}{x - t},$$

where x is any real number in the open interval other than t; this expression is sometimes called the *Newton quotient*. If by choosing x close to t the quotient can be made arbitrarily close to one and only one real number, then the number is called the *derivative of f at t* and is denoted by $f'(t)$. The process for finding this number is called *differentiation*. The function defined by the ordered pairs $(t, f'(t))$ is called the *derived function* of f, or the derivative of f. The derivative of f is a function denoted by f'.

If f is the function defined by $f(x) = x^2$, then the derivative of f at 2 is $f'(2) = 4$. Furthermore, the derivative f' is defined by $f'(x) = 2x$.

To give a routine method for finding the derivative of a function and to justify the procedure, it is necessary to give a more explicit definition of the derivative. But in order to do this, we must first define what is meant by the limit of a function f at t. The limit concept is one of the fundamental ideas of calculus.

4-2. THE LIMIT CONCEPT

If f is the function defined by $f(x) = \dfrac{x^2 - 4}{x - 2}$, then the limit of f as

x approaches 2 is 4; this is denoted by

$$\lim_{x \to 2} f(x) = 4.$$

The *limit* is 4; the number 2 is called the *limit point*. When discussing the limit of a function as x approaches 2, the value of the function at 2 [that is, $f(2)$] is immaterial to the limit of f at 2. In fact, as in this example, the limit point need not be in the domain of the function. The limit of f at 2 is 4, since for any positive number ϵ we can find an interval containing 2 such that the distance between $f(x)$ and 4 is less than ϵ for every number in the interval, except 2.

Definition. A function f has limit L at t (or as x approaches t) if for every $\epsilon > 0$ *there exists* a $\delta > 0$ such that $|f(x) - L| < \epsilon$ for every x satisfying $0 \neq |x - t| < \delta$. Symbolically, $\lim_{x \to t} f(x) = L$.

From this definition, we conclude that if we want to *prove* that $\lim_{x \to 4} (3x + 2) = 14$, it is necessary to find an interval containing 4 such that for any $\epsilon > 0$, $|(3x + 2) - 14| < \epsilon$ for every x in the interval different from 4. This can be accomplished by noting that

$$|(3x + 2) - 14| < \epsilon$$

if and only if $|3x - 12| < \epsilon$. Furthermore, $|3x - 12| < \epsilon$ if and only if $|x - 4| < \epsilon/3$. Thus, if x satisfies $|x - 4| < \epsilon/3$, then $|(3x + 2) - 14| < \epsilon$; hence, we choose δ to be $\epsilon/3$. Of course δ could be chosen to be any positive number less than $\epsilon/3$.

If we consider the graph of f defined by $f(x) = 3x + 2$, it is geometrically obvious how close numbers in the domain must be to 4 so that the function values are within ϵ of 14. Draw lines parallel to the x-axis from $14 + \epsilon$ and $14 - \epsilon$ on the y-axis to the graph of f and drop perpendiculars from these intersection points to the x-axis. Since the graph of f is a straight line with slope 3, the foot of each perpendicular on the x-axis will be $\epsilon/3$ on each side of 4. The function values for all numbers in the interval $(4 - \epsilon/3, 4 + \epsilon/3)$ will be within ϵ of 14. (See Fig. 4-2.)

Although the positive number ϵ need not be "small," it is evident that if an interval containing t can be chosen such that $|f(x) - L|$ is less

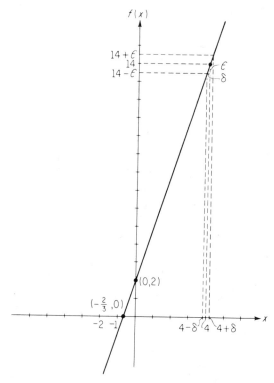

FIG. 4-2. $\lim_{x \to 4} (3x + 2) = 14.$

than, say, 0.01 for all x satisfying $0 \neq |x - t| < \delta$, then it follows that $|f(x) - L| < \epsilon$ for any $\epsilon > 0.01$ for the same x.

It is quite difficult to prove limits exist using the ϵ, δ definition. However, a few basic limit theorems make the task of finding limits relatively easy for most functions. These we now state without proof but note they can be proved from the definition of limit.

Theorem 4-1. If f is the constant function defined by $f(x) = c$, then $\lim_{x \to t} f(x) = c$.

Example 1. If f is defined by $f(x) = 7$, then $\lim_{x \to t} f(x) = 7$. (Since the function values are always 7, it should be obvious that an interval can be found containing t such that the function values can be made as close to 7 as we wish.)

Theorem 4-2. If f is the identity function defined by $f(x) = x$, then $\lim_{x \to t} f(x) = t$.

Example 2. If f is defined by $f(x) = x$, then $\lim_{x \to 3} f(x) = 3$. It should be obvious from the graph of the identity function that an interval containing 3 so that the function values will be within ϵ of 3 is

$$3 - \epsilon < x < 3 + \epsilon.$$

Theorem 4-3. If $\lim_{x \to t} f(x)$ exists, then $\lim_{x \to t} cf(x) = c \lim_{x \to t} f(x)$ where c is a given real number. (This is sometimes stated as: The limit of a constant times a function is the constant times the limit of the function.)

Example 3.

$$\lim_{x \to 5} 7x = 7 \left(\lim_{x \to 5} x \right) = (7)(5) = 35.$$

Theorem 4-4. If $\lim_{x \to t} f(x)$ and $\lim_{x \to t} g(x)$ exist, then

$$\lim_{x \to t} f(x)g(x) = \left[\lim_{x \to t} f(x) \right] \left[\lim_{x \to t} g(x) \right].$$

(This is sometimes stated as: The limit of the product of two functions is the product of the limits of the functions.)

Example 4.

$$\lim_{x \to 6} x^2 = \lim_{x \to 6} x \cdot x = \left[\lim_{x \to 6} x \right] \left[\lim_{x \to 6} x \right] = (6)(6) = 36.$$

Theorem 4-5. If $\lim_{x \to t} f(x)$ and $\lim_{x \to t} g(x)$ exist, then

$$\lim_{x \to t} [f(x) + g(x)] = \lim_{x \to t} f(x) + \lim_{x \to t} g(x).$$

(This is sometimes stated as: The limit of the sum of two functions is the sum of the limits.)

Example 5.

$$\lim_{x \to 3} (x^2 + 5x) = \lim_{x \to 3} x^2 + \lim_{x \to 3} 5x = 9 + 15 = 24.$$

Theorem 4-6. If P is a polynomial function defined by

$$P(x) = a_0 x^n + a_1 x^{n-1} + a_2 x^{n-2} + \cdots + a_{n-1} x + a_n,$$

then $\lim_{x \to t} P(x) = P(t)$. (This theorem, which states that the limit of any polynomial function at t is the function value $P(t)$, is an immediate consequence of the preceding theorems.)

Example 6.

$$\lim_{x \to 2} (3x^2 - 5x + 17) = 3(2)^2 - 5(2) + 17 = 19.$$

Theorem 4-7. If $\lim_{x \to t} f(x)$ and $\lim_{x \to t} g(x)$ exist, and if $\lim_{x \to t} g(x) \neq 0$, then

$$\lim_{x \to t} \frac{f(x)}{g(x)} = \frac{\lim_{x \to t} f(x)}{\lim_{x \to t} g(x)}.$$

(This theorem is sometimes stated as: The limit of the quotient of two functions is the quotient of the limits, provided the limit of the denominator is not zero.)

Example 7.

$$\lim_{x \to 2} \frac{x^2 + 7x}{x^2 - 1} = \frac{\lim_{x \to 2} (x^2 + 7x)}{\lim_{x \to 2} (x^2 - 1)} = \frac{18}{3}.$$

The preceding theorems pertain to the limits of the sum, difference, product, and quotient of functions. The next theorem has to do with the composition of functions.

Theorem 4-8. If $\lim_{x \to t} g(x) = s$ and $\lim_{x \to s} f(x) = f(s)$, then

$$\lim_{x \to t} f(g(x)) = f\left(\lim_{x \to t} g(x)\right) = f(s).$$

(This theorem is sometimes stated as: The limit of f of g is f of the limit of g.)

Example 8. To find $\lim_{x \to 2} \sqrt{x^3 + 1}$, let $f(x) = \sqrt{x}$ and let $g(x) = x^3 + 1$. Then, $f(g(x)) = \sqrt{x^3 + 1}$. Since $\lim_{x \to 2} f(g(x)) = f\left(\lim_{x \to 2} g(x)\right)$, $\lim_{x \to 2} \sqrt{x^3 + 1} = \sqrt{\lim_{x \to 2} (x^3 + 1)} = \sqrt{9} = 3$.

We complete our list of limit theorems with one that is often very useful in finding limits of the types of functions that arise naturally in the study of calculus.

Theorem 4-9. Assume that $\dfrac{f(x)}{g(x)} = \dfrac{F(x)}{G(x)}$ for all $x \neq t$. If $\lim_{x \to t} f(x) = 0$, $\lim_{x \to t} g(x) = 0$, $\lim_{x \to t} F(x)$ and $\lim_{x \to t} G(x)$ exist, and $\lim_{x \to t} G(x) \neq 0$, then

$$\lim_{x \to t} \frac{f(x)}{g(x)} = \frac{\lim_{x \to t} F(x)}{\lim_{x \to t} G(x)}.$$

As we discovered at the beginning of this chapter, the Newton quotient $\dfrac{f(x) - f(t)}{x - t}$ is of considerable interest. It should be clear that since $\lim_{x \to t} (x - t) = 0$ it will be necessary to rely heavily on Theorem 4-9 to find the limit of the Newton quotient as x approaches t. However, Theorem 4-9 does not provide any method for finding $F(x)$ and $G(x)$ such that the hypotheses of the theorem are satisfied. Sometimes for functions f and g, $f(x) = F(x)g(x)$; in this case, $f(x)/g(x) = F(x)$ and $\lim_{x \to t} F(x)$ may exist. The functions f and g can also have a common factor h; in this case, $f(x) = h(x)F(x)$, $g(x) = h(x)G(x)$ and $\dfrac{f(x)}{g(x)} = \dfrac{h(x)F(x)}{h(x)G(x)} = \dfrac{F(x)}{G(x)}$ where

$\lim\limits_{x \to t} \dfrac{F(x)}{G(x)}$ may exist. In Chapter 11, we shall present a more efficient method for finding limits of functions such as those hypothesized in Theorem 4-9. The following examples will exhibit some of the algebraic manipulations that can be used to find the limits which are important to our development of the derivative.

Example 9. Let f be defined by $f(x) = x^3$. Find $\lim\limits_{x \to 3} \dfrac{f(x) - f(3)}{x - 3}$.

Since

$$\frac{x^3 - 3^3}{x - 3} = \frac{(x - 3)(x^2 + 3x + 9)}{x - 3}$$

$$= \frac{x^2 + 3x + 9}{1},$$

provided $x \neq 3$,

$$\lim_{x \to 3} \frac{x^3 - 27}{x - 3} = \lim_{x \to 3} (x^2 + 3x + 9) = 27.$$

Example 10. Find $\lim\limits_{x \to 2} \dfrac{x^2 - 5x + 6}{x^2 + 5x - 14}$. Notice that $\lim\limits_{x \to 2} (x^2 - 5x + 6) = 0$ and $\lim\limits_{x \to 2} (x^2 + 5x - 14) = 0$. Since

$$\frac{x^2 - 5x + 6}{x^2 + 5x - 14} = \frac{(x - 2)(x - 3)}{(x - 2)(x + 7)}$$

$$= \frac{x - 3}{x + 7},$$

provided $x \neq 2$,

$$\lim_{x \to 2} \frac{x^2 - 5x + 6}{x^2 + 5x - 14} = \frac{\lim\limits_{x \to 2} (x - 3)}{\lim\limits_{x \to 2} (x + 7)} = -\frac{1}{9}.$$

Example 11. Find $\lim\limits_{x \to 2} \dfrac{x - 2}{\sqrt{x + 2} - 2}$. Notice that $\lim\limits_{x \to 2} (x - 2) = 0$ and $\lim\limits_{x \to 2} (\sqrt{x + 2} - 2) = 0$. Since

$$\frac{(x - 2)}{\sqrt{x + 2} - 2} = \frac{(x - 2)(\sqrt{x + 2} + 2)}{(\sqrt{x + 2} - 2)(\sqrt{x + 2} + 2)}$$

$$= \frac{(x - 2)(\sqrt{x + 2} + 2)}{x - 2}$$

$$= \sqrt{x + 2} + 2,$$

provided $x \neq 2$,

$$\lim_{x \to 2} \frac{x - 2}{\sqrt{x + 2} - 2} = \lim_{x \to 2} (\sqrt{x + 2} + 2) = 4.$$

As we have seen, many functions, such as the polynomial functions, have the important property that $\lim\limits_{x \to t} f(x) = f(t)$; that is, if t is in the domain of f, then the limit of f as x approaches t exists and the limit is the value of f at t. A function with this property is said to be *continuous at t*. If f is continuous at t, this insures that t is in the domain of f and that for real numbers "near" t the function values are "near" $f(t)$; geometrically, points $(x, f(x))$ on the graph of f are close to $(t, f(t))$ if x is close to t. If $\lim\limits_{x \to t} f(x) = f(t)$ for every number t in some open interval of the domain of f, then f is said to be continuous in the open interval. If a function is not continuous at t, it is said to be *discontinuous* at t.

In the following examples, for each function f we find the indicated limit and state for what numbers the function is continuous.

Example 12. If $f(x) = \dfrac{x^2 + 9}{x^2 - 4}$, find $\lim\limits_{x \to 3} f(x)$.

$$\lim_{x \to 3} f(x) = \frac{9 + 9}{9 - 4} = \frac{18}{-5}.$$

f is continuous for all real numbers except 2 and -2.

Example 13. If $f(x) = \dfrac{x^2 - 1}{x^3 - 1}$, find $\lim\limits_{x \to 1} f(x)$.

$$\lim_{x \to 1} \frac{x^2 - 1}{x^3 - 1} = \lim_{x \to 1} \frac{(x - 1)(x + 1)}{(x - 1)(x^2 + x + 1)}$$

$$= \lim_{x \to 1} \frac{x + 1}{x^2 + x + 1} = \frac{2}{3}.$$

f is continuous for all real numbers except 1.

Example 14. If $f(x) = \dfrac{\sqrt{x + 1} - 3}{x - 8}$ for $x \neq 8$ and $f(8) = \dfrac{1}{6}$, find $\lim\limits_{x \to 8} f(x)$.

$$\lim_{x \to 8} \frac{\sqrt{x + 1} - 3}{x - 8} = \lim_{x \to 8} \frac{\sqrt{x + 1} - 3}{x - 8} \cdot \frac{\sqrt{x + 1} + 3}{\sqrt{x + 1} + 3}$$

$$= \lim_{x \to 8} \frac{x - 8}{(x - 8)(\sqrt{x + 1} + 3)}$$

$$= \lim_{x \to 8} \frac{1}{\sqrt{x + 1} + 3}$$

$$= \frac{1}{6}.$$

Since $\lim\limits_{x \to 8} f(x) = f(8)$, f is continuous for every x in the domain of the function. That is, f is continuous for $x \geq -1$.

Example 15. If $f(x) = \dfrac{x - 2}{\sqrt[3]{3x + 2} - 2}$ for $x \neq 2$ and $f(2) = 0$, find $\lim\limits_{x \to 2} f(x)$.

$$\lim_{x \to 2} \frac{x - 2}{(3x + 2)^{1/3} - 2} = \lim_{x \to 2} \frac{x - 2}{(3x + 2)^{1/3} - 8^{1/3}}$$

$$\cdot \frac{(3x + 2)^{2/3} + (3x + 2)^{1/3}8^{1/3} + 8^{2/3}}{(3x + 2)^{2/3} + (3x + 2)^{1/3}8^{1/3} + 8^{2/3}}$$

$$= \lim_{x \to 2} \frac{(x - 2)[(3x + 2)^{2/3} + 2(3x + 2)^{1/3} + 4]}{(3x + 2) - 8}$$

$$= \lim_{x \to 2} \frac{(x - 2)[(3x + 2)^{2/3} + 2(3x + 2)^{1/3} + 4]}{3(x - 2)}$$

$$= \lim_{x \to 2} \frac{(3x + 2)^{2/3} + 2(3x + 2)^{1/3} + 4}{3}$$

$$= \frac{12}{3} = 4.$$

Thus f is continuous for all real numbers except 2.

Example 16. If $f(x) = \dfrac{1}{2x^2 + 3x - 14} - \dfrac{1}{3x^2 - x - 10}$, find $\lim\limits_{x \to 2} f(x)$.

$$\lim_{x \to 2} \left[\frac{1}{(2x + 7)(x - 2)} - \frac{1}{(3x + 5)(x - 2)} \right] = \lim_{x \to 2} \frac{(3x + 5) - (2x + 7)}{(2x + 7)(x - 2)(3x + 5)}$$

$$= \lim_{x \to 2} \frac{x - 2}{(2x + 7)(x - 2)(3x + 5)}$$

$$= \lim_{x \to 2} \frac{1}{(2x + 7)(3x + 5)}$$

$$= \frac{1}{(11)(11)} = \frac{1}{121}.$$

Thus f is continuous for all real numbers except 2, $-7/2$, and $-5/3$.

EXERCISES

Find the indicated limits.

1. $\lim\limits_{x \to -5} \dfrac{2x^2 - 3x + 11}{x - 7}$.

2. $\lim\limits_{x \to 3} \left(\dfrac{1}{x + 7} - \dfrac{2x}{3x - 2} \right)$.

3. $\lim\limits_{x \to 0} \dfrac{x^2 + 5x}{2x^2 + 3x}$.

4. $\lim\limits_{x \to 3} \dfrac{x^2 - 9}{x - 3}$.

5. $\lim\limits_{x \to 4} \dfrac{\sqrt{x + 5} - 3}{x - 4}$.

6. $\lim\limits_{x \to 5} \dfrac{x - 5}{\sqrt{3x + 1} - 4}$.

7. $\lim\limits_{x \to -3} \dfrac{\dfrac{x-1}{3x+1} - \dfrac{1}{2}}{x+3}$.

8. $\lim\limits_{x \to 0} \dfrac{x^2}{x}$.

9. $\lim\limits_{x \to t} \dfrac{x^{1/3} - t^{1/3}}{x - t}$.

10. $\lim\limits_{x \to 3} \dfrac{\sqrt[3]{3x-1} - 2}{x - 3}$.

11. $\lim\limits_{x \to t} \dfrac{\dfrac{1}{x^{3/2}} - \dfrac{1}{t^{3/2}}}{x - t}$, $t > 0$.

12. $\lim\limits_{x \to t} \dfrac{x^4 - t^4}{x - t}$.

$\star$**13.** Consider the function f defined by $f(x) = (1 + x)^{1/x}$ where $x > -1$. Use at least seven-place logarithm tables to find the following values. (a) $f(0.01)$. (b) $f(0.001)$. (c) $f(0.0001)$. (d) $f(0.00001)$. (e) $f(-0.01)$. (f) $f(-0.001)$. (g) $f(-0.0001)$. (h) $f(-0.00001)$. (i) Would you assume that this function has a limit as x approaches zero? (j) If so, give a three-place decimal approximation of the limit.

4-3. THE DERIVATIVE

Let f be a function with the real number t in its domain. The derivative of f at t is defined by

$$f'(t) = \lim_{x \to t} \frac{f(x) - f(t)}{x - t},$$

provided this limit exists. The function $\{(t, f'(t))\}$ is called the *derivative* of f and is denoted by f'.

Since the derivative of f at t is the slope of the tangent line to the graph of f at $(t, f(t))$, we already have one application of the derivative. It is geometrically obvious that if $f'(t) > 0$ the slope is positive and the tangent line "leans to the right"; thus, if $f'(t) > 0$ the function must be

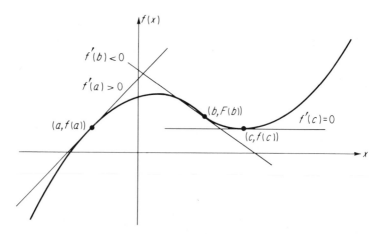

FIG. 4-3. Increasing at $(a, f(a))$.   Decreasing at $(b, f(b))$. $(c, f(c))$ is a minimum point.

increasing at t. Similarly, if $f'(t) < 0$, the function is decreasing at t. Consequently, at a local maximum, or local minimum, the derivative must be zero or undefined. (See Fig. 4-3.) In Chapter 6 we elaborate on these ideas and make an extensive study of the applications of the derivative. First, however, we turn our attention to the differentiation theorems and the techniques for finding derivatives.

Example 1. If f is the constant function defined by $f(x) = c$, where c is a real number, find $f'(t)$.

Solution:

$$f'(t) = \lim_{x \to t} \frac{f(x) - f(t)}{x - t}$$

$$= \lim_{x \to t} \frac{c - c}{x - t}$$

$$= \lim_{x \to t} \frac{0}{x - t}$$

$$= 0,$$

since $\dfrac{0}{x - t} = 0$ for every $x \neq t$. Thus the derivative of a constant function is zero.

Example 2. If f is the identity function defined by $f(x) = x$, find $f'(t)$.

Solution:

$$f'(t) = \lim_{x \to t} \frac{f(x) - f(t)}{x - t}$$

$$= \lim_{x \to t} \frac{x - t}{x - t}$$

$$= 1,$$

since $\dfrac{x - t}{x - t} = 1$ for every $x \neq t$. Thus, the derivative of the identity function is 1.

Example 3. If f is defined by $f(x) = x^{1/2}$ where $x \geq 0$, find $f'(t)$.

Solution:

$$f'(t) = \lim_{x \to t} \frac{x^{1/2} - t^{1/2}}{x - t}$$

$$= \lim_{x \to t} \frac{1}{x^{1/2} + t^{1/2}}$$

$$= \frac{1}{2t^{1/2}},$$

provided $t \neq 0$. Although f is defined for $x \geq 0$, notice that f' is defined only for positive numbers.

Example 4. If f is defined by $f(x) = \dfrac{2x + 7}{x}$, find $f'(3)$.

Solution:

$$f'(3) = \lim_{x \to 3} \frac{\dfrac{2x + 7}{x} - \dfrac{13}{3}}{x - 3}$$

$$= \lim_{x \to 3} \frac{\dfrac{6x + 21 - 13x}{3x}}{x - 3}$$

$$= \lim_{x \to 3} \frac{-7(x - 3)}{3x(x - 3)}$$

$$= \lim_{x \to 3} \frac{-7}{3x}$$

$$= -\frac{7}{9}.$$

Example 5. If f is defined by $f(x) = x^{2/3}$, find $f'(t)$.

Solution:

$$f'(t) = \lim_{x \to t} \frac{x^{2/3} - t^{2/3}}{x - t}$$

$$= \lim_{x \to t} \frac{(x^2)^{1/3} - (t^2)^{1/3}}{x - t} \cdot \frac{(x^2)^{2/3} + (x^2)^{1/3}(t^2)^{1/3} + (t^2)^{2/3}}{(x^2)^{2/3} + (x^2)^{1/3}(t^2)^{1/3} + (t^2)^{2/3}}$$

$$= \lim_{x \to t} \frac{x^2 - t^2}{(x - t)[x^{4/3} + x^{2/3}t^{2/3} + t^{4/3}]}$$

$$= \lim_{x \to t} \frac{x + t}{x^{4/3} + x^{2/3}t^{2/3} + t^{4/3}}$$

$$= \frac{2t}{3t^{4/3}} = \frac{2}{3t^{1/3}}.$$

For a function f, $f'(t)$ is called the *rate of change* of f with respect to the independent variable at t. For example, the function f defined by $f(x) = 16x^2$ gives the distance in feet that a free falling body falls in x seconds; the derivative f' is the rate of change of distance with respect to time and $f'(t) = 32t$ is the velocity in feet per second of a free falling body at the end of t seconds.

Example 6. In an earlier example we established the break-even point by considering the profit function to be linear with positive slope. However, the theory of diminishing returns states there is some level of sales at which the rate of return on sales (profit) will decline either due to inability to maintain price or because of increasing costs of production or both.

Assume that the sales price p is constant for all levels of sales x, but that production cost is an increasing function given by

$$C(x) = F + V\left(\frac{x}{k}\right)^{3/2},$$

where F and V are as previously defined and k is a positive constant. Now

$$P(x) = px - \left[F + V\left(\frac{x}{k}\right)^{3/2}\right].$$

The graphs of the three functions follow the form shown in Fig. 4-4. To find the rate at which profit is changing as production increases we compute $P'(t)$.

$$P'(t) = \lim_{x \to t} \frac{P(x) - P(t)}{x - t}$$

$$= \lim_{x \to t} \frac{\left\{px - \left[F + V\left(\frac{x}{k}\right)^{3/2}\right]\right\} - \left\{pt - \left[F + V\left(\frac{t}{k}\right)^{3/2}\right]\right\}}{x - t}$$

$$= \lim_{x \to t} \left\{\left[\frac{p(x - t)}{x - t}\right] - \frac{V}{k^{3/2}}\left[\frac{x^{3/2} - t^{3/2}}{x - t}\right]\right\}$$

$$= \lim_{x \to t} \left\{p - \left(\frac{V}{k^{3/2}}\right)\left[\frac{x^{3/2} - t^{3/2}}{x - t} \cdot \frac{x^{3/2} + t^{3/2}}{x^{3/2} + t^{3/2}}\right]\right\}$$

$$= p - \frac{V}{k^{3/2}} \lim_{x \to t} \frac{x^3 - t^3}{(x - t)(x^{3/2} + t^{3/2})}$$

$$= p - \frac{V}{k^{3/2}} \lim_{x \to t} \frac{x^2 + xt + t^2}{x^{3/2} + t^{3/2}}$$

$$= p - \frac{3Vt^{1/2}}{2k^{3/2}}.$$

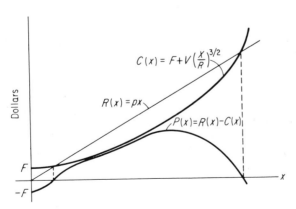

FIG. 4-4

Example 7. It has been observed that the production rate of an employee performing a new task increases as experience is gained in performing the new task. Also as learning progresses the total cost of production decreases not only due to the increased production rate but also due to a reduction in waste of materials and defective production. This phenomenon is often described by a mathematical formula called a *learning curve* which describes the progress of the worker from original instruction in the task to the attainment of a standard production rate. If we let $C(1)$ be the cost of producing the first item and $C(2)$ the cost of the second, the learning parameter a is given by

$$a = \frac{C(2)}{C(1)},$$

or, in general,

$$a = \frac{C(i + 1)}{C(i)}.$$

Thus

$$C(i + 1) = aC(i).$$

If we decompose this last formula by

$$C(2) = aC(1)$$
$$C(3) = aC(2) = a^2C(1)$$
$$C(4) = aC(3) = a^3C(1)$$
$$\cdot \quad \cdot \quad \cdot \quad \cdot \quad \cdot$$
$$C(i + 1) = aC(i) = a^iC(1),$$

which should be recognized as a geometric sequence with $r = a$, and if learning does reduce cost, $C(i + 1) < C(i)$ and thus $0 < a < 1$. The total cost of producing n items is

$$S_n = \frac{C(1) - C(1)a^n}{1 - a}.$$

(It has been shown that this formulation of the learning curve is rather inaccurate in that cost reduction is considerably slower than that given by the formula. The major reason for this inaccuracy is that $a \neq \dfrac{C(i + 1)}{C(i)}$ for all i. We shall, however, postpone development of a more accurate curve until a later chapter.)

The graph of the learning curve generally resembles the one shown in Fig. 4-5. If we wish to compute the rate at which the cost of producing an item is decreasing we must first reconcile a contradiction between our function (sequence) and the conditions under which the derivative exists. In Fig. 4-5 the discrete points which represent the cost of producing the ith unit have been joined by a continuous curve which is the graph of $f(x) =$

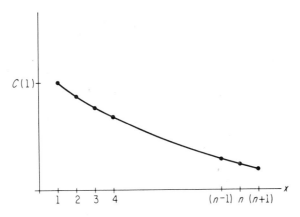

FIG. 4-5. Learning curve.

$\dfrac{C(1) - C(1)a^x}{1 - a}$. This same difficulty arises in many (if not most) applications of the calculus to business decision processes and the means of
reconciling the contradiction is by considering the function to have the set
of all real numbers as its domain and to adjust solutions to restore the
discrete nature of the independent variable. Making this assumption,

$$f'(t) = \lim_{x \to t} \frac{f(x) - f(t)}{x - t}$$

$$= \lim_{x \to t} \frac{\dfrac{C(1) - C(1)a^x}{1 - a} - \dfrac{C(1) - C(1)a^t}{1 - a}}{x - t}$$

$$= \lim_{x \to t} \frac{-C(1)(a^x - a^t)}{(1 - a)(x - t)}$$

$$= \frac{-C(1)}{1 - a} \lim_{x \to t} \frac{a^x - a^t}{x - t}.$$

This final limit exists but requires application of techniques not yet introduced and will therefore be deferred until Chapter 9.

If f is a function differentiable at t, then $\lim\limits_{x \to t} \dfrac{f(x) - f(t)}{x - t}$ exists. Since
$\lim\limits_{x \to t} (x - t) = 0$, for $\dfrac{f(x) - f(t)}{x - t}$ to have a limit as x approaches t,
$\lim\limits_{x \to t} [f(x) - f(t)]$ must have zero as its limit. Hence, $f(x)$ must be "close"
to $f(t)$ when x is "close" to t; this means f is continuous at t. We now
prove the important fact that every differentiable function is continuous.

Assume $f'(t)$ exists. Since $f(x) = \dfrac{f(x) - f(t)}{x - t} (x - t) + f(t)$ for every $x \neq t$,

$$\lim_{x \to t} f(x) = \lim_{x \to t} \left[\frac{f(x) - f(t)}{x - t} (x - t) + f(t) \right]$$

$$= \lim_{x \to t} \frac{f(x) - f(t)}{x - t} \lim_{x \to t} (x - t) + \lim_{x \to t} f(t).$$

Notice that $f(t)$ is a constant and thus $\lim_{x \to t} f(t) = f(t)$. Therefore

$$\lim_{x \to t} f(x) = f'(t)[0] + f(t)$$

and

$$\lim_{x \to t} f(x) = f(t).$$

Consequently, f is continuous at t by the definition of continuity.

EXERCISES

1. If f is defined by $f(x) = x^3$, find $f'(t)$.
2. If f is defined by $f(x) = x^5$, find $f'(t)$.
3. If f is defined by $f(x) = x^{1/2}$, find $f'(t)$.
4. If f is defined by $f(x) = x^{1/3}$, find $f'(t)$.
5. If f is defined by $f(x) = x^{-1/2}$, find $f'(t)$.
6. If f is the function defined by $f(x) = x^r$ where r is a rational number, what conjecture would you make concerning $f'(t)$?

7. (a) If f is defined by $f(x) = \dfrac{x^2 + 1}{x}$, find $f'(t)$. (b) For what numbers is the derivative zero? (c) Solve $f'(t) < 0$. (d) Solve $f'(t) > 0$.

8. Consider the continuous function f defined by $f(x) = |x|$. Graph f and show that $f'(0)$ does not exist.

9. (a) If f is defined by $f(x) = \dfrac{8}{3} x^3 + 18x^2 + 36x + 12$, find $f'(t)$. (b) For what numbers is the derivative zero? (c) Solve $f'(t) < 0$. (d) Solve $f'(t) > 0$.

10. (a) If in Example 6 of Sec. 4-3 we let $p = \$25$, $F = \$250,000$, $V = \$10$ and $k = 500$, find the rate of change in profit. (b) Graph the three functions and approximate the point at which the profit rate is maximum. (c) Evaluate the derivative at this point. (d) What can you surmise about the tangent to the graph of the profit function P at its maximum point?

11. For Example 7 of Sec. 4-3, find how many items must be produced to reduce the initial production cost to one half the cost of the first item if the learning parameter $a = 0.9$.

5

Techniques of Differentiation

5-1. DERIVATIVE OF THE SUM OF TWO FUNCTIONS

It should be clear after working through the examples and exercises of Chapter 4 that finding the derivative of a function by direct use of the definition can be quite complicated. We turn our attention now to stating and proving the general differentiation theorems which simplify the task of finding derivatives by providing routine procedures for differentiation.

In Chapter 4 we proved that if f is defined by $f(x) = c$, then $f'(t) = 0$; furthermore, if $f(x) = x$, then $f'(t) = 1$. We now prove that if $f(x) = x^n$ for any positive integer n, then $f'(t) = nt^{n-1}$.

Theorem 5-1. If f is defined by $f(x) = x^n$ for any positive integer n, then $f'(t) = n \cdot t^{n-1}$.

Proof:

$$f'(t) = \lim_{x \to t} \frac{f(x) - f(t)}{x - t}$$

$$= \lim_{x \to t} \frac{x^n - t^n}{x - t}$$

$$= \lim_{x \to t} \frac{(x - t)(x^{n-1} + x^{n-2}t + x^{n-3}t^2 + \cdots + xt^{n-2} + t^{n-1})}{x - t}$$

$$= \lim_{x \to t} (x^{n-1} + x^{n-2}t + x^{n-3}t^2 + \cdots + xt^{n-2} + t^{n-1})$$

$$= \underbrace{(t^{n-1} + t^{n-1} + t^{n-1} + \cdots + t^{n-1} + t^{n-1})}_{n \text{ terms}}$$

$$= n \cdot t^{n-1}.$$

Example 1. If f is defined by $f(x) = x^6$, then $f'(t) = 6t^5$ for any real number t. Since the letter used to define a function is immaterial, f' could be defined by $f'(u) = 6u^5$, $f'(y) = 6y^5$, or $f'(x) = 6x^5$. For 2 in the domain of f, we have $f'(2) = 6(2)^5 = 192$.

Let g be the function defined by $g(x) = 8x^3$. Since the derivative of f defined by $f(x) = x^3$ is given by $f'(t) = 3t^2$, we would like to assert that g' is given by $g'(t) = 8f'(t) = 8(3t^2) = 24t^2$. More precisely, we want

73

to prove that the derivative of $g(x) = cf(x)$, where c is a given real number (constant), is given by $g'(t) = cf'(t)$, provided f is a differentiable function. This fact is often stated as *the derivative of a constant times a function is the constant times the derivative of the function.*

Theorem 5-2. Let f be a differentiable function. If g is a function defined by $g(x) = cf(x)$ where c is a real number, then $g'(t) = cf'(t)$.

Proof:

$$g'(t) = \lim_{x \to t} \frac{g(x) - g(t)}{x - t} \qquad \text{[Definition of } g'(t).]$$

$$= \lim_{x \to t} \frac{cf(x) - cf(t)}{x - t} \qquad \text{[Definition of } g(x).]$$

$$= \lim_{x \to t} \frac{c[f(x) - f(t)]}{x - t} \qquad \text{[Factoring.]}$$

$$= c \lim_{x \to t} \frac{f(x) - f(t)}{x - t} \qquad \begin{array}{l}\text{[The limit of a constant times a} \\ \text{function is the constant times the} \\ \text{limit of the function.]}\end{array}$$

$$= cf'(t). \qquad \begin{array}{l}\text{[The limit of the Newton quotient} \\ \text{for } f \text{ at } t \text{ is } f'(t) \text{ since it is given} \\ \text{that } f \text{ is differentiable.]}\end{array}$$

Example 2. Let $h(x) = 9x^5$. Then, $h'(x) = 45x^4$ and $h'(1) = 45$. [Note that $h'(2)$ is the value of the derivative of h at 2. Unfortunately, a student occasionally reasons incorrectly as follows. Since $h(2) = 9(2)^5 = 288$, $h'(2) = 0$. This is a misunderstanding of the notation for derivative.]

Theorems 5-1 and 5-2 can be used in a rather trivial way to find the derivative of any polynomial function. If h is defined by $h(x) = x^4 + 6x^3$, then $h'(x) = 4x^3 + 18x^2$. More precisely, if h is the sum of two differentiable functions f and g ($h = f + g$), then h is differentiable and $h' = f' + g'$; that is, $h'(t) = f'(t) + g'(t)$. This theorem is often stated as *the derivative of the sum of two functions is the sum of the derivatives.* Occasionally, we do not choose to introduce a letter, such as h, to represent the sum of f and g. In such a case, the symbolism $(f + g)'$ is used to denote the derivative of the sum of f and g, and this differentiation rule is stated as $(f + g)' = f' + g'$.

Theorem 5-3. Let h be the sum of two differentiable functions f and g. Then, $h'(t) = f'(t) + g'(t)$.

Proof:

$$h'(t) = \lim_{x \to t} \frac{h(x) - h(t)}{x - t}$$

$$= \lim_{x \to t} \frac{[f(x) + g(x)] - [f(t) + g(t)]}{x - t}$$

$$= \lim_{x \to t} \frac{[f(x) - f(t)] + [g(x) - g(t)]}{x - t}$$

$$= \lim_{x \to t} \frac{f(x) - f(t)}{x - t} + \lim_{x \to t} \frac{g(x) - g(t)}{x - t}$$

$$= f'(t) + g'(t).$$

If h is the sum of three differentiable functions u, v, and w, then h can be defined by $h = u + (v + w)$. Thus, $h' = u' + (v + w)'$, and by the repeated use of Theorem 5-3, $h' = u' + v' + w'$. More generally, the derivative of the sum of a finite number of differentiable functions is the sum of the derivatives of the functions. Consequently, if $F(x) = 7x^4 + 11x^3 + 3x^2 + x + 17$, then $F'(x) = 28x^3 + 33x^2 + 6x + 1$.

Let f and g be two differentiable functions. If $h = f - g$, then $h = f + (-g) = f + (-1)g$. Thus

$$h' = f' + (-1)g'$$

$$= f' - g'.$$

In other words, *the derivative of the difference of two differentiable functions is the difference of the derivatives.* For example, if $h(x) = 3x^5 - x^2$, then $h'(x) = 15x^4 - 2x$.

EXERCISES

In Exercises 1 through 6, find $f'(x)$ and $f'(2)$.

1. $f(x) = 12x^3 + 5x - 3$. **2.** $f(x) = 14x^2 - 6x + 8$.
3. $f(x) = 5x^4 - 13x^2$. **4.** $f(x) = x^3/3 + 11x$.
5. $f(x) = x^5/2 - 42$. **6.** $f(x) = 19x + 3$.

In Exercises 7 through 12, solve (a) $f'(x) = 0$, (b) $f'(x) < 0$, and (c) $f'(x) > 0$.

7. $f(x) = x^3 - 3$. **8.** $f(x) = x^2 + 4$.
9. $f(x) = 3x + 11$. **10.** $f(x) = 11$.
11. $f(x) = 2x^3 - 15x^2 - 36x + 11$. **12.** $f(x) = x^3 - 6x$.
13. If $f(x) = (3x + 5)^3$, find $f'(x)$.
14. If $f(x) = (x^2 + 3)^3$, find $f'(x)$.
15. If f is defined by $f(x) = x^3 - 4x^2 + 7x - 5$, for what x is $f'(x) = 3$?
16. If the revenue function R is given by $R(x) = 10x - x^2/100$, and the cost function C is given by $C(x) = 75 + 5x + x^2/500$, find the rate at which the profit function $P(x) = R(x) - C(x)$ is changing.
17. In economics, marginal revenue is defined as the derivative of the revenue function, and marginal cost is defined as the derivative of the cost function. According to a theorem which will be proved in Chapter 6, total profit is maximum when marginal revenue equals marginal cost. For

the functions given in Exercise 16, find the level of production which produces the largest profit.

5-2. DERIVATIVE OF THE PRODUCT OF TWO FUNCTIONS

Although the derivative of a constant times a function is the constant times the derivative of the function and the derivative of the sum of two functions is the sum of the derivatives, it is generally *not* true that the derivative of the product of two functions is the product of the derivatives. This fact is easy to illustrate. Let h be defined by $h(x) = x^7$. From Theorem 5-1, we have that $h'(x) = 7x^6$. Now, h can be expressed as a product fg, where $f(x) = x^3$ and $g(x) = x^4$. Since $f'(x) = 3x^2$ and $g'(x) = 4x^3$ and since $(3x^2)(4x^3) \neq 7x^6$, obviously $h' \neq f'g'$. We now state and prove the product theorem.

Theorem 5-4. Let f and g be differentiable functions and let h be the product function defined by $h(x) = f(x)g(x)$. Then

$$h'(t) = f(t)g'(t) + f'(t)g(t).$$

Proof:

(1) $\quad h'(t) = \lim_{x \to t} \dfrac{h(x) - h(t)}{x - t}$

(2) $\quad = \lim_{x \to t} \dfrac{f(x)g(x) - f(t)g(t)}{x - t}$

(3) $\quad = \lim_{x \to t} \dfrac{f(x)g(x) - f(x)g(t) + f(x)g(t) - f(t)g(t)}{x - t}$

(4) $\quad = \lim_{x \to t} f(x) \dfrac{[g(x) - g(t)]}{x - t} + \lim_{x \to t} g(t) \dfrac{[f(x) - f(t)]}{x - t}$

(5) $\quad = \lim_{x \to t} f(x) \lim_{x \to t} \dfrac{g(x) - g(t)}{x - t} + g(t) \lim_{x \to t} \dfrac{f(x) - f(t)}{x - t}$

(6) $\quad = f(t)g'(t) + g(t) f'(t).$

Let us first review each step in the proof of Theorem 5-4 to be certain the proof is clear. Step 1 follows from the definition of the derivative of h at t. Step 2 follows from the definition of h. In step 3 we add $f(x)g(t) - f(x)g(t)$ (that is, zero) to the numerator of the fraction. In step 4 we use some elementary algebraic identities and the fact that the limit of a sum is the sum of the limits; of course, we must prove that the individual limits exist. In step 5 we use the fact that the limit of a product is the product of the limits; again, we must show that the limits exist. Since $g(t)$ is a constant, we use the fact that the limit of a constant times a function is the constant times the limit of the function to obtain $g(t) \lim_{x \to t} \dfrac{f(x) - f(t)}{x - t}$. Since it is given that f is differentiable, we conclude that $\lim\limits_{x \to t} \dfrac{f(x) - f(t)}{x - t} = f'(t)$; similarly, $\lim\limits_{x \to t} \dfrac{g(x) - g(t)}{x - t} = g'(t)$. To jus-

tify the fact that $\lim\limits_{x \to t} f(x) = f(t)$, we need only recall that the differenti-

bility of f implies that f is continuous, and, by definition, f is continuous at t if and only if $\lim\limits_{x \to t} f(x) = f(t)$.

Returning to our example where $h(x) = x^7 = f(x)g(x)$, $f(x) = x^3$, and $g(x) = x^4$, we verify the product theorem. Since $f'(x) = 3x^2$ and $g'(x) = 4x^3$,

$$
\begin{aligned}
h'(x) &= f(x)g'(x) + f'(x)g(x) \\
&= (x^3)(4x^3) + (3x^2)(x^4) \\
&= 4x^6 + 3x^6 \\
&= 7x^6,
\end{aligned}
$$

the desired result.

If h is the product of three differentiable functions u, v, and w, then h can be defined by $h = u(vw)$. Thus, $h' = u(vw)' + u'(vw)$, and by repeated use of Theorem 5-4,

$$h' = u(vw' + v'w) + u'(vw).$$

Thus,

$$h' = uvw' + uv'w + u'vw.$$

It is important to notice that if $u = v = w$, then $h' = 3u^2u'$. For example, if $h(x) = (x^2 + 5x + 2)^3$, then h is the product of three equal functions u defined by $u(x) = x^2 + 5x + 2$; hence,

$$
\begin{aligned}
h'(x) &= 3[u(x)]^2 u'(x) \\
&= 3(x^2 + 5x + 2)^2(2x + 5).
\end{aligned}
$$

It should be clear that finding the derivative of h by this method is easier than expanding $(x^2 + 5x + 2)^3$ and then differentiating the resulting polynomial term by term.

EXERCISES

In Exercises 1 through 6, find $f'(x)$.

1. $f(x) = (x^2 + 3x + 5)(x^2 - 3x + 7)$.
2. $f(x) = (x^3 + 7x - 1)(x^2 + 2x + 5)$.
3. $f(x) = (x^3 + 7x^2 + 3x + 11)^2$.
4. $f(x) = (x^3 - 5x + 1)^3$.
5. $f(x) = (3x^5 + 7x^2 - 2)^3$.
6. $f(x) = (x - 3)(2x + 1)(5x - 7)$.
7. (a) If u, v, w, and z are differentiable functions and $h = uvwz$, show that $h' = u'vwz + uv'wz + uvw'z + uvwz'$. (b) Use part (a) to find the derivative of h if $h(x) = (2x + 3)(3x^2 + 11)(5x - 11)(x^3 + 7)$. (Do not simplify your answer.) (c) Prove that if u is a differentiable function

and $h(x) = [u(x)]^4$, then $h'(x) = 4[u(x)]^3 u'(x)$. (d) Use part (c) to find the derivative of $h(x) = (3x^3 + 7x + 2)^4$.

⋆8. Use the product theorem and mathematical induction to prove that if $f(x) = x^n$, then $f'(x) = nx^{n-1}$ for every positive integer n. (HINT: $x^{k+1} = x^k \cdot x$.)

⋆9. Assume that f is a differential function. Use the product theorem and mathematical induction to prove that if $h(x) = [f(x)]^n$, then $h'(x) = n[f(x)]^{n-1} f'(x)$ for every positive integer n. Show that the theorem in Exercise 8 is a special case of this theorem.

5-3. DERIVATIVE OF THE QUOTIENT OF TWO FUNCTIONS

In the preceding section it was proved that *the derivative of the product of two functions is the first factor times the derivative of the second plus the second factor times the derivative of the first.* We now prove that *the derivative of the quotient of two functions is the denominator times the derivative of the numerator less the numerator times the derivative of the denominator all divided by the denominator squared.*

Theorem 5-5. Let f and g be differentiable functions and let h be the quotient defined by $h(x) = \dfrac{f(x)}{g(x)}$. Then

$$h'(t) = \frac{g(t)f'(t) - f(t)g'(t)}{[g(t)]^2},$$

provided $g(t) \neq 0$.

Proof:

$$h'(t) = \lim_{x \to t} \frac{h(x) - h(t)}{x - t}$$

$$= \lim_{x \to t} \frac{\dfrac{f(x)}{g(x)} - \dfrac{f(t)}{g(t)}}{x - t}$$

$$= \lim_{x \to t} \frac{f(x)g(t) - g(x)f(t)}{g(x)g(t)(x - t)}$$

$$= \lim_{x \to t} \frac{f(x)g(t) - f(t)g(t) - g(x)f(t) + f(t)g(t)}{g(x)g(t)(x - t)}$$

$$= \lim_{x \to t} \frac{g(t)}{g(x)g(t)} \cdot \frac{f(x) - f(t)}{x - t} - \lim_{x \to t} \frac{f(t)}{g(x)g(t)} \cdot \frac{g(x) - g(t)}{x - t}$$

$$= \lim_{x \to t} \frac{g(t)}{g(x)g(t)} \lim_{x \to t} \frac{f(x) - f(t)}{x - t} - \lim_{x \to t} \frac{f(t)}{g(x)g(t)} \lim_{x \to t} \frac{g(x) - g(t)}{x - t}$$

$$= \frac{g(t)}{[g(t)]^2} \cdot f'(t) - \frac{f(t)}{[g(t)]^2} \cdot g'(t)$$

$$= \frac{g(t)f'(t) - f(t)g'(t)}{[g(t)]^2}.$$

The steps in the proof of this theorem are rather similar to the steps in the proof of the product theorem with one important exception. Although it is given that $g(t) \neq 0$, it need not be true that $g(x) \neq 0$ for every x in the domain of g so we must be concerned about $g(x)$ being zero in the denominator in some of the steps of the proof. Since g is differentiable, it is continuous; furthermore, since $g(t) \neq 0$, there must exist an interval containing t such that $g(x) \neq 0$ for every x in this interval. Roughly speaking, if the graph of a continuous function is above the x-axis at t, the graph must be above the axis in some interval containing t. (This geometrically obvious theorem is not easy to prove.) We assume in the proof of the quotient theorem that x is in an interval containing t such that $g(x) \neq 0$.

Earlier, we proved that if $f(x) = x^p$ where p is a positive integer, then $f'(x) = px^{p-1}$. The quotient theorem can be used to prove that this formula is also valid if p is a negative integer. Let $p = -n$ be a negative integer. If $f(x) = x^p = x^{-n}$, then

$$f(x) = \frac{1}{x^n},$$

where n is a positive integer. Using the quotient theorem,

$$f'(x) = \frac{x^n(0) - 1(n)x^{n-1}}{(x^n)^2}$$

$$= \frac{-nx^{n-1}}{x^{2n}}$$

$$= -nx^{-n-1}$$

$$= px^{p-1}.$$

To prove this result when $p = 0$ is trivial; thus if $f(x) = x^p$, then $f'(x) = px^{p-1}$ for any integer p. In the next section we shall prove that if $f(x) = x^p$, where p is any rational number, then $f'(x) = px^{p-1}$.

Example 1. One of the major applications of mathematics to business decision processes is in the area of inventory control, or, as it is frequently called, *inventory theory*. Basic to this application is the square root formula for order size. To develop this model we must first note the hypotheses and assumptions underlying its formulation.

1. The firm buys and sells only one product.

2. Demand for the product is known and is constant throughout a stated time period.

3. Deliveries to the firm are instantaneous. The consequence of this assumption is that the firm will always let the inventory of the product become zero before ordering a new shipment.

4. Orders from customers must be filled when the order is placed. This assumption prohibits back orders or what might be considered negative inventory.

5. The firm is concerned with only three costs: C_1, the purchase price

of the product. C_2, the cost of placing an order including such factors as the clerical costs, delivery charges, cost of initial warehousing, inspection costs, etc. This cost is independent of the size of the order. C_3, the cost of holding one unit in inventory per time period where the time period is the same as that in assumption 2. This cost includes such items as interest on capital invested in inventory, deterioration, insurance, etc.

As a consequence of assumptions 2, 3, and 4 the number of units of the product in inventory will follow the "sawtooth" graph as shown in Fig. 5-1. It should be noted that the graph is not really smooth as shown in the figure because the number of units in inventory is necessarily an integer.

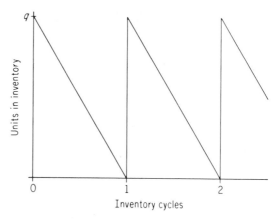

FIG. 5-1

Letting q be the quantity ordered on each order, we shall refer to the time period required to sell q units as an inventory cycle. Since demand— and thus sales—is constant throughout the cycle it should be obvious that the average inventory during a cycle is $q/2$. Letting D be the demand for a year, the total number of orders placed during the year will be D/q. Since D was stated as the annual demand, C_3 must be stated as the cost of carrying one unit in inventory for one year, and, as we have already seen, the average number in inventory is $q/2$.

Based upon these assumptions, the total cost of providing the product for one year may be stated as

$$\text{Total cost} = \begin{array}{c}\text{total cost} \\ \text{of purchase}\end{array} + \begin{array}{c}\text{total ordering} \\ \text{cost}\end{array} + \begin{array}{c}\text{total holding} \\ \text{cost}\end{array}$$

$$TC(q) = C_1 D + C_2 \frac{D}{q} + C_3 \frac{q}{2}, \text{ for } 0 < q \le D.$$

The domain of q is the half open interval $(0, D]$. By assumption 4, we cannot make the decision to do nothing; also, it would be economic nonsense to order more than is required for the entire year since unnecessary holding costs would be incurred.

Obviously $TC(q)$ is not a continuous function since it is defined only for integral values of q, but, by making a continuity assumption as explained in Chapter 4, the rate at which total costs are changing as the order size is varied is given by

$$TC'(q) = -C_2 \frac{D}{q^2} + \frac{C_3}{2}.$$

Since the rational entrepreneur would search for the order size which leads to the lowest total cost, we search for the number in the range for which $TC(q)$ is a minimum. As shown in the next chapter, if $TC'(q)$ is negative then $TC(q)$ is decreasing, and if $TC'(q) > 0$, then $TC(q)$ is increasing. We note that

$$-C_2 \frac{D}{q^2} + \frac{C_3}{2} > 0 \qquad \text{if } C_2 \frac{D}{q^2} < \frac{C_3}{2}$$

$$-C_2 \frac{D}{q^2} + \frac{C_3}{2} < 0 \qquad \text{if } C_2 \frac{D}{q^2} > \frac{C_3}{2}$$

$$TC'(q) = 0 \qquad \text{if } -C_2 \frac{D}{q^2} + \frac{C_3}{2} = 0.$$

Solving the last expression yields

$$q = \sqrt{\frac{2DC_2}{C_3}}.$$

Since the function is decreasing to the left of $\sqrt{\dfrac{2DC_2}{C_3}}$ and increasing to the right of this number, this number makes $TC(q)$ a minimum.

To verify geometrically that $\sqrt{\dfrac{2DC_2}{C_3}}$ is the order size which leads to the minimum value of $TC(q)$, we first note that $C_1 D$ is a constant and although it affects the minimum value of $TC(q)$ it does not affect the determination of the q which makes the function a minimum. Now consider the graphs $O(q) = C_2 \dfrac{D}{q}$, $H(q) = C_3 \dfrac{q}{2}$, and $TC(q) = C_2 \dfrac{D}{q} + C_3 \dfrac{q}{2}$ as shown in Fig. 5-2. From the figure, we see that the minimum total cost coincides with the intersection of the graphs of the ordering cost and holding cost. Solving for this intersection, from

$$C_2 \frac{D}{q} = C_3 \frac{q}{2}$$

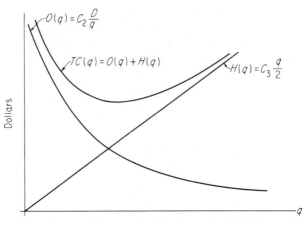

FIG. 5-2

we obtain

$$q = \sqrt{\frac{2DC_2}{C_3}}.$$

The number $\sqrt{\dfrac{2DC_2}{C_3}}$ is referred to as the *economic lot size* or economic order quantity. We shall further investigate this model and its derivation in later chapters.

EXERCISES

1. If $f(x) = \dfrac{1}{x}$, find $f'(x)$.

2. If $f(x) = \dfrac{x^2 + 7x + 2}{x + 2}$, find $f'(1)$.

3. If $f(x) = \dfrac{x^2 + 3x + 4}{x + 3}$, for what x is $f'(x) = 0$? $f'(x) > 0$? $f'(x) < 0$?

4. If $f(x) = \dfrac{2x^2 + 3x - 3}{x + 5}$, for what x is $f'(x) = 0$? $f'(x) > 0$? $f'(x) < 0$?

5. If $f(x) = \dfrac{x^3 + 5x^2 - 7x}{x^2 + 1}$, find $f'(x)$.

6. If $g(x) = \dfrac{x}{x^2 + 1}$, find $g'(x)$.

7. If $f(x) = \dfrac{3x + 5}{2x - 1}$, find $f'(x)$.

8. If $f(x) = \left(\dfrac{3x - 7}{x^2 + 4}\right)^2$, find $f'(x)$.

9. In earlier examples and exercises we have frequently used the function $C(x) = F + Vx$, where $C(x)$ is the total cost of producing x units of the product. Let C_a be the average cost per unit of product. C_a may be computed by noting that the cost of each unit is composed of the unit variable cost plus the incremental fixed cost. Thus $C_a = V + F/x$. Let the sales price of the product be p and suppose there exists some upper level of the sales price P_0 at which no sales will be made. For p in the interval $0 < p \leq P_0$, it is known that the total sales of the product is given by $x = P_0/p - 1$. Assuming that production is set at the same level as sales and recalling that profit is the difference between sales revenue and production costs, find the rate at which profit changes as the sales price is varied.

5-4. COMPOSITE FUNCTION THEOREM

For differentiable functions f and g, we have proved the following:

$$(f + g)' = f' + g'$$
$$(f - g)' = f' - g'$$
$$(fg)' = fg' + f'g$$
$$(f/g)' = \frac{gf' - fg'}{g^2}.$$

Our final general differentiation theorem is called the composite function theorem for differentiation; it gives us the technique for finding the derivative of $f(g)$, the composition of two differentiable functions.

Theorem 5-6. Let f and g be differentiable functions. If $h(x) = f(g(x))$, then

$$h'(x) = f'(g(x)) \cdot g'(x).$$

The composite function theorem, which is frequently called the *Chain Rule*, often is stated in the following way: *The derivative of f of g is f' of g times g'.* Symbolically,

$$[f(g)]' = f'(g) \cdot g'.$$

In this theorem, it should be noted that $f'(g)$ is the composition of the derivative of f and g. For example, let $h(x) = (x^2 + 2x + 3)^{15}$, $f(x) = x^{15}$, and $g(x) = x^2 + 2x + 3$. Then

$$h(x) = f(g(x)) = (x^2 + 2x + 3)^{15}.$$

Since $f'(x) = 15x^{14}, f'(g(x)) = 15(x^2 + 2x + 3)^{14}$, and $g'(x) = 2x + 2$,

$$h'(x) = 15(x^2 + 2x + 3)^{14}(2x + 2).$$

We now prove three significant consequences of the composite function theorem.

I. Let g be a differentiable function and let $h(x) = [g(x)]^n$ where n is an integer. If we let $f(x) = x^n$, then $f'(x) = nx^{n-1}$ and $h(x) = f(g(x))$. Hence

$$h'(x) = f'(g(x)) \cdot g'(x)$$
$$= n[g(x)]^{n-1} g'(x).$$

In other words, the derivative of a function to the nth power is n times the function raised to the $(n - 1)$st power times the derivative of the function. (See Sec. 5-2, Exercise 9, for a different proof of this important result when n is a positive integer. Note that in this proof we used the result proved in Sec. 5-3 that $f'(x) = nx^{n-1}$ for any *integer*.)

Example 1. If $h(x) = (2x^3 + 7x - 1)^{-3}$, then
$$h'(x) = -3(2x^3 + 7x - 1)^{-4}(6x^2 + 7).$$

II. Let g be defined by $g(x) = x^{1/n}$ where $x > 0$. Thus, $[g(x)]^n = x$. Since $[g(x)]^n$ is the identity function, its derivative is 1; that is,

$$n[g(x)]^{n-1} g'(x) = 1$$

$$g'(x) = \frac{1}{n[g(x)]^{n-1}}$$

$$= \frac{1}{n[x^{1/n}]^{n-1}}$$

$$= \frac{1}{nx^{1-1/n}}$$

$$= \frac{1}{n} x^{1/n-1}.$$

Hence for a positive rational p of the form $1/n$, where n is a positive integer, if $g(x) = x^p$, then $g'(x) = px^{p-1}$.

III. Let $h(x) = x^{m/n}$, where $x > 0$, m and n are integers, and $n > 0$. (Notice that assuming $n > 0$ places no restriction on the sign of the rational number m/n.) Now,

$$h(x) = (x^{1/n})^m.$$

Combining the results of I and II,

$$h'(x) = m(x^{1/n})^{m-1} \cdot \frac{1}{n} x^{1/n-1}$$

$$= \frac{m}{n} x^{m/n - 1/n} \cdot x^{1/n-1}$$

$$= \frac{m}{n} x^{m/n-1}.$$

Thus if p is any rational number and $h(x) = x^p$, then $h'(x) = px^{p-1}$.

EXERCISES

1. Let $h(x) = [g(x)]^p$, where $g(x) > 0$ and p is any rational number. If g is differentiable, prove that $h'(x) = p[g(x)]^{p-1}g'(x)$.

In Exercises 2 through 10 find the derivative of the functions defined.

2. $h(x) = x^2(x^3 - 7x)^{11}$.

3. $t(x) = x(x^2 + 1)^{3/2}$.

4. $g(x) = (2x + 1)\sqrt{x^2 + 9}$.

5. $h(x) = \dfrac{\sqrt{x^2 + 1}}{2x + 1}$.

6. $h(x) = \dfrac{(x^2 + 5x + 1)^{1/3}}{5x - 2}$.

7. $g(x) = x^2(3x^3 + 1)^{2/3}$.

8. $f(x) = \sqrt{\dfrac{3x + 1}{2x - 5}}$.

9. $f(x) = [(x^2 + 1)^{1/2} + 7x]^2$.

10. $h(x) = \sqrt{3x + \sqrt{x^2 + 4}}$.

11. $f(x) = x\sqrt{5x + 7}$.

5-5. HIGHER DERIVATIVES AND IMPLICIT DIFFERENTIATION

As we shall learn in the next chapter, it is often quite important to study the derivative of the derivative of some function f. For this reason, the derivative f' is sometimes called the *first derivative of* f. The derivative of f' is often denoted by f'' and is called the *second derivative of* f. For example, if

$$f(x) = x^2,$$

then

$$f'(x) = 2x$$

and

$$f''(x) = 2.$$

The derivative of the second derivative is called the *third derivative of* f; in general, the derivative of the nth derivative of f where n is a positive integer is called the $(n + 1)$st derivative of f. The third derivative of f is often denoted by f'''. The nth derivatives of f where $n \geq 2$ are called *higher derivatives of* f.

It should be obvious that although the symbol f''''' could be used for the fifth derivative it is not a very good choice of notation. This leads us to discuss some of the other (and often used) notations for derivatives. For a function f, if we let $y = f(x)$, then the following are all standard notations for the first derivative:

$$f', \quad D_x y, \quad f'(x), \quad y', \quad \frac{dy}{dx}, \quad \frac{d}{dx}f(x), \quad \text{and} \quad Df(x).$$

The most used notations for the second derivative are the following:

$$f''(x), \quad y'', \quad \frac{d^2 y}{dx^2}, \quad \frac{d^2}{dx^2}f(x), \quad \text{and} \quad D_x^2 y.$$

The following are all notations for the fourth derivative of f:

$$f^{(\mathrm{IV})}(x),\quad f^{(4)}(x),\quad \frac{d^4 y}{dx^4},\quad \frac{d^4}{dx^4}f(x),\quad \text{and}\quad D_x^4 y.$$

Although there are several frequently used notations for the first derivative, we have intentionally avoided the introduction of the other notations until now for two reasons. (1) The extra unfamiliar and unnecessary notation is an additional burden that tends to interfere with grasping the derivative concept and the differentiation theorems. (2) Occasionally, the mnemonic advantages of the $\dfrac{dy}{dx}$ notation obscure the basic features of the composite function theorem. Let us explain this last remark.

Suppose $y = f(g(x))$ and $u = g(x)$. Then $y = f(u)$. Now

$$\frac{dy}{dx} = [f(g(x))]',\quad \frac{du}{dx} = g'(x),\quad \text{and}\quad \frac{dy}{du} = f'(u) = f'(g(x)).$$

Hence, since

$$[f(g(x))]' = f'(g(x)) \cdot g'(x),$$

then

$$\frac{dy}{dx} = \frac{dy}{du} \cdot \frac{du}{dx}.$$

If we were allowed to treat dy/dx as a fraction, then the second expression for the composite function theorem is "obviously" valid. Although it is not easy to prove, the notation dy/dx can be treated as a fraction; thus, the notation serves as a memory device for remembering some of the differentiation theorems. For example, if $F(x) = f(g(h(x)))$, then by repeated use of the composite function theorem we can prove that

$$F'(x) = f'(g(h(x))) \cdot g'(h(x)) \cdot h'(x).$$

If we let $u = h(x)$, $v = g(u)$, and $F = f(v)$, then the formula for $F'(x)$ is equivalent to

$$\frac{dF}{dx} = \frac{dF}{dv} \cdot \frac{dv}{du} \cdot \frac{du}{dx}.$$

To this point in the section we have only defined what is meant by higher derivatives and discussed derivative notation. Let us again turn our attention to techniques for finding the derivatives of functions. This is the last "tool" we present for finding derivatives before discussing many of the important applications of differential calculus.

For the equation $x^2 + y^2 = 25$, the set S of ordered pairs (x, y) satisfying this equation is not a function since, for example $(3, 4)$ and $(3, -4)$ are in S. (See Fig. 5-3.) However, if we restrict $y \geq 0$, the set of pairs (x, y) satisfying $x^2 + y^2 = 25$ is a function. In fact, the graph of this func-

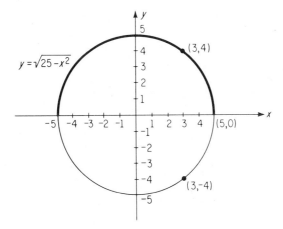

FIG. 5-3. $x^2 + y^2 = 25$.

tion is the semicircle defined by $y = \sqrt{25 - x^2}$, or $f(x) = \sqrt{25 - x^2}$. The equation $x^2 + y^2 = 25$ is said to define a function *implicitly*. We now discuss a method for differentiating functions defined implicitly by equations; the process is called *implicit differentiation*.

Assume $x^2 + y^2 = 25$ defines a function with ordered pairs $(x, f(x))$. Then

$$x^2 + [f(x)]^2 = 25.$$

Differentiating both sides,

$$2x + 2f(x) \cdot f'(x) = 0.$$

Solving,

$$f'(x) = \frac{-x}{f(x)}.$$

If $f(x) > 0$, then

$$f'(x) = \frac{-x}{\sqrt{25 - x^2}}.$$

This is the same result obtained by differentiating (explicitly) the function defined by $f(x) = \sqrt{25 - x^2}$ since

$$f'(x) = \frac{1}{2}(25 - x^2)^{-1/2} \cdot (-2x) = \frac{-x}{\sqrt{25 - x^2}}.$$

Example 1. Assume $y^2 + 2xy + x^3 = 25$ defines a function implicitly. Let $f(x)$ be the unique number in the range corresponding to x in the domain. Thus

$$[f(x)]^2 + 2xf(x) + x^3 = 25.$$

Differentiating,

$$2f(x) \cdot f'(x) + 2xf'(x) + 2f(x) + 3x^2 = 0.$$

Thus

$$f'(x) = \frac{-3x^2 - 2f(x)}{2x + 2f(x)}.$$

Notice that $f'(x)$ is given in terms of x and $f(x)$.

Example 2. Find the slope of the tangent line to the curve $x^3 - 2x^2y^2 + 3y = x - 2$ at $(1, 2)$.

Solution: Let $f(x)$ be the number in the range of the function f defined by the equation paired with x in the domain. Thus

$$x^3 - 2x^2[f(x)]^2 + 3f(x) = x - 2.$$

Differentiating,

$$3x^2 - \{2x^2(2)f(x)f'(x) + 4x[f(x)]^2\} + 3f'(x) = 1$$

$$3f'(x) - 4x^2f(x)f'(x) = 4x[f(x)]^2 + 1 - 3x^2$$

$$f'(x) = \frac{4x[f(x)]^2 + 1 - 3x^2}{3 - 4x^2f(x)}.$$

Since $f(1) = 2$,

$$f'(1) = \frac{4(2)^2 + 1 - 3}{3 - 4(2)} = -\frac{14}{5},$$

the slope of the tangent line at $(1, 2)$.

Example 3. If $x^3 + 3xy + y^2 = 7$ defines a function f implicitly, find $f''(x)$.

Solution:

$$x^3 + 3xf(x) + [f(x)]^2 = 7$$

$$3x^2 + 3xf'(x) + 3f(x) + 2f(x)f'(x) = 0. \tag{1}$$

Differentiating again,

$$6x + 3xf''(x) + 3f'(x) + 3f'(x) + 2f(x)f''(x) + 2[f'(x)]^2 = 0.$$

Solving for $f''(x)$,

$$f''(x) = -\frac{6x + 6f'(x) + 2[f'(x)]^2}{3x + 2f(x)}. \tag{2}$$

The second derivative could be expressed in terms of x and $f(x)$ by solving Eq. 1 for $f'(x)$ and substituting in Eq. 2.

EXERCISES

1. If $f(x) = x^{30}$, find $f'(x)$, $f''(x)$, $f^{(4)}(x)$, $f^{(30)}(x)$, and $f^{(31)}(x)$.

2. If $y = x(x^2 + 3)^3$, find $\dfrac{dy}{dx}$, $\dfrac{d^2y}{dx^2}$, and $\dfrac{d^8y}{dx^8}$.

3. Let $3x^2y + 2x^3y - 3x^3 = 2x - 57$ define a function $y = f(x)$. (a) By implicit differentiation, find y'. (b) Solve the equation for y and find y' explicitly. (c) Compare your answers.

4. If $x^3 + 4xy + 7x = y^2$ defines a function implicitly, find $f''(x)$.

5. For the economic-lot-size example on page 79, assume management has identified a fourth cost, C_4, the cost of warehousing one unit for a year, and wishes to include consideration of this cost in computing the order size. Using an approach similar to that used in the example, show that the number for which $TC(q)$ is a minimum is given by

$$q = \sqrt{\frac{2DC_2}{C_3 + C_4}}.$$

HINT: The average quantity being stored in the warehouse is $q/2$.

6. Develop a "proof" that each inventory cycle in the economic-lot-size example is of the same length and thus prove that the economic lot size is the same for each order in the total time period.

7. The revenue produced at time t by a machine which costs $500,000 when new is

$$R(t) = \frac{875,000}{t} - 75,000.$$

As the machine ages, not only does its ability to produce revenue decline but the cost M of maintaining it increases in accordance with the function

$$M(t) = 1,000 + 75t + 800t^2.$$

(a) If all other costs are constant throughout the life of the machine, find the rate at which revenue and maintenance costs are changing. (b) If profit is maximum when marginal cost $M'(t)$ equals marginal revenue $R'(t)$, how long should the machine be used? (c) When should the machine be replaced so as to minimize average annual cost?

8. If $x^2 + 3xy + y = 11$ defines a function implicitly, find $f''(x)$.

9. If $y^3 - 3xy^2 - 2x = y$ defines a function implicitly, find $f''(x)$.

10. If $y^2 - 2x^2y^2 + 7x = 11 + y$ defines a function implicitly, find $f''(x)$.

6

Applications of the Derivative

6-1. INCREASING AND DECREASING FUNCTIONS

In Chapter 2 we said that a function f is an increasing function at a point t in its domain if for some interval containing t,

$$f(x) < f(t) \quad \text{for } x < t$$

and

$$f(x) > f(t) \quad \text{for } x > t.$$

Furthermore, we indicated in Chapter 4 that if f is differentiable and $f'(t) > 0$, then f is increasing at t. This can be proved in the following manner.

Assume $f'(t) > 0$. Thus

$$\lim_{x \to t} \frac{f(x) - f(t)}{x - t}$$

exists and is a positive number. A geometrically obvious theorem (though not easy to prove) is that if the limit of a function is positive at some point t in its domain, then the function must be positive in some interval containing t. Using this fact, there exists some interval containing t such that

$$\frac{f(x) - f(t)}{x - t} > 0.$$

For this quotient to be positive,

$$f(x) - f(t) < 0 \quad \text{for } x - t < 0$$

and

$$f(x) - f(t) > 0 \quad \text{for } x - t > 0.$$

That is,

$$f(x) < f(t) \quad \text{for } x < t$$

and

$$f(x) > f(t) \quad \text{for } x > t.$$

Consequently, if $f'(t) > 0$, f is an increasing function at t. Geometrically, if the slope of the tangent line is positive, then the graph of f "moves up" as x "moves to the right."

Notice we did not prove that if the function is increasing and differentiable at t then $f'(t) > 0$. In fact, this need not be true. For example,
if f is defined by $f(x) = x^3$, then $f'(x) = 3x^2$. Since $f'(x) > 0$ for all
$x \neq 0$, the function is increasing for all $x \neq 0$. Although $f'(0) = 0$, it is
obvious that f is also increasing at $x = 0$; if $x < 0$ then $x^3 < 0$ and if
$x > 0$ then $x^3 > 0$. (See Fig. 6-1.)

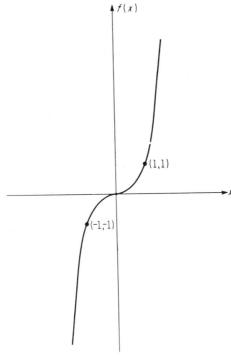

FIG. 6-1. $f(x) = x^3$.

It should be obvious that points where the derivative is zero or undefined require separate consideration when finding the numbers in the
domain of the function such that f is either increasing or decreasing. A
real number t such that $f'(t) = 0$ is sometimes called a *stationary point* and
$f(t)$ is called a *stationary value* of the function.

If $f'(t) < 0$, then f is *decreasing* at t. To prove this statement we need
to use the fact that if the limit of a function at some point t in its domain is
negative then there exists an interval containing t where the function is
negative. Since

$$\lim_{x \to t} \frac{f(x) - f(t)}{x - t} < 0,$$

there exists an interval containing t such that

$$f(x) - f(t) > 0 \quad \text{for } x - t < 0$$

and

$$f(x) - f(t) < 0 \quad \text{for } x - t > 0.$$

That is,

$$f(x) > f(t) \quad \text{for } x < t$$

and

$$f(x) < f(t) \quad \text{for } x > t.$$

Example 1. In a study of the effects of change in subway fare for the New York rapid transit system, it was estimated that the number of passengers using the system was a linear function g of the fare charged p, where

$$g(p) = a - bp$$

and a and b were positive constants. If we let p be any real number, the graph of this function is a straight line with slope $-b$; thus, it is a decreasing function. Note that $g'(p) = -b$ is a negative number and that the number of passengers decreases as the fare p increases.

The revenue R earned by the system is the product of the number of passengers and the fare. Thus

$$R(p) = g(p) \cdot p$$
$$= (a - bp)p = ap - bp^2$$

and

$$R'(p) = a - 2bp.$$

Since the derivative of the revenue function is positive when $a > 2bp$, R is an increasing function for all p such that $p < a/2b$. If $p > a/2b$, R is a decreasing function.

Example 2. For the function f given by $f(x) = x^{2/3}$, $f'(x) = \frac{2}{3} x^{-1/3} = \frac{2}{3\sqrt[3]{x}}$. For any number $t > 0$, $f'(t) > 0$; thus, the function increases for all positive real numbers. For any number $t < 0$, $f'(t) < 0$; thus, the function decreases for all negative real numbers. In any interval containing zero, f is positive on both sides of zero; hence, f is neither increasing nor decreasing at zero. (See Fig. 6-2.)

Example 3. For the function given by $f(x) = x^{1/3}$,

$$f'(x) = \frac{1}{3} x^{-2/3} = \frac{1}{3x^{2/3}} = \frac{1}{3\sqrt[3]{x^2}}.$$

Since $f'(x) > 0$ for all $x \neq 0$, the function increases for all real numbers different from zero. As in Example 2, although zero is not in the domain of f', it is in the domain of f. Furthermore, since $f(x) < f(0)$ when $x < 0$

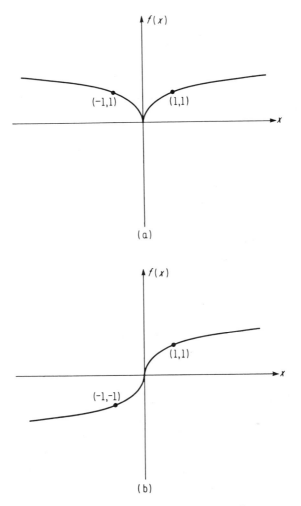

Fig. 6-2. (a) $f(x) = x^{2/3}$. (b) $f(x) = x^{1/3}$.

and $f(x) > f(0)$ when $x > 0$, f is an increasing function at $x = 0$. Consequently, f increases for all real numbers. (See Fig. 6-2.)

6-2. CONCAVITY AND INFLECTION POINTS

The graph of a function f is said to be *concave upward at* t if the derivative f' is an increasing function at t. The graph is said to be *concave downward at* t if f' is a decreasing function at t. Geometrically, the graph of f is concave upward (downward) at t if the tangent at $(t, f(t))$ is below (above) the curve in some interval containing t. Note that since concavity

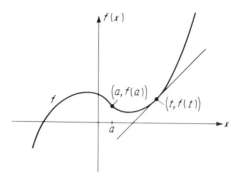

FIG. 6-3. Concave upward: $x > a$. Concave downward: $x < a$. Point of inflection: $(a, f(a))$.

is defined in terms of the derivative we have restricted the concept of concavity to points where the function is differentiable and continuous.

We proved in Sec. 6-1 that if the derivative of some function exists and is positive at t then the function is increasing at t. Thus, if $f''(t) > 0$ for a function f, then f' is an increasing function at t and the graph of f is concave upward at t. Similarly, if $f''(t) < 0$, then f' is a decreasing function at t and the graph of f is concave downward at t. (See Fig. 6-3.)

Although we have assumed that f' exists in order to discuss the concavity of the graph of a function f at t, $f''(t)$ need not be defined. Similar to the preceding section, points where the second derivative is zero or undefined will have to be considered separately to find if the derivative f' is increasing or decreasing.

Example 1. If f is defined by $f(x) = x^4$, then $f'(x) = 4x^3$ and $f''(x) = 12x^2$. If $x \neq 0$, then $f''(x) > 0$ and f' is an increasing function. The graph of f is concave upward for $x \neq 0$. Since

$$f'(x) < f'(0) \text{ for } x < 0$$

and

$$f'(x) > f'(0) \text{ for } x > 0,$$

f' is an increasing function at 0. Hence, the graph of f is concave upward for every real number. (See Fig. 6-4.)

Example 2. If f is defined by $f(x) = x^{1/3}$, $f'(x) = \dfrac{1}{3x^{2/3}}$ and $f''(x) = -\dfrac{2}{9x^{5/3}}$. If $x > 0$, $f''(x) < 0$ so the graph of f is concave downward for $x > 0$. If $x < 0$, $f''(x) > 0$ so the graph of f is concave upward for $x < 0$. Since 0 is not in the domain of f', the graph of f is neither concave upward or downward at 0. (See Fig. 6-4.)

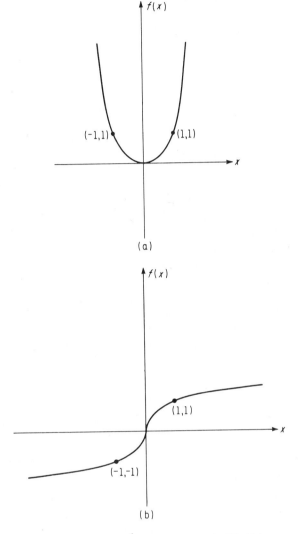

FIG. 6-4. (a) $f(x) = x^4$; concave upward. (b) $f(x) = x^{1/3}$. Concave upward: $x < 0$; concave downward: $x > 0$; inflection point: $(0,0)$.

Example 3. In an earlier example of this chapter the revenue function of the New York subway system was estimated as

$$R(p) = ap - bp^2.$$

$R'(p) = a - 2bp$ and $R''(p) = -2b$. Since $-2b$ is a negative constant, $R''(p) < 0$ for all p and the graph of R is concave downward for every real number.

A point on the graph of a function where the curve "changes" concavity is called an *inflection point*; that is, $(t, f(t))$ is an inflection point if
there is an interval containing t such that f is concave upward (downward)
for $x < t$ and concave downward (upward) for $x > t$. In the preceding
three examples, only the graph of $f(x) = x^{1/3}$ has an inflection point; it is
$(0, 0)$. Since $f''(t) > 0$ (or $f''(t) < 0$) implies that the curve is concave
upward (or concave downward), *necessary* conditions for f to have an
inflection point at $(t, f(t))$ are that $f''(t) = 0$ or $f''(t)$ be undefined.
Three different sufficient conditions for the graph of a function f to have
an inflection point at $(t, f(t))$ are as follows. (See Fig. 6-5.)

I. If $f''(t) = 0$ and if, in some interval containing t, $f''(x)$ is positive
on one side of t and negative on the other, then $(t, f(t))$ is an inflection
point. [If f'' "changes signs" at t, then f must be concave upward on one
side of t and concave downward on the other. Thus $(t, f(t))$ is an inflection point.]

II. If $f''(t) = 0$ and if $f'''(t) \neq 0$, then $(t, f(t))$ is an inflection point.
[If $f'''(t) \neq 0$, f'' is either increasing or decreasing at t. Since $f''(t) = 0$,
f'' must have different signs on each side of t; thus, the graph is concave
upward on one side and concave downward on the other.]

III. Assume t is in the domain of f, but assume $f''(t)$ is undefined.
If $f''(x)$ exists and has opposite signs in some interval containing t, then
$(t, f(t))$ is an inflection point.

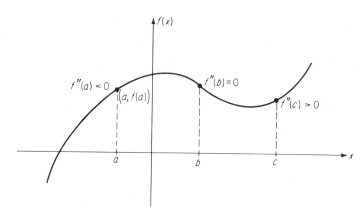

FIG. 6-5. Concave downward at $(a, f(a))$.   Concave upward at
$(c, f(c))$. $(b, f(b))$ is an inflection point.

EXERCISES

For the functions of Exercises 1 through 7 determine the following:
(a) The subsets of the domain where the function is increasing. (b) The
subsets of the domain where the function is decreasing. (c) The coordi-

nates of any inflection points on the graph of the function. (d) The subsets of the domain where the graph of the function is concave upward.
(e) The subsets of the domain where the graph of the function is concave
downward.

   1. $f(x) = x^{2/3}$.   **2.** $f(x) = x^{4/3}$.

   3. $f(x) = x^3 - 3x^2$.   **4.** $f(x) = \dfrac{x}{x + 1}$.

   5. $f(x) = 2x^3 + 5x^2 - 8x + 1$.   **6.** $f(x) = x^3 + 4x^2 - 3x + 1$.

   7. $f(x) = 4x^3 - 7x^2$.

   8. Let g be the inverse of f as defined in Exercise 4. Find $g'(3)$.

6-3. MAXIMA AND MINIMA

   A function f is said to have $f(t)$ as a relative maximum (or local maximum) at t if there is some interval containing t in the domain of f such
that $f(x) \le f(t)$ for every x in the interval. Similarly, a function f is said
to have $f(t)$ as a relative minimum (or local minimum) at t if there is some
interval containing t in the domain of f such that $f(x) \ge f(t)$. As defined
in Chapter 2, if $f(t) \ge f(x)$ for every x in the domain of f, then $f(t)$ is the
absolute maximum, or global maximum, of the function.   Similarly, if
$f(t) \le f(x)$ for every x in the domain of f, then $f(t)$ is an absolute minimum, or a global minimum. It should be noted that an absolute maximum is also a local maximum; similarly, an absolute minimum is a local
minimum.

   As shown in Fig. 6-6, a relative maximum for a function may be less
than a relative minimum. Of course, if a function has both an absolute

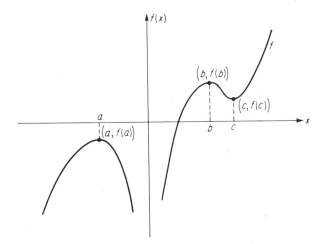

FIG. 6-6. Relative maxima: $f(a)$ and $f(b)$; relative minimum: $f(c)$.

maximum and absolute minimum, then the absolute maximum is greater than or equal to the absolute minimum.

Example 1. Let f be given by $f(x) = 2 + (x - 3)^2$. Since $(x - 3)^2 \geq 0$ for every real number x, the function has an absolute minimum at $x = 3$; the absolute minimum is $f(3) = 2$. (See Fig. 6-7.)

Example 2. Let f be given by $f(x) = \sqrt{x^2 - 1}$. The domain of f is $\{x \mid x \geq 1 \text{ or } x \leq -1\}$. Since $f(x) \geq f(1)$ for all $x \geq 1$, we have that $f(1) = 0$ is a relative minimum for f. Similarly, since $f(x) \geq f(-1)$ for all $x \leq -1$, $f(-1) = 0$ is also a relative minimum. Furthermore, zero is the absolute minimum for f. Notice that for, say, $x > 7$, $y \approx \sqrt{x^2}$; likewise, if $x < -7$, $y \approx \sqrt{x^2}$. Consequently, $y \approx x$ for $x > 7$ and $y \approx -x$ for $x < -7$. The lines $y = x$ and $y = -x$ are called *asymptotes* for the graph of the function; the lines approximate the graph for "large" x. (See Fig. 6-7.) It is geometrically obvious that f does not have any local maxima.

Example 3. Let f be given by $f(x) = 6$. At any point t in the domain of f, there always exists an interval containing t such that $f(x) \geq f(t)$ and $f(x) \leq f(t)$ for every x in the interval. Hence every point in the domain of f is a relative minimum and every point is a relative maximum; both are 6. In fact, 6 is also the absolute maximum and absolute minimum.

Example 4. In the economic-lot-size problem of Chapter 5 we assumed the minimum total cost occurred at the intersection of the ordering cost function $C_2 D/q$ and the carrying cost function $C_3 q/2$. Based on this assumption, we determined the economic lot size to be

$$q = \sqrt{\frac{2 C_2 D}{C_3}}.$$

If we evaluate the total cost function

$$TC(q) = C_1 D + \frac{C_2 D}{q} + \frac{C_3 q}{2}$$

for this value of q, then

$$TC(q) = C_1 D + \frac{C_2 D \sqrt{C_3}}{\sqrt{2 C_2 D}} + \frac{C_3 \sqrt{2 C_2 D}}{2 \sqrt{C_3}}$$

$$= C_1 D + \sqrt{\frac{C_2 C_3 D}{2}} + \sqrt{\frac{C_2 C_3 D}{2}}$$

$$= C_1 D + \sqrt{2 C_2 C_3 D}.$$

Now assume we increase q by some "small" positive number ϵ and then

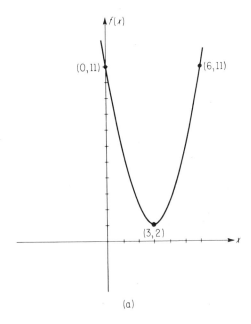

(a)

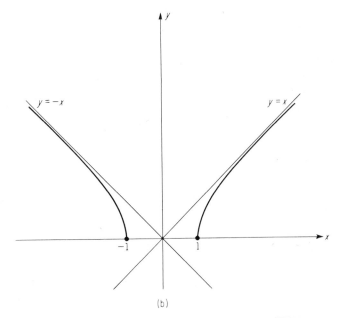

(b)

FIG. 6-7. (a) $f(x) = 2 + (x - 3)^2$. (b) $f(x) = \sqrt{x^2 - 1}$.

evaluate the cost function at $\sqrt{\dfrac{2C_2 D}{C_3}} + \epsilon$.

$$TC = C_1 D + \frac{C_2 D}{\sqrt{\dfrac{2C_2 D}{C_3}} + \epsilon} + \left(\frac{C_3 \sqrt{\dfrac{2C_2 D}{C_3}} + \epsilon}{2} \right)$$

$$= C_1 D + \frac{C_2 D \sqrt{C_3}}{\sqrt{2C_2 D} + \epsilon \sqrt{C_3}} + \frac{\sqrt{2C_2 C_3 D} + \epsilon C_3}{2}$$

$$= C_1 D + \frac{2C_2 D \sqrt{C_3} + \epsilon C_3 \sqrt{2C_2 D}}{\sqrt{2C_2 D} + \epsilon \sqrt{C_3}} + \frac{\epsilon^2 C_3^{3/2}}{2(\sqrt{2C_2 D} + \epsilon C_3)}$$

$$= C_1 D + \sqrt{2C_2 C_3 D} + \frac{\epsilon^2 C_3^{3/2}}{2(\sqrt{2C_2 D} + \epsilon \sqrt{C_3})}.$$

Since this differs only by the last term, which is always positive, the total cost function increases as q is increased above $q = \sqrt{\dfrac{2C_2 D}{C_3}}$, and we have completed one half of a proof that the calculated value of q makes TC a minimum. The reader should complete the proof by verifying that the total cost is more if we use an order size of $q - \epsilon$, where ϵ is some "small" positive number.

If f is a continuous function on a closed interval $[a, b]$, then it should be geometrically obvious that there exists a number $v \in [a, b]$ such that $f(v) \geq f(x)$ for all $x \in [a, b]$. Similarly, there exists a $u \in [a, b]$ such that $f(u) \leq f(x)$ for all $x \in [a, b]$. In other words, a function that is continuous on a closed interval attains both its maximum and minimum on the interval. It is important to note that a function which is continuous on an *open* interval may not have a maximum (or minimum). For example, let f be defined by $f(x) = 1/x$ where $0 < x < 10$. This function does not have a maximum value (or minimum value) in its domain.

We now show how to use the techniques of calculus to find local maxima and minima on *some open interval* (a, b). If the domain of a function f is a closed interval $[a, b]$, then in finding local maxima and minima the end point values $f(a)$ and $f(b)$ must be considered separately; these are sometimes called *end-point extrema*.

If f is a differentiable function and $f'(t) \neq 0$, then f is either an increasing function or a decreasing function at t. Thus, the numbers in the domain of f such that $f'(t) = 0$ or $f'(t)$ is undefined are the "candidates" for points where the function has a relative maximum or relative minimum. At a local maximum $(t, f(t))$ the function is increasing for $x < t$ and decreasing for $x > t$. Hence, if $f'(t) = 0$, or $f'(t)$ is undefined, and

$f'(x)$ is positive for $x < t$ and $f'(x)$ is negative for $x > t$, then $f(t)$ is a local maximum value of the function. By a similar argument, we see that if $f'(t) = 0$, or $f'(t)$ is undefined, and f' "changes" signs from minus to the left of t and to plus to the right of t, then f changes from a decreasing function to an increasing function at $(t, f(t))$ and $f(t)$ is a local minimum value of f. (See Fig. 6-8.)

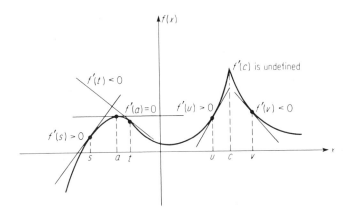

FIG. 6-8. $(a, f(a))$ is a local maximum point. $(c, f(c))$ is a local maximum point.

Another test to find relative maxima and minima is the following. If $f'(t) = 0$ and $f''(t) < 0$, then $f(t)$ is a relative maximum for the function f. Notice that if $f''(t) < 0$, the graph is concave downward and the point $(t, f(t))$ where the tangent line is parallel to the x-axis is a maximum point. If $f'(t) = 0$ and if $f''(t) > 0$, then the graph of f is concave upward and $f(t)$ is a relative minimum value of f. If $f'(t) = 0$ and $f''(t) = 0$, $(t, f(t))$ may or may not be a maximum or minimum point; it is then necessary to use the technique exhibited in Example 7 on page 103.

At end points in the domain of a function defined on a closed interval or at points of discontinuity the techniques we have just discussed for finding maxima or minima are not applicable. For example, let f be the function defined by

$$f(x) = \begin{cases} \dfrac{x^2 - 4}{x - 2} & x \neq 2 \text{ and } x \in [-1, 6] \\ 17 & x = 2. \end{cases}$$

Note that since $\dfrac{x^2 - 4}{x - 2} = x + 2$ for $x \neq 2$, the graph of f is the point $(2, 17)$ and the graph of $y = x + 2$ where $-1 \leq x \leq 6$ except for a "hole" at $x = 2$. It is obvious that $f(2) \geq f(x)$ for every x in some interval con-

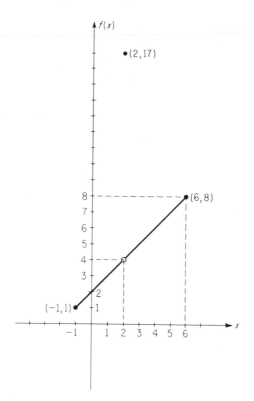

FIG. 6-9. For f, 1 is a relative and absolute minimum value; 6 is a relative maximum value; and 17 is a relative and absolute maximum value.

taining 2; in fact, $f(2) \geq f(x)$ for every x in the domain of the function. Therefore 17 is not only a relative maximum value of f but is also the absolute maximum of the function. Since $f(-1) \leq f(x)$ for every x in the domain of f, $f(-1)$ is the absolute minimum of the function. If we consider the function values at the other end point, we see that there is an interval containing 6 such that $f(x) \leq f(6)$ for every x in this interval. Thus $f(6) = 8$ is a relative maximum of f although it is not the absolute maximum. (See Fig. 6-9.)

Example 5. Let f be the function defined by $f(x) = x^3 - \dfrac{15}{2}x^2 - 18x + \dfrac{3}{2}$. Then, $f'(x) = 3x^2 - 15x - 18$ and $f''(x) = 6x - 15$. Since f is differentiable for every number in its domain, the only "candidates" for maximum or minimum points are the numbers x such that $3x^2 - 15x - 18 = 0$.

Since $f'(-1) = 0$ and $f''(-1) = -21$, a negative number, there is a relative maximum at $x = -1$. The relative maximum is $f(-1) = 11$.

Since $f'(6) = 0$ and $f''(6) = 21$, a positive number, there is a relative minimum at $x = 6$. The relative minimum is $f(6) = -321/2$. (See Fig. 6-10.)

Example 6. Let h be the function defined by $h(x) = x + \dfrac{4}{x}$. Then, $h'(x) = 1 - 4/x^2$ and $h''(x) = 8/x^3$. Since both $h(x)$ and $h'(x)$ are undefined for $x = 0$, the function cannot have a maximum or minimum at zero. The only possible numbers in the domain for which the function can have a maximum or minimum is where $h'(x) = 0$; that is, $x = 2$, $x = -2$.

Since $h''(2) = 1$, we conclude that $h(2) = 4$ is a relative minimum. Since $h''(-2) = -1$, we conclude that $h(-2) = -4$ is a relative maximum. This is an example of a function whose relative maximum is less than its relative minimum. (See Fig. 6-10.)

Example 7. Let g be the function defined by $g(x) = \sqrt{x^2 + 4}$. Then

$$g'(x) = \frac{x}{\sqrt{x^2 + 4}}.$$

Since g' is defined for all real x and $g'(0) = 0$, the only possible maximum or minimum point must be at $x = 0$.

Although we can find $g''(x)$ and evaluate $g''(0)$ to determine whether or not $g(0)$ is a relative maximum or relative minimum, this is an example of a function where just considering g' is much simpler. Since $\sqrt{x^2 + 4}$ is always positive, we see immediately that $\dfrac{x}{\sqrt{x^2 + 4}}$ is negative where $x < 0$ and positive where $x > 0$. Hence, since g' "changes" signs from negative to positive, g has a relative minimum at zero; the relative minimum is $g(0) = 2$. NOTE: For "large" x, $g(x) \approx |x|$. (See Fig. 6-11.)

Example 8. Let f be defined by $f(x) = (x - 1)^{1/2} - x/2$. $f'(x) = (1/2)(x - 1)^{-1/2} - 1/2$ and $g''(x) = -(1/4)(x - 1)^{-3/2}$. Since $f'(2) = 0$ and since $f''(2) = -1/4$, a negative number, we conclude that $f(2) = 0$ is a relative maximum for f.

Since f is not defined when $x < 1$, to determine if $x = 1$ is a maximum or minimum point, we find for what numbers f' is positive and for what numbers f' is negative.

$$\frac{1}{2}(x - 1)^{-1/2} - \frac{1}{2} > 0$$

$$\frac{1/2}{(x - 1)^{1/2}} > \frac{1}{2}$$

$$1 > (x - 1)^{1/2}.$$

We conclude that $f'(x)$ is positive where $1 < x < 2$. Similarly, $f'(x)$ is negative for all $x > 2$.

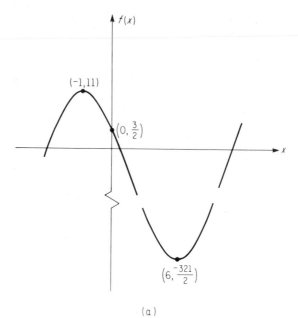

(a)

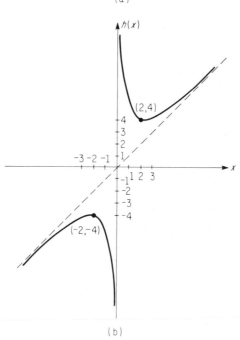

(b)

FIG. 6-10. (a) $f(x) = x^3 - \dfrac{15}{2}x^2 - 18x + \dfrac{3}{2}$.

(b) $h(x) = x + \dfrac{4}{x}$.

Since $f'(x)$ is positive where $1 < x < 2$, f is increasing in the interval. Thus, f has a relative minimum at the end point $x = 1$; thus, $f(1) = -\frac{1}{2}$ is a relative minimum. Since $f'(x) < 0$ where $x > 2$, f decreases for all $x > 2$. Thus, $f(2)$ is also the absolute maximum of f; the function has no absolute minimum. (See Fig. 6-11.)

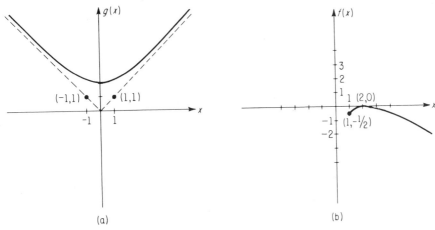

Fig. 6-11. (a) $g(x) = \sqrt{x^2 + 4}$. (b) $f(x) = (x - 1)^{1/2} - \frac{x}{2}$.

Example 9. In Chapter 5 we assumed the economic-lot-size problem could be determined algebraically and we thus obtained the square-root formula $\bar{q} = \sqrt{\dfrac{2C_2 D}{C_3}}$. We now verify our assumption by calculating the extrema of the total cost function

$$TC(q) = CD + \frac{C_2 D}{q} + \frac{C_3 q}{2}, \quad q \in (0, D]$$

$$TC'(q) = -\frac{C_2 D}{q^2} + \frac{C_3}{2}$$

$$TC''(q) = \frac{2C_2 D}{q^3}.$$

Since $TC'(\bar{q}) = 0$ when $\bar{q} = \sqrt{\dfrac{2C_2 D}{C_3}}$, and since $TC''(\bar{q}) > 0$, $TC(\bar{q})$ is a relative minimum. We have already computed the value of $TC(\bar{q})$. Since $TC''(q) > 0$ for all q in the domain, $TC(\bar{q})$ is the absolute minimum.

Example 10. A sheet of tin 28 ft long and 16 in. wide is to be made into a trough by turning up equal "sides" at right angles to the bottom.

Find the dimensions which give the maximum volume if the ends are to be closed with some other material.

Solution: Since the length is fixed, it is the maximum cross-sectional area that will make the volume a maximum. If x inches are turned up on each side, the cross-sectional area in square inches is given by

$$A(x) = x(16 - 2x).$$

Thus

$$A'(x) = 16 - 4x$$

and

$$A''(x) = -4.$$

Since $A'(4) = 0$ and $A''(4)$ is negative, the area is a maximum where $x = 4$. Since $A''(x)$ is negative for all x in the domain of A, $A(4)$ is not only a relative maximum but also the absolute maximum.

$$A(4) = 32 \text{ sq in.} = \frac{2}{9} \text{ sq ft.}$$

Example 11. If a box with a square bottom is open at the top and has a given surface area S, find the ratio of the height to the width of the base so that the volume will be a maximum.

Solution: If w is the width of the base and h is the height, then the area of the base is w^2 and the area of one of the sides is wh. Therefore, the total surface area is

$$S = w^2 + 4wh,$$

where S is a constant. Hence h as a function of w is given by

$$h = \frac{S - w^2}{4w}. \tag{1}$$

If x is the ratio of the height to the width, we have $x = h/w$; that is, $h = wx$. Substituting for h in Eq. 1,

$$wx = \frac{S - w^2}{4w},$$

$$4w^2 x = S - w^2,$$

$$w^2 = \frac{S}{4x + 1},$$

and

$$w = \left(\frac{S}{4x + 1}\right)^{1/2}. \tag{2}$$

Since the volume of the box is $V = hw^2 = xw^3$, from Eq. 2 we find that the volume V as a function of x is given by

$$V(x) = x\left(\frac{S}{4x + 1}\right)^{3/2}$$

$$= S^{3/2} \frac{x}{(4x + 1)^{3/2}}.$$

Thus

$$V'(x) = \frac{S^{3/2}\left[(4x + 1)^{3/2} - x\left(\frac{3}{2}\right)(4x + 1)^{1/2}(4)\right]}{(4x + 1)^3}$$

$$= \frac{S^{3/2}(1 - 2x)}{(4x + 1)^{5/2}}.$$

Since $V'\left(\frac{1}{2}\right) = 0$ and since there is an interval containing $\frac{1}{2}$, namely

$0 < x < 1$, such that $V'(x) > 0$ where $x < \frac{1}{2}$ and $V'(x) < 0$ where

$x > \frac{1}{2}$, $V(x)$ is a maximum for $x = \frac{1}{2}$. Therefore if the ratio of the height

to the width is $\frac{1}{2}$, then for a fixed surface area the volume of the box is a

maximum.

Example 12. In Exercise 17, Sec. 5-1, it was stated that profit is maximum when marginal cost (the derivative of the cost function) is equal to marginal revenue (the derivative of the revenue function). In developing a proof of this statement we shall assume the cost and revenue functions to be differentiable functions for all production levels. Since profit is negative for all production levels less than the break-even point $x = \dfrac{FC}{p - v}$

(see page 27), we need only consider $x \geq \dfrac{FC}{p - v}$. Three cases must be considered.

(a) If $P(x) = R(x) - C(x)$ is linear for production greater than the break-even point and $P'(x) > 0$ for all $x \geq \dfrac{FC}{p - v}$, no maximum exists, and thus the statement does not apply. This is, however, a most unlikely case since it implies that both costs and sales are increasing at constant rates and producing identical increments of profit at all production levels. (Note that if $P(x)$ is linear and $P'(x) \leq 0$, no break-even point exists and profit thus never exceeds zero.)

(b) Suppose the graph of P is concave upward for all levels of production. If $P'(x) > 0$, no maximum exists and the analysis of case (a) applies. If $P'(x) < 0$ for all x, break-even does not exist and the maximum of P is negative and again we decide the rational decision is to do nothing. If $P'(t) = 0$ for some t, then $(t, f(t))$ is a minimum point and no maximum exists.

(c) The more interesting and most commonly occurring case is when the graph of P is concave downward, a fact resulting from increasing production costs as volume exceeds some level and the inability to maintain price as the market becomes saturated. In this case P attains its absolute

maximum where $P'(x) = 0$; that is, where
$$R'(x) - C'(x) = 0,$$
or
$$R'(x) = C'(x).$$

EXERCISES

For each of the functions in Exercises 1 through 12, determine the following. (a) The subsets of the domain where the function is increasing. (b) The subsets of the domain where the function is decreasing. (c) The coordinates of any inflection points on the graph of the function. (d) The subsets of the domain where the graph of the function is concave upward. (e) The subsets in the domain where the graph of the function is concave downward. (f) Relative maxima of the function. (g) Relative minima of the function. (h) Absolute maximum. (i) Absolute minimum.

1. $f(x) = x^3 - \dfrac{15}{2} x^2 - 18x + \dfrac{3}{2}$.   2. $f(x) = x^3 + x^2 - 8x + 3$.

3. $f(x) = 2x^3 + \dfrac{7}{2} x^2 - 5x - \dfrac{7}{2}$.   4. $f(x) = 3 + \sqrt{x - 2}$.

5. $f(x) = \dfrac{x^2 + 2}{x}$.   6. $f(x) = 2x - 2(x - 2)^{3/2}$.

7. $f(x) = (x - 3)^{1/2} - 2x$.   8. $f(x) = \dfrac{3x + 7}{2x - 5}$.

9. $f(x) = \dfrac{5x - 6}{3x + 11}$.   10. $f(x) = x^{1/3} \sqrt{64 - x^2}$.

11. $f(x) = (3x + 1)^2(x - 5)$.   12. $f(x) = (x + 3)(2x - 7)^3$.

13. A man on an island is 3 miles from a straight shore and he wishes to reach, as soon as possible, a point on the shore 4 miles from the closest point on shore. If he can average 2 mph rowing in a boat and 4 mph walking, what route should he take?

14. A closed cylindrical can is to have a given volume. The cost of the material for the top and the bottom is k times the cost per square unit of the material for the side. Find the most economical ratio of the altitude to the radius.

15. Find the dimensions of the cylinder of maximum volume that can be inscribed in a sphere of fixed radius R.

16. A length of wire 100 in. long is to be cut into two pieces. One piece of wire is to be bent into a square and the other into a circle. How should the wire be cut so that the sum of the area of the square and circle is minimum?

17. Let x be the demand for a product for one time period when the selling price is set at p and $x = 75 - \dfrac{3}{5} p$. If manufacturing and selling costs

are $(x^2 + 15x + 500)$ dollars, show that profit is maximum when approximately 21 units are produced.

18. In Exercise 17, assume the government imposes a tax of t dollars on each unit sold by the manufacturer. The manufacturer adds the tax to his production costs before determining his best production schedule. (a) Determine the increase in the selling price as a result of the tax. (b) Express the government's revenue from the tax in terms of t and find the tax that maximizes the government's revenue. (c) Show that when the value of t found in part (b) is used, the selling price is increased by about 20 percent.

19. Assume the manufacturing costs of producing x items in one time period follow the general quadratic $ax^2 + bx + c$; $a, b, c > 0$. The firm sells its product through a manufacturing agent and must pay a commission of k dollars on each unit the agent sells. If the expense of the commission is considered another cost and is to be passed on to the customer and if the price p at which each unit can be sold is $p = \beta - \alpha x$; $\alpha, \beta > 0$, show that the agent maximizes his income when $k = \dfrac{1}{2}(\beta - b)$. Also show that the increase in price resulting from passing on the commission is always less than the commission.

20. Two farmers desire to build an irrigation pumping station which is to serve both farms. If the stream from which they will take their water is straight and if the distances from farms A and B to the stream are 300 and 800 yd respectively and if the perpendiculars from the farms to the stream are 500 yd apart, find the location of the pumping station which minimizes the pumping distance to both farms.

21. The costs of land, excavation, architect fees, and foundation for an office building are \$1,250,000 and are assumed to be independent of the height of the building. The cost of erecting the first floor is \$500,000, the second \$550,000, and the third \$600,000, etc. The minimum height of the building is to be five stories and the maximum height fifty stories. If the net annual income (profit) from each floor is \$75,000, how many stories should be constructed in order to maximize the annual rate of return on the investment in the building. Rate of return is defined as net income divided by total investment.

6-4. MEAN VALUE THEOREM

Let f be a differentiable function on a closed interval $[a, b]$. Since f is continuous on a closed interval, f attains its maximum and minimum value in the interval. If $f(a) = f(b) = 0$ and if f is not the zero function, then f must attain its maximum, or minimum, in the *open* interval (a, b). Since f is differentiable and since the derivative cannot be positive or negative at a maximum or minimum point, there exists a $t \in (a, b)$ such that $f'(t) = 0$. If f were the zero function defined by $f(x) = 0$, then $f'(t) = 0$ for every $t \in [a, b]$. Consequently, we have the following theorem.

Rolle's Theorem.   Let f be a continuous function defined on $[a, b]$ with the following properties: (1) $f'(x)$ exists for every $x \in (a, b)$. (2) $f(a) = f(b) = 0$. Then, there exists a $t \in (a, b)$ such that $f'(t) = 0$.

Rolle's theorem is a special case of the important mean value theorem of differential calculus. Geometrically, the mean value theorem states that if the graph of a continuous function on a closed interval $[a, b]$ has a nonvertical tangent at each point in the open interval (a, b) then at least one tangent line is parallel to the line containing $(a, f(a))$ and $(b, f(b))$. (See Fig. 6-12.)

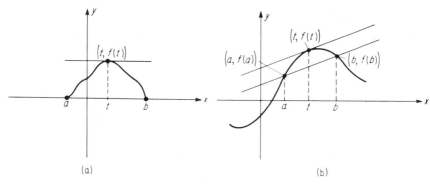

(a)   (b)

FIG. 6-12. (a) Rolle's theorem. (b) Mean value theorem: $f'(t) = \dfrac{f(b) - f(a)}{b - a}$.

Since the slope of the line containing $(a, f(a))$ and $(b, f(b))$ is $\dfrac{f(b) - f(a)}{b - a}$, the mean value theorem asserts that there exist a $t \in (a, b)$ such that

$$f'(t) = \frac{f(b) - f(a)}{b - a}.$$

By drawing the graphs of a few continuous functions, it should be evident that the number t is a number which makes the vertical distance between the graph of f and the line containing $(a, f(a))$ and $(b, f(b))$ a maximum. (See Fig. 6-12.)

The equation of the line containing $(a, f(a))$ and $(b, f(b))$ is

$$\frac{y - f(a)}{x - a} = \frac{f(b) - f(a)}{b - a},$$

or

$$y = \frac{f(b) - f(a)}{b - a} (x - a) + f(a).$$

Thus, the vertical distance between the graph of this line and the graph of the function for any x is defined by

$$g(x) = f(x) - \left[\frac{f(b) - f(a)}{b - a} (x - a) + f(a) \right].$$

This function g is used to prove the mean value theorem.

Mean Value Theorem.   Let f be a function continuous on $[a, b]$ and differentiable on (a, b). Then, there exists a $t \in (a, b)$ such that

$$f'(t) = \frac{f(b) - f(a)}{b - a}.$$

Proof: Let $g(x) = f(x) - \dfrac{f(b) - f(a)}{b - a} (x - a) - f(a)$. Then, $g(a) = 0$ and $g(b) = 0$. Furthermore, g is differentiable on (a, b) and

$$g'(x) = f'(x) - \frac{f(b) - f(a)}{b - a}.$$

Since g satisfies the hypotheses of Rolle's theorem, there exists a $t \in (a, b)$ such that $g'(t) = 0$; thus

$$f'(t) - \frac{f(b) - f(a)}{b - a} = 0.$$

Consequently,

$$f'(t) = \frac{f(b) - f(a)}{b - a}.$$

Note that the mean value theorem is an existence theorem; it does not provide a way to find a number t such that

$$f'(t) = \frac{f(b) - f(a)}{b - a}.$$

It should also be noted that the number t need not be unique; in fact, for a constant function, any t in the domain of the function will make

$$f'(t) = \frac{f(b) - f(a)}{b - a}.$$

One of the main uses for the mean value theorem is to prove other theorems in analysis. For example, assume f is a differentiable function such that $f'(x) = 0$ for every x in the domain of f. If b is in the domain of f, then for any $x \neq b$ we have by the mean value theorem that there exists a t between x and b such that

$$f'(t) = \frac{f(b) - f(x)}{b - x}.$$

But since $f'(t) = 0$, we conclude that $f(b) - f(x) = 0$, or $f(x) = f(b)$. That is, f is the constant function with $\{f(b)\}$ as its range set.

In Chapter 4 we proved that if f is a constant function, then $f'(x) = 0$ for every x in the domain. Now, we have used the mean value theorem to prove the converse of this theorem. We shall see the importance of this converse theorem in the next section.

6-5. ANTIDERIVATIVES

Having considered the process of finding derivatives as an operation, it is natural to consider the "inverse" operation. For example, we know that the derivative of f defined by $f(x) = x^2$ is $f'(x) = 2x$, but for what function g is $g'(x) = \dfrac{x^2 + 1}{x}$?

Let f and g be functions such that $f'(x) = g(x)$ for every x in the domain of f' and g. Then, g is the derivative of f and f is an *antiderivative* of g. For example, $g(x) = 2x$ is the derivative of $f(x) = x^2$, and $f(x) = x^2$ is an antiderivative of $g(x) = 2x$. Since the derivative of $F(x) = x^2 + 6$ also is $g(x) = 2x$, F is another antiderivative of g.

Before developing techniques for finding antiderivatives of functions, let us prove that any two antiderivatives of a given function can differ only by a constant. Let $F'(x) = g(x)$ and let $f'(x) = g(x)$ for every x in the domains of F', f', and g. Then F and f are antiderivatives of g. Let

$$H(x) = F(x) - f(x).$$

Thus

$$H'(x) = F'(x) - f'(x)$$
$$= g(x) - g(x)$$
$$= 0.$$

Since $H'(x) = 0$ for every x, $H(x) = C$, where C is a constant. Thus,

$$F(x) - f(x) = C,$$

or

$$F(x) = f(x) + C.$$

A standard notation for an antiderivative of a function g is $\int g$, or $\int g(x)\,dx$. An antiderivative is often called an *indefinite integral*. Thus

$$\int 2x\,dx = x^2 + C,$$

and we say that $x^2 + C$ is the indefinite integral of $2x$.

Obviously, if we have differentiated a hundred functions, then we have a hundred antiderivative "formulas" available. However, we should be interested in general techniques of finding antiderivatives. Most of this task will be postponed until Chapter 10; at present, we give a few general formulas that are immediate consequences of our differentiation theorems.

$$\int x^p \, dx = \frac{x^{p+1}}{p+1} + C, \ p \neq -1. \tag{I}$$

$$\int k f(x) \, dx = k \int f(x) \, dx. \tag{II}$$

$$\int [f(x) + g(x)] \, dx = \int f(x) \, dx + \int g(x) \, dx. \tag{III}$$

$$\int [f(x)]^p f'(x) \, dx = \frac{[f(x)]^{p+1}}{p+1} + C, \ p \neq -1. \tag{IV}$$

Each of the above can be verified directly by differentiation. For example, let $g(x) = \dfrac{x^{p+1}}{p+1} + C$; then, $g'(x) = x^p$. Consequently, Formula I is verified.

EXERCISES

In Exercises 1 through 5, find a t in the open interval (a, b) that satisfies the conditions of the mean value theorem.

1. $f(x) = x^3$, $[a, b] = [2, 3]$.
2. $f(x) = x^2 + 6x - 3$, $[a, b] = [1, 3]$.
3. $f(x) = x^2 + 4x + 2$, $[a, b] = [-1, 3]$.
4. $f(x) = 3x + 1$, $[a, b] = [2, 5]$.
5. $f(x) = x^3 - 2x^2 + 5x - 6$, $[a, b] = [0, 2]$.
6. Verify the indefinite integral Formula II given above.
7. Verify the indefinite integral Formula III given above.
8. Verify the indefinite integral Formula IV given above.

In Exercises 9 through 24, find the antiderivative of each of the given functions.

9. $f(x) = x^3$.
10. $f(x) = x^{2/3}$.
11. $f(x) = 3x^{7/5}$.
12. $f(x) = 3x^2 - 6x + 7$.
13. $f(x) = 4x^2 + 5x - 11$.
14. $f(x) = 8x^3 - 6x^2 + 11$.
15. $f(x) = (3x + 5)^3$.
16. $f(x) = 3(3x + 5)^3$.
17. $f(x) = 2(2x + 1)^{15}$.
18. $f(x) = 7(7x - 3)^4$.
19. $f(x) = 2x(x^2 + 4)^{3/2}$.
20. $f(x) = 3x^2(x^3 - 2)^4$.
21. $f(x) = x(3x^2 + 4)^{4/3}$.
22. $f(x) = x^2(6x^3 + 11)^{9/5}$.
23. $f(x) = (3x^2 + 4x - 13)^5(6x + 4)$.
24. $f(x) = (4x^2 + 2x + 11)^{5/3}(4x + 1)$.

6-6. DIFFERENTIALS

Finding the function values for many functions requires extensive arithmetic calculations. Often, we can use approximation techniques which substantially reduce the amount of labor required. To illustrate one technique, consider a method for approximating $\sqrt[3]{29}$. If f is defined by $f(x) = x^{1/3}$, we seek an approximation of $f(29)$. It is obvious

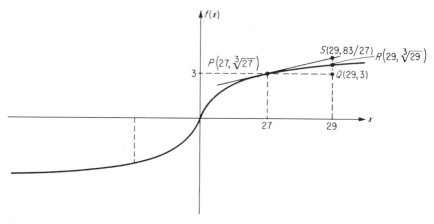

FIG. 6-13. $\sqrt[3]{29} = 3 + |QR|$; $|QR| \approx |QS|$; $\sqrt[3]{29} \approx 3 + |QS|$.

that $f(27) = \sqrt[3]{27} = 3$. If k is the difference in the range values of f corresponding to 27 and 29 in the domain of f, then $\sqrt[3]{29}$ is $3 + k$.

In Fig. 6-13 we see that $\sqrt[3]{29} - \sqrt[3]{27} = |QR|$; thus

$$\sqrt[3]{29} = 3 + |QR|.$$

Furthermore, $|QR| \approx |QS|$ so $\sqrt[3]{29} \approx 3 + |QS|$. The slope of the tangent line at $(27, 3)$ is

$$f'(27) = -\frac{1}{3(27)^{2/3}} = \frac{1}{27}.$$

Therefore the equation of the tangent line is $x - 27y = -54$. Since the x-coordinate of S is 29, the y-coordinate of S is given by

$$-27y = -54 - 29,$$

or

$$y = \frac{83}{27}.$$

Thus

$$|QS| = \frac{83}{27} - 3 = \frac{83}{27} - \frac{81}{27} = \frac{2}{27}.$$

Consequently,

$$\sqrt[3]{29} \approx 3 + \frac{2}{27} = 3.074.$$

A check with cube-root tables shows that $\sqrt[3]{29} = 3.072$ correct to three decimal places.

To generalize this approximation process, we note that if a point S, as shown in Fig. 6-14, has x-coordinate $t + h$, the y-coordinate of S can be found from the equation of the tangent line. Since the slope of the tangent

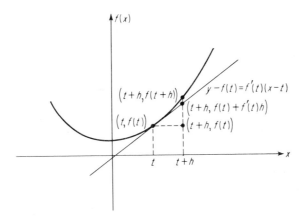

Fig. 6-14. $f(t + h) \approx f(t) + f'(t)h$; $f(t + h) - f(t) \approx f'(t)h = dy$.

line is $f'(t)$, the equation of the line is

$$y - f(t) = f'(t)(x - t).$$

Thus where $x = t + h$,

$$y = f(t) + f'(t)h.$$

Consequently,

$$f(t + h) \approx f(t) + f'(t)h.$$

Example 1. If f is defined by $f(x) = x^3$ and we wish to approximate $f(2.001) = (2.001)^3$, we let $t = 2$ and $h = 0.001$. Thus

$$f(2.001) = f(2 + 0.001)$$
$$\approx f(2) + [f'(2)](0.001)$$
$$\approx 8 + 3(2)^2(0.001)$$
$$\approx 8.012.$$

Actually, $f(2.001) = 8.012006001$; thus, the error introduced by this method of approximation is 0.000006001.

We define $f'(t)h$ to be the *differential of the function f at t with increment h*. It is denoted by dy or df. Notice that dy is a function of two variables since its value depends on t and h. The increment h is more often denoted by dx and is called the *differential of the independent variable*. Consequently, we have

$$dy = f'(x) \, dx$$

and

$$\frac{dy}{dx} = f'(x).$$

Thus, the derivative of f is equal to the *quotient* of dy divided by dx.

In summary, the differential dy of a function f with increment dx is given by $dy = f'(x)\,dx$ and for "suitable" choices of dx,

$$f(x) + dy$$

is a close approximation of $f(x + dx)$.

EXERCISES

1. The volume of a sphere is given by

$$V = \frac{4}{3}\pi x^3 \quad \text{where } x \text{ is the radius.}$$

Find the approximate volume of a spherical shell with outside diameter of 10 in. and wall thickness of $\frac{1}{16}$ in.

2. For a certain application of the economic-lot-size problem, C_2, the cost of placing an order, is estimated to be \$4. It is believed that the maximum error in this estimate is \$1.25. Use the differential method to approximate the maximum error in ordering costs for a fixed D.

6-7. NEWTON'S METHOD OF ROOT APPROXIMATION

Let us consider the problem of finding $\sqrt[3]{29}$ from a viewpoint different from that discussed in Sec. 6-6. Algebraically, calculating $\sqrt[3]{29}$ is equivalent to finding the real root of the equation $x^3 = 29$. In other words, we seek the real zero of the polynomial

$$f(x) = x^3 - 29,$$

the number t for which $f(t) = 0$.

For $x = 3$, $f(x) = 27 - 29 = -2$; thus, take $x_1 = 3$ as a first approximation of the zero of the polynomial. (See Fig. 6-15.) Constructing a tangent line to the graph of f at $(3, f(3))$, we let x_2 be the x-intercept of this tangent line. Next consider the tangent line to the graph of f at $(x_2, f(x_2))$. It is geometrically obvious that the x-intercept, x_3, of this second tangent line is a better approximation of the zero of the polynomial than x_1 or x_2. Now consider the problem in a more general manner in order to develop formulas for the x-intercepts of successive tangent lines.

Let f be a polynomial function. Let x_1 be the first approximation of the zero of the function f; that is, choose x_1 such that $f(x_1) \approx 0$. (See Fig. 6-15.) The slope of the tangent line at $(x_1, f(x_1))$ is $f'(x_1)$ and the equation of the tangent line is

$$y - f(x_1) = f'(x_1)(x - x_1).$$

Since the x-intercept of this line is at $y = 0$,

$$-f(x_1) = f'(x_1)x - f'(x_1)x_1$$

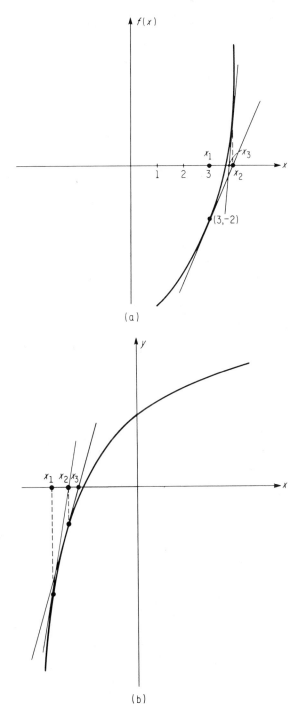

FIG. 6-15. Newton's method. (a) $f(x) = x^3 - 29$.

(b) $x_n = x_{n-1} - \dfrac{f(x_{n-1})}{f'(x_{n-1})}$.

and

$$f'(x_1)x = f'(x_1)x_1 - f(x_1),$$

and

$$x = x_1 - \frac{f(x_1)}{f'(x_1)}$$

is the x-intercept of the tangent line to the curve at $(x_1, f(x_1))$. [Note that we pick x_1 so that $f'(x_1) \neq 0$.]

Taking the x-intercept of this first tangent line to the curve as our second approximation for the zero of f, we let

$$x_2 = x_1 - \frac{f(x_1)}{f'(x_1)}.$$

Similarly, it can be shown that the x-intercept of the tangent line to the curve at $(x_2, f(x_2))$ is

$$x_3 = x_2 - \frac{f(x_2)}{f'(x_2)}.$$

Continuing, x_n is given by the formula

$$x_n = x_{n-1} - \frac{f(x_{n-1})}{f'(x_{n-1})}.$$

Using the sequence $x_1, x_2, x_3, x_4, \ldots$ to approximate the zeros of the polynomial f and thus the roots of the equation $f(x) = 0$ is called *Newton's method* of root approximation.

Returning to our original example to illustrate the use of Newton's method, we approximate the root of the equation $x^3 - 29 = 0$. Let $f(x) = x^3 - 29$, and choosing $x_1 = 3$,

$$x_2 = 3 - \frac{f(3)}{f'(3)}$$

$$= 3 - \frac{(-2)}{27}$$

$$= \frac{83}{27}.$$

Next,

$$x_3 = \frac{83}{27} - \frac{f\left(\frac{83}{27}\right)}{f'\left(\frac{83}{27}\right)}$$

$$= \frac{83}{27} - \frac{(83/27)^3 - 29}{3(83/27)^2}$$

$$= \frac{83}{27} - \frac{83}{81} + \frac{29(27)^2}{3(83)^2}$$

$$= \frac{166}{81} + \frac{21141}{20667}$$

$$\approx 2.049382 + 1.022935$$

$$\approx 3.072317.$$

This approximation of $\sqrt[3]{29}$ is *correct to six decimal places* after using the formula only twice, ample verification of the usefulness of Newton's method.

EXERCISES

In Exercises 1 through 4, find the differential dy in terms of x and dx.

1. $y = x^3$.   **2.** $y = (x + 2)^{3/2}$.

3. $y = x\sqrt{x^2 + 3}$.   **4.** $y = \sqrt{1 - 3x}$.

5. (a) Use differentials to calculate the approximate volume of a cube that is 3.012 cm on each edge. (b) Find the actual volume of the cube in part (a).

6. Use differentials to approximate $1/10.023$. HINT: Find the approximate change in y where $y = 1/x$ when x "changes" from 10 to 10.023.

7. Use differentials to approximate (a) $\sqrt[3]{127}$ and (b) $(2.013)^5$.

8. Use Newton's method to approximate the positive real root of $x^4 - 18 = 0$.

9. Use Newton's method to approximate the positive real root of $x^4 - 2x^3 - 8x - 16 = 0$. [HINT: Let $f(x) = x^4 - 2x^3 - 8x - 16$. Show $f(3) < 0$ and $f(4) > 0$.]

10. Use Newton's method to approximate the positive real root of $x^4 - 4x^3 - 4x - 1 = 0$.

6-8. TAYLOR'S POLYNOMIALS

When we discussed differentials in an earlier section, we found that the first-degree polynomial

$$p(x) = f(t) + f'(t)(x - t)$$

whose graph is the tangent line to the graph of f at $(t, f(t))$ approximated $f(x)$ for x "close" to t. In fact, by the mean value theorem we found that there exists a number c between x and t such that

$$f(x) = f(t) + f'(c)(x - t).$$

For improving numerical calculations and from mathematical interest, we are led to seek a second-degree polynomial function p which approximates the graph of a given function f. If $f(t) = p(t)$, if the slopes of p and f are equal at t [that is, $f'(t) = p'(t)$], and if the concavity or the rates of change of the slopes are equal at t [that is, $f''(t) = p''(t)$], then this polynomial function should better approximate the graph of f in some interval containing t than the linear polynomial I. (See Fig. 6-16.)

If the polynomial $p(x) = a_0 + a_1(x - t) + a_2(x - t)^2$ is to approximate a differentiable function f under the conditions that $f(t) = p(t)$,

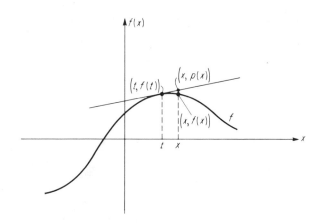

FIG. 6-16. Taylor polynomial: $p(x) = f(t) + f'(t)(x - t)$.

$f'(t) = p'(t)$, and $f''(t) = p''(t)$, it must be that $a_0 = f(t)$ since $p(t) = a_0$. Furthermore, since

$$p'(x) = a_1 + 2a_2(x - t),$$
$$p'(t) = a_1;$$

thus

$$f'(t) = a_1.$$

Also, since

$$p''(x) = 2a_2,$$
$$p''(t) = 2a_2;$$

thus

$$a_2 = \frac{f''(t)}{2}.$$

Consequently, $p(x) = f(t) + f'(t)(x - t) + \dfrac{f''(t)}{2}(x - t)^2$ should approximate f in some interval containing t. This is called the *second degree Taylor polynomial of f at t*.

We can actually prove that for some c between x and t that

$$f(x) = f(t) + f'(t)(x - t) + \frac{f''(c)}{2}(x - t)^2.$$

Instead, we make the expected generalization and give an nth degree polynomial which approximates f in some interval containing t.

The polynomial p defined by

$$p(x) = f(t) + f'(t)(x - t) + \frac{f''(t)}{2!}(x - t)^2 + \cdots + \frac{f^{(n)}(t)}{n!}(x - t)^n$$

is called the *nth degree Taylor polynomial of the function f at t*. As for the first-degree Taylor polynomial, $p(x)$ approximates $f(x)$ for x "close" to t. Also, as for the first-degree polynomial, we can *prove* that for some c between x and t,

$$f(x) = f(t) + f'(t)(x - t) + \frac{f''(t)}{2!}(x - t)^2 + \cdots$$

$$+ \frac{f^{(n-1)}(t)}{(n - 1)!}(x - t)^{n-1} + \frac{f^{(n)}(c)}{n!}(x - t)^n.$$

This is often called *Taylor's formula for a function f at t*. Note for $n = 1$, this is the mean value theorem; thus, Taylor's formula is also referred to as the generalized mean value theorem.

Generalized Mean Value Theorem. Let the function f and its first $(n - 1)$ derivatives be continuous on the closed interval $[a, b]$ and let the nth derivative exist on the open interval (a, b). Let $t \in (a, b)$. Then, for any $x \in [a, b]$ there exists a c between t and x such that

$$f(x) = f(t) + f'(t)(x - t) + \frac{f''(t)}{2!}(x - t)^2 + \cdots$$

$$+ \frac{f^{(n-1)}(t)}{(n - 1)!}(x - t)^{n-1} + \frac{f^{(n)}(c)}{n!}(x - t)^n.$$

The last term $\dfrac{f^{(n)}(c)}{n!}(x - t)^n$ in Taylor's formula is called the *remainder* term. It gives a way to approximate the error in using the Taylor polynomial at t to approximate $f(x)$. Consider the following example.

Example 1. If $f(x) = x^{1/3}$, approximate $f(28)$ by the Taylor polynomial of degree three at 27. Give an upper bound on the error.

Solution: For $x = 28$ and $t = 27$, there exists a $c \in (27, 28)$ such that

$$f(28) = f(27) + f'(27)(1) + \frac{f''(27)}{2!}(1)^2 + \frac{f'''(27)}{3!}(1)^3 + \frac{f^{IV}(c)(1)^4}{4!}.$$

Since

$$f(x) = x^{1/3},$$

$$f'(x) = \frac{1}{3}x^{-2/3},$$

$$f''(x) = -\frac{2}{9}x^{-5/3},$$

$$f'''(x) = \frac{10}{27}x^{-8/3},$$

and

$$f^{IV}(x) = -\frac{80}{81}x^{-11/3},$$

$$f(27) = 3, \quad f'(27) = \frac{1}{3^3}, \quad f''(27) = \frac{-2}{3^7}, \quad f'''(27) = \frac{10}{3^{11}},$$

and

$$f^{IV}(c) = \frac{-80}{3^4 c^{11/3}}.$$

Thus,

$$f(28) = 3 + \frac{1}{3^3} - \frac{1}{3^7} + \frac{5}{3^{12}} - \frac{80}{3^4 c^{11/3}(4!)}.$$

Since $c \in (27, 28)$,

$$\frac{80}{3^4 c^{11/3}(4!)} < \frac{80}{3^4(27)^{11/3}4!} = \frac{80}{3^{15} \cdot 4!} = \frac{10}{3^{16}}.$$

Hence,

$$\frac{3^{13} + 3^9 - 3^5 + 5}{3^{12}}$$

approximates $f(28)$ with $\frac{10}{3^{16}}$ as an upper bound of the error. Consequently, $\sqrt[3]{28} = 3.03658919$ with error less than $0.00000024 = 24 \times 10^{-8}$.

EXERCISES

Use the Taylor polynomial of f at the given t of degree n to approximate the indicated function values. Give an upper bound of your error.

1. If $f(x) = x^{1/5}$, approximate $f(33)$. Let $t = 32, n = 3$.
2. If $f(x) = x^{1/3}$, approximate $f(7)$. Let $t = 8, n = 3$.
3. If $f(x) = x^{2/7}$, approximate $f(1.1)$. Let $t = 1, n = 2$.
4. If $f(x) = x^4$, approximate $f(2.01)$. Let $t = 2, n = 2$.

7

Functions of Several Variables

7-1. FUNCTIONS OF TWO VARIABLES

To this point we have considered only real functions of one variable; that is, sets of ordered pairs of real numbers with no two first elements the same. We now turn our attention to real functions of two variables; these are sets of ordered pairs whose first elements (domain) are themselves ordered pairs of real numbers. For example,

$$f = \{((x, y), z) \mid z = x^2 + 4y^2\},$$

where x and y are real numbers, is a function of two variables. Since $2^2 + 4(3^2) = 4 + 36 = 40$, $((2, 3), 40)$ is an element of f. Since 40 is the number in the range associated with $(2, 3)$ in the domain, the value of f at $(2, 3)$ should be denoted by $f((2, 3))$ to be consistent with our previous definition of functional notation; however, it is standard practice to omit one set of parentheses and write $f(2, 3) = 40$ and say that $f(x, y) = x^2 + 4y^2$ defines the function f.

For any real function f of two variables, the number $f(x, y)$ associated with the pair (x, y) is either positive, zero, or negative. We have available a rather easy way to associate a point in three dimensions with each ordered pair $((x, y), f(x, y))$ of f. Take a horizontal plane with an xy-coordinate system in it as being the plane to associate the points (x, y) of the domain. We now "graph" the function values of f in the following way. If (a, b) is in the domain of f, then $f(a, b) = t$ where $t = 0$, $t < 0$, or $t > 0$. If $t = 0$, then $((a, b), t)$ is the point in the plane with xy-coordinates (a, b). If $t > 0$, then $((a, b), t)$ is the point directly above (a, b) at distance t from the plane. If $t < 0$, then $((a, b), t)$ is the point directly below (a, b) at distance $|t|$ from the plane. (See Fig. 7-1.)

This leads us directly to a method of associating points in three dimensions with ordered triples of real numbers; it is called the *cartesian*, or *rectangular*, coordinate system for three dimensions.

Consider any plane in three dimensions and construct the familiar two-dimensional rectangular xy-coordinate system in this plane. Now construct a number line perpendicular to this plane at the origin $(0, 0)$ and

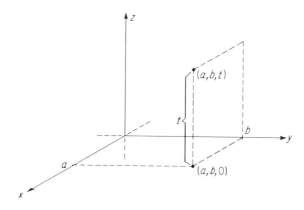

Fig. 7-1

let the origin of this number line, which is generally called the *z-axis*, coincide with the point $(0,0)$ in the *xy*-plane. Obviously, one direction from the origin on *z*-axis is positive and the other is negative.

If $(3,4)$ is a point in the *xy*-plane, then the ordered triple of real numbers $(3,4,0)$ is the three-dimensional coordinates assigned to this point. If the positive *z*-axis is "up," $(3,4,5)$ are the three-dimensional coordinates of the point five units above $(3,4,0)$. Similarly, $(3,4,-6)$ are the three-dimensional coordinates of the point six units below $(3,4,0)$. For the point $(3,4,5)$, 3 is called the *x-coordinate*, 4 is the *y-coordinate*, and 5 is the *z-coordinate*. (See Fig. 7-2.)

From the discussion, it should be apparent that there are essentially two different ways to construct a rectangular coordinate system for three dimensions. The positive *z*-axis can be oriented in two different directions from the *xy*-plane. If when we look "down" from the side of

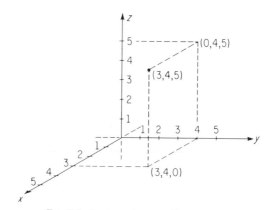

Fig. 7-2. Rectangular coordinate system.

the xy-plane with the positive z-axis the positive y-axis is 90° counter-clockwise from the x-axis, then the system is called a *right-hand* coordinate system. If when we look "down" from the side of the xy-plane with the positive z-axis the positive y-axis is 90° clockwise from the positive x-axis, then the system is called a *left-hand* coordinate system. We shall restrict ourselves to the use of the right-hand coordinate system. (See Fig. 7-3.)

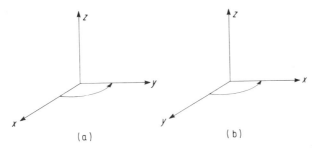

FIG. 7-3. (a) Right-hand system. (b) Left-hand system.

If $P(x_1, y_1, z_1)$ and $Q(x_2, y_2, z_2)$ are two points in three-space, perpendicular projections of the two points onto the xy-plane are $R(x_1, y_1, 0)$ and $S(x_2, y_2, 0)$, respectively. (See Fig. 7-4.) We have

$$|RS| = \sqrt{(x_2 - x_1)^2 + (y_2 - y_1)^2}$$

from the formula for the distance between two points in two dimensions. In the rectangle $RPTS$, $|PT| = |RS|$ and T has coordinates (x_2, y_2, z_1). Furthermore, $|TQ| = |z_2 - z_1|$ and by the Pythagorean theorem,

$$|PQ| = \sqrt{|PT|^2 + |QT|^2}$$
$$= \sqrt{(x_2 - x_1)^2 + (y_2 - y_1)^2 + (z_2 - z_1)^2}.$$

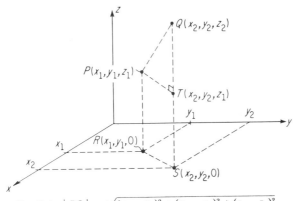

FIG. 7-4. $|PQ| = \sqrt{(x_2 - x_1)^2 + (y_2 - y_1)^2 + (z_2 - z_1)^2}.$

The reader should recognize the similarity between the formulas for finding the distance between two points in two dimensions and two points in three dimensions. If $P(x_1, y_1, z_1)$ and $Q(x_2, y_2, z_2)$ are two points in three dimensions, then the coordinates of the midpoint of the line segment joining P and Q are found in a fashion similar to that for two dimensions. We leave as an exercise for the student to prove that the midpoint is

$$\left(\frac{x_1 + x_2}{2}, \frac{y_1 + y_2}{2}, \frac{z_1 + z_2}{2} \right).$$

If $z = f(x, y)$ where $f(x, y) = 3x + 4y - 7$, then the equation $z = 3x + 4y - 7$ is a linear equation in three unknowns; the graph of the set of ordered triples satisfying this equation is the graph of a three-dimensional surface. It can be proved that a linear function in two variables such as $f(x, y) = 3x + 4y - 7$ has a plane as its graph in three dimensions. The collection of all points where $z = 0$ are in the xy-plane and the coordinates satisfy $3x + 4y - 7 = 0$; thus, the points of intersection of the plane surface and the xy-plane be on the straight line with equation $3x + 4y = 7$.

The curves of intersection (they might be lines) between any three-dimensional surface and the three-dimensional coordinate planes are called *traces* in the planes. For example, $3x + 4y = 7$ is the trace in the xy-plane of the intersection of the surface $z = 3x + 4y - 7$ and the xy-plane. The trace in the xy-plane is found by letting $z = 0$; the trace in the xz-plane is found by letting $y = 0$; and the trace in the yz-plane is found by letting $x = 0$. (See Fig. 7-5.)

Graphing a three-dimensional surface on a two-dimensional surface such as a piece of paper can be a rather difficult task. However, it is important that some facility in graphing three-dimensional surfaces be devel-

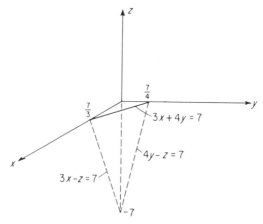

FIG. 7-5. $f(x, y) = 3x + 4y - 7$.

oped, usually obtained through practice. We now consider some examples of graphs of functions of two variables.

Let f be defined by $f(x, y) = x^2 + y^2$. It should be obvious that the range of this function is the set of nonnegative real numbers since $x^2 + y^2 \geq 0$. Except for the point $(0, 0, 0)$, the graph is above the xy-plane. Where $f(x, y) = 9$, that is $x^2 + y^2 = 9$, the plot is a circle with center on the z-axis and radius 3 in the plane where $z = 9$. The trace in the xz-plane is the parabola $z = x^2$ and the trace in the yz-plane is the parabola $z = y^2$. This surface is sometimes called a *parabola of revolution*,

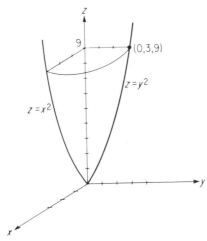

FIG. 7-6. $f(x, y) = x^2 + y^2$.

since it can be obtained by rotating a parabola about its axis. (See Fig. 7-6.) Other surfaces are given in Fig. 7-7.

It should be apparent from our discussion of functions of one variable that not all equations in x, y, and z define functions of two variables. For example, the collection of all points in the three-dimensional coordinate system at distance 5 from the origin is a sphere whose coordinates satisfy the equation

$$x^2 + y^2 + z^2 = 25.$$

Since two different numbers are assigned to z by a given pair of numbers x and y, the equation does not define a function. If we let

$$z = \sqrt{25 - x^2 - y^2},$$

then z is uniquely determined for each pair of numbers x and y where $x^2 + y^2 \leq 25$. The graph of $z = \sqrt{25 - x^2 - y^2}$ is a hemisphere.

Example 1. A single production facility is capable of manufacturing two different products, say A and B. Let x_1 and x_2 be the number of units

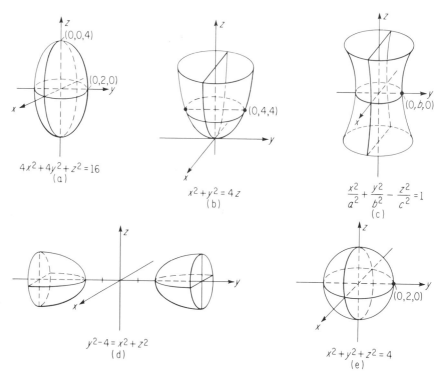

FIG. 7-7. (a) Ellipsoid. (b) Paraboloid of revolution. (c) Hyperboloid of one sheet. (d) Hyperboloid of two sheets. (e) Sphere.

of A and B produced, respectively, in a one-month period and let c_1 and c_2 be the respective costs of producing one unit each of A and B. Again letting FC be the fixed cost, the total production cost is given by the function

$$C(x_1, x_2) = FC + c_1 x_1 + c_2 x_2,$$

a linear function of the two variables x_1 and x_2. Since x_1 and x_2 are never negative, the graph of $C(x_1, x_2)$ is a plane in the first octant of the three-dimensional rectangular system; this is where $x \geq 0$, $y \geq 0$, and $z \geq 0$.

Letting p_1 and p_2 be the respective selling prices of A and B and assuming the total production will be sold, the revenue function $R(x_1, x_2)$ is given by

$$R(x_1, x_2) = p_1 x_1 + p_2 x_2.$$

Again defining profit as the difference between revenue and cost,

$$P(x_1, x_2) = p_1 x_1 + p_2 x_2 - (FC + c_1 x_1 + c_2 x_2).$$

Recalling that break-even was defined for the single product as that level of production at which profit is zero, one might assume there exists a similar number for the combined production of Products A and B. At break-even,

$$p_1 x_1 + p_2 x_2 - FC - c_1 x_1 - c_2 x_2 = 0,$$

or

$$x_1(p_1 - c_1) + x_2(p_2 - c_2) = FC.$$

We are unable to find a unique solution for break-even because $P(x_1, x_2)$ is a function of two variables. However, any solution of

$$x_1 = \frac{FC - (p_2 - c_2)x_2}{p_1 - c_1}$$

will provide a point lying on the "break-even curve," the intersection of the graph of P and the x_1, x_2-plane.

Example 2. The total cost of producing a unit of product is often defined as the sum of direct costs and unit overhead. Direct costs are composed of labor costs actually used in producing the unit, materials consumed in creating it, and any other costs that would not have been incurred had the unit not been produced. Unit overhead or indirect cost is defined as the pro rata share of all costs not included in the direct charges. There exist many methods of allocating overhead to individual units of production. For Example 1, assume the allocation policy is that each unit of A will be allocated 0.75 of the overhead allocation to Product B. Since all overhead must be allocated, the total charged to the two products must equal the total overhead which we shall call K. If a_2 is the unit overhead rate for the second product, then

$$0.75 a_2 x_1 + a_2 x_2 = K$$

and

$$a_2 = \frac{K}{0.75 x_1 + x_2}.$$

Since the number a_2 is constant for a given month and assuming the quantity we have referred to as fixed cost is one of the components of overhead, we rewrite the profit function as

$$
\begin{aligned}
P(x_1, x_2) &= (p_1 - c_1)x_1 + (p_2 - c_2)x_2 \\
&\quad - 0.75\left(\frac{K}{0.75 x_1 + x_2}\right)x_1 - \left(\frac{K}{0.75 x_1 + x_2}\right)x_2 \\
&= (p_1 - c_1)x_1 + (p_2 - c_2)x_2 - K.
\end{aligned}
$$

EXERCISES

1. For Example 1, sketch the profit plane if $FC = \$50,000$, $c_1 = \$1.25$, $c_2 = \$1.50$, $p_1 = \$2.15$, and $p_2 = \$2.55$.

2. Sketch the overhead allocation formula of Example 2 using

$100,000 for K and different choices of x_1 and x_2 chosen in such a way that $x_1 + x_2 = 10,000$.

3. Graph each of the following points in a right-hand cartesian coordinate system: $(3, 5, 8)$, $(1, 1, 1)$, and $(-2, 8, 5)$.

4. (a) Find the distance between $(1, 2, 5)$ and $(-3, 7, 2)$. (b) What are the coordinates of the midpoint of the line segment joining the given points?

5. (a) Find the distance between $(2, -3, 6)$ and $(4, 1, 7)$. (b) What are the coordinates of the midpoint of the line segment joining the given points?

6. Sketch the graph of the plane $3x + 5y + 6z = 10$.

7. Sketch the graph of the plane $6x + 4y + 2z = 11$.

8. Sketch the graph of the function defined by $f(x, y) = 3x - 4y + 7$.

9. Sketch the graph of the function defined by $f(x, y) = x^2 + y^2 - 2$.

10. Discuss any features that you can determine about the graph of $f(x, y) = xy + x^2$.

7-2. PARTIAL DERIVATIVES

If $f(x, y) = \sqrt{25 - x^2 - y^2}$ where $x^2 + y^2 \le 25$, then the graph of the function f defined by this equation is a hemisphere. (See Fig. 7-8.)

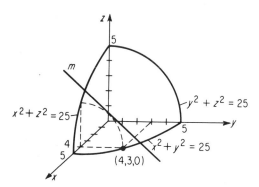

Fig. 7-8. $f(x, y) = \sqrt{25 - x^2 - y^2}$;

$$m = f_y(4, y) = \frac{-y}{\sqrt{9 - y^2}}.$$

If we let $x = 4$, then $f(4, y) = \sqrt{9 - y^2}$ is the equation of the intersection of the plane $x = 4$ and the hemisphere; the intersection is a semicircle of radius 3. Now,

$$H(y) = \sqrt{9 - y^2}$$

is a differentiable function of one variable and

$$H'(y) = \frac{-y}{\sqrt{9 - y^2}}$$

is the slope of the tangent line to the semicircle in the plane $x = 4$ for all y in the domain of H'.

The derivative obtained by differentiating a function of two variables such as $f(x, y) = \sqrt{25 - x^2 - y^2}$ by treating one of the variables as a constant is called a *partial derivative* of f. If we treat x as a constant then the partial derivative of f is said to be *with respect to y* and is denoted by f_y, $f_y(x, y)$, or $\partial f/\partial y$. Thus, if $f(x, y) = \sqrt{25 - x^2 - y^2}$,

$$f_y = f_y(x, y) = \frac{\partial f}{\partial y} = \frac{-y}{\sqrt{25 - x^2 - y^2}},$$

$$f_y(4, y) = \frac{-y}{\sqrt{9 - y^2}},$$

and

$$f_y(4, 2) = \frac{-2}{\sqrt{5}} = \frac{-2\sqrt{5}}{5}.$$

The *partial derivative of f with respect to x* is obtained by treating y as a constant; it is denoted by f_x, $f_x(x, y)$, or $\partial f/\partial x$.

The following are definitions of the first partial derivatives of a function of two variables.

$$f_x(x, y) = \lim_{h \to 0} \frac{f(x + h, y) - f(x, y)}{h}$$

$$f_y(x, y) = \lim_{h \to 0} \frac{f(x, y + h) - f(x, y)}{h}.$$

Example 1. Let $f(x, y) = x^2 + 3xy + 6$. Then $f_x(x, y) = 2x + 3y$ and $f_y(x, y) = 3x$.

Example 2. Let $f(x, y) = x^3 + 3x^2 y + y^3$. Then $f_x(x, y) = 3x^2 + 6xy$ and $f_y(x, y) = 3x^2 + 3y^2$.

Example 3. Let $f(x, y) = \dfrac{x}{y} + \dfrac{y}{x}$. Then $\dfrac{\partial f}{\partial x} = \dfrac{1}{y} - \dfrac{y}{x^2}$ and $\dfrac{\partial f}{\partial y} = -\dfrac{x}{y^2} + \dfrac{1}{x}$.

Since there are two first partial derivatives of a function f, one can obtain four "different" partial derivatives of the first partial derivatives. These are called *second partial* derivatives and are denoted by the following symbols.

$$\frac{\partial}{\partial x}\left(\frac{\partial f}{\partial x}\right) = \frac{\partial^2 f}{\partial x^2} = f_{xx} \qquad \text{Partial of } \frac{\partial f}{\partial x} \text{ with respect to } x.$$

$$\frac{\partial}{\partial y}\left(\frac{\partial f}{\partial x}\right) = \frac{\partial^2 f}{\partial y \partial x} = f_{xy} \qquad \text{Partial of } \frac{\partial f}{\partial x} \text{ with respect to } y.$$

$$\frac{\partial}{\partial x}\left(\frac{\partial f}{\partial y}\right) = \frac{\partial^2 f}{\partial x \partial y} = f_{yx} \qquad \text{Partial of } \frac{\partial f}{\partial y} \text{ with respect to } x.$$

$$\frac{\partial}{\partial y}\left(\frac{\partial f}{\partial y}\right) = \frac{\partial^2 f}{\partial y^2} = f_{yy} \qquad \text{Partial of } \frac{\partial f}{\partial y} \text{ with respect to } y.$$

For example, let $f(x, y) = x^2 + 3y^3 + 4xy + 13$. Then,

$$f_x(x, y) = 2x + 4y \qquad\qquad f_y(x, y) = 9y^2 + 4x$$
$$f_{xx}(x, y) = 2 \text{ and } f_{xy}(x, y) = 4 \quad f_{yx}(x, y) = 4 \text{ and } f_{yy}(x, y) = 18y$$

(It is no accident in our example that $f_{xy} = f_{yx}$. It can be proved for any function f, if f_x, f_y, and f_{xy} are continuous functions, then $f_{xy} = f_{yx}$.)

EXERCISES

Find the first and second partial derivatives of each of the following functions.

1. $f(x, y) = x^2 + 3y^2 + 7x$.
2. $f(x, y) = x^2 y + 7xy + 6y + 17$.
3. $f(x, y) = x^2 y^3 + 6x + 5y$.
4. $f(x, y) = x^2 y^3 + 6x^3 y - 3xy + 11$.
5. $f(x, y) = x^3 y - 3x^2 y^2 + 7x - 5y$.
6. $f(x, y) = 4x^4 y + 3x^2 y^3 - 7x + 2$.

7-3. THE TOTAL DIFFERENTIAL

Consider the function of two variables that gives the area of a rectangle with length x and width y: $f(x, y) = xy$. For $x = 2$ and $y = 3$, $f(2, 3) = 6$ is the area of the rectangle. Suppose the length were increased by $h = 0.003$ and the width by $t = 0.002$; what would be the change in the area? One way to answer this question is to multiply 2.003 times 3.002 and find the difference of this product from 6. Multiply

$$
\begin{array}{r}
3.002 \\
\underline{2.003} \\
9006 \\
6004 \\
\hline
6.013006 \\
\end{array}
$$

Subtract
$$
\begin{array}{r}
6 \\
\hline
0.013006 \\
\end{array}
$$

We get some interesting results if we look more carefully at what is involved in such a problem. What we want to find is

$$f(2 + h, 3 + t) - f(2, 3).$$

Now,

$$f(2 + h, 3 + t) - f(2, 3)$$
$$= f(2 + h, 3 + t) - f(2, 3 + t) + f(2, 3 + t) - f(2, 3).$$

If t is a fixed number, by the mean value theorem we have

$$f(2 + h, 3 + t) - f(2, 3 + t) = [f_x(u, 3 + t)] \cdot h$$

where u is between 2 and $2 + h$. Since $f_x(x, y) = y$ is a continuous function, for h and t "close" to zero

$$f_x(u, 3 + t) \approx f_x(2, 3).$$

So

$$f(2 + h, 3 + t) - f(2, 3 + t) \approx [f_x(2, 3)] \cdot h.$$

Similarly,

$$f(2, 3 + t) - f(2, 3) \approx [f_y(2, 3)] \cdot t.$$

Consequently,

$$f(2 + h, 3 + t) - f(2, 3) \approx h f_x(2, 3) + t f_y(2, 3).$$

To check this result, notice that $f_x(2, 3) = 3$ and $f_y(2, 3) = 2$. Thus,

$$f_x(2, 3) \cdot h + f_y(2, 3) \cdot t = 3(0.003) + 2(0.002)$$
$$= 0.009 + 0.004$$
$$= 0.013.$$

The number 0.013 differs from the actual change in the area by only 0.000006. For "small" h and t we can use

$$f_x(x, y) \cdot h + f_y(3, y) \cdot t$$

to approximate

$$f(x + h, y + t) - f(x, y).$$

We call $f_x(x, y) \cdot h + f_y(x, y) \cdot t$ the *total differential* of f at (x, y) with respect to h and t; it is denoted by df, or $df(x, y)$; thus

$$df(x, y) = f_x(x, y) \cdot h + f_y(x, y) \cdot t.$$

Often, dx and dy are used to represent the increments in x and y, respectively. In this case, the total differential is usually expressed by

$$df = \frac{\partial f}{\partial x} dx + \frac{\partial f}{\partial y} dy.$$

Physically, $df(x, y)$ gives the approximate incremental change in $f(x, y)$ when x and y are incremented, respectively, by dx and dy.

Example 1.　Earlier we developed the "square root formula" for the economic order size

$$q = \sqrt{\frac{2 c_2 D}{c_3}} \, .$$

The numbers c_2, the cost of placing an order, and c_3, the cost of carrying one unit in inventory, are parameters whose exact value cannot usually be obtained. To investigate the effect of error in estimates of these quantities we will assume that the true c_2 is overestimated by a quantity h and c_3 contains an error of t and compute the incremental change in q.

$$dq(c_2, c_3) = \frac{\partial q}{\partial c_2} h + \frac{\partial q}{\partial c_3} t$$

$$= h \frac{1}{2} \left(\frac{2D}{c_3}\right)^{1/2} (c_2)^{-1/2} - t \frac{1}{2} (2c_2 D)^{1/2} (c_3)^{-3/2}$$

$$= \frac{1}{2} \sqrt{\frac{2c_2 D}{c_3}} \left(\frac{h}{c_2} - \frac{t}{c_3}\right)$$

$$= \frac{q}{2} \left(\frac{h}{c_2} - \frac{t}{c_3}\right).$$

Since the quantities h/c_2, t/c_3 are relative errors which may be expressed as percentages, we note that if the percentage error is approximately the same in both estimates, the net effect, in this example, is essentially zero because the errors offset each other.

EXERCISES

1. For the example of this section, determine the effect on the economic order size q where c_2 is overestimated by a "small" quantity h and c_3 is underestimated by a "small" quantity t, i.e., $c_2^* = c_2 + h$ and $c_3^* = c_3 - t$.

2. Assume the cost of operating at a level x is defined by $c(x) = x^2 - 2x + 25$, and that x is a function of the price p at which the product is sold given by $x = 30 - \frac{1}{4} p$. Form the profit function and determine the incremental change in profit resulting from an increase in the selling price p.

3. Suppose a metal can is to have an inner radius of 3 in. and an inner height of 7 in. If the can is to be 0.1 in. thick, approximate the amount of metal in cubic inches necessary to make the can. [HINT: Volume of a right circular cylinder is given by $V(r, h) = \pi r^2 h$, where r is the radius and h is the height.]

4. (a) A box with a square base is to be increased from 12.2 in. on a side to 12.3 in.; its height is to be increased from 17.3 to 17.34 in. Find the actual change in volume of the box. (b) Using the total differential, find the approximate change in the volume.

5. (a) Find the product 2.037×7.98. (b) Use the total differential to approximate this product. [HINT: Let $f(x, y) = xy$. Then, $f(2, 8) = 16$

and $f(2 + h, 8 + t) \approx f(2, 8) + f_x(2, 8)h + f_y(2, 8)t$, where $h = 0.037$ and $t = -0.02$.]

7-4. MAXIMA AND MINIMA

In the preceding chapter, we found that a necessary condition for the existence at t of a maximum or minimum value of a differentiable function f of one variable is that $f'(t) = 0$. We also found that if $f'(t) = 0$ and $f''(t) \neq 0$, then the function has a maximum or minimum value at t. Now consider the corresponding problem for a function of two variables.

A function f of two variables is said to have $f(a, b)$ as a local maximum value if $f(a, b)$ is greater than or equal to $f(x, y)$ at all points (x, y) in the domain of f "near" (a, b). More specifically, if there exists an $r > 0$ such that $f(x, y) \leq f(a, b)$ for all x and y satisfying

$$(x - a)^2 + (y - b)^2 < r,$$

then $f(a, b)$ is a *relative* (or *local*) maximum value of f. Geometrically, this means there is a circle of radius r with (a, b) as center in the xy-plane such that $f(a, b)$ is greater than or equal to every other function value $f(x, y)$ where the point (x, y) is in the interior of the circle. Similarly, $f(a, b)$ is a relative minimum value for f if $f(a, b) \leq f(x, y)$ for every (x, y) in some neighborhood of (a, b). (See Fig. 7-9.)

If $f(a, b) \geq f(x, y)$ [or $f(a, b) \leq f(x, y)$] for every (x, y) in the domain of f, then $f(a, b)$ is the *absolute maximum* (or *absolute minimum*) of f. A careful analysis of Fig. 7-9 shows that a necessary condition for a function of two variables to have a maximum or minimum at (a, b) is that $f_x(a, b) = f_y(a, b) = 0$, provided the partial derivatives exist. If $f(a, b)$ is a relative maximum for the function, then the curve

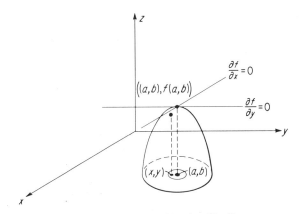

FIG. 7-9. $z = f(x, y); f(x, y) \leq f(a, b)$.

which is the intersection of the surface and the plane $y = b$ must have a relative maximum at $x = a$ and thus $f_x(a, b) = 0$. The statement that necessary conditions for a relative maximum or minimum to exist at (a, b) are that both partial derivatives must be zero at (a, b) means that such an ordered pair (a, b) is a "candidate" for a maximum or minimum point. It is also geometrically obvious that this condition is not sufficient. For example, consider what is called a *saddle point* as shown in Fig. 7-10. It is obvious at the saddle point (c, d) that $f_x(c, d) = f_y(c, d) = 0$ and that $f(c, d)$ is neither a local maximum nor a local minimum.

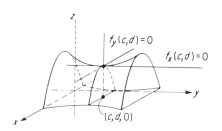

FIG. 7-10. Saddle point.

The sufficient conditions for a function of two variables to have a maximum or minimum value at (a, b) are given in the following theorem which is stated without proof since the details are beyond the scope of our work.

Theorem 7-1. Let f be a function of two variables defined in some neighborhood of (a, b). Assume (1) $f_x(a, b) = 0$ and $f_y(a, b) = 0$, (2) $f_{xx}(a, b) \cdot f_{yy}(a, b) - [f_{xy}(a, b)]^2 > 0$, and (3) f_{xx}, f_{xy}, and f_{yy} are continuous at (a, b). Then $f(a, b)$ is a local maximum if $f_{xx}(a, b) < 0$, and $f(a, b)$ is a local minimum if $f_{xx}(a, b) > 0$.

NOTE: If $f_{xx}(a, b) f_{yy}(a, b) - [f_{xy}(a, b)]^2 < 0$, there is a saddle point at (a, b) and f has no maximum or minimum at (a, b). If $f_{xx}(a, b) f_{yy}(a, b) - [f_{xy}(a, b)]^2 = 0$, f may or may not have a maximum or minimum at (a, b).

Example 1. Suppose a rectangular box of fixed volume V is to be manufactured from three different materials. The lid costs 6 cents per square unit of area, the sides cost 3 cents per square unit of area, and the bottom costs 10 cents per square unit of area. Find the most economical dimensions for the box.

Solution: The volume V is xyz where x is the width of the rectangular bottom and top, y is its length, and z is the height of the box. The cost of the bottom is $10xy$ cents, two sides cost $3xz$ cents each, the two other sides cost $3yz$ cents each, and the cost of the top is $6xy$. Thus, the total cost T is $10xy + 6xz + 6yz + 6xy$. Since $V = xyz$, $z = V/xy$ and the total cost as a function of x and y is

$$T(x, y) = 10xy + 6x \frac{V}{xy} + 6y \frac{V}{xy} + 6xy$$

$$= 16xy + \frac{6V}{y} + \frac{6V}{x} .$$

Now,

$$T_x(x, y) = 16y - \frac{6V}{x^2}$$

and

$$T_y(x, y) = 16x - \frac{6V}{y^2} .$$

To solve

$$\begin{cases} 16y - \dfrac{6V}{x^2} = 0 & \text{(1)} \\[2mm] 16x - \dfrac{6V}{y^2} = 0 & \text{(2)} \end{cases}$$

simultaneously, solve Eq. 1 for y and substitute in Eq. 2. From Eq. 1,

$$y = \frac{3}{8} \frac{V}{x^2},$$

and substituting in Eq. 2,

$$16x - (6V) \frac{64x^4}{9V^2} = 0$$

$$3Vx - 8x^4 = 0$$

$$x(3V - 8x^3) = 0$$

$$x = 0 \text{ or } 3V - 8x^3 = 0.$$

Thus

$$x = \frac{\sqrt[3]{3V}}{2} = \frac{3^{1/3} V^{1/3}}{2}$$

is the only positive solution for x. Substituting,

$$x = \frac{3^{1/3} V^{1/3}}{2}$$

in $y = \dfrac{3}{8} \dfrac{V}{x^2},$

$$y = \frac{3V}{8} \left(\frac{2}{3^{1/3} V^{1/3}} \right)^2 = \frac{3^{1/3} V^{1/3}}{2} .$$

Now $T_{xx}(x, y) = \dfrac{12V}{x^3}$, $T_{yy}(x, y) = \dfrac{12V}{x^3}$, and $T_{xy}(x, y) = 16$. At $x = \dfrac{3^{1/3} V^{1/3}}{2}$ and $y = \dfrac{3^{1/3} V^{1/3}}{2}$,

$$T_{xx}(x,y) \cdot T_{yy}(x,y) - [T_{xy}(x,y)]^2 = \frac{12V}{x^3} \frac{12V}{y^3} - 256$$

$$= \frac{8(12)V}{3V} \frac{8(12)V}{3V} - 256$$

$$= 1024 > 0.$$

Since $T_{xx}(x,y)$ is also positive at the given point, the function has a minimum at that point.

Although x and y depend on the volume, an important fact to note is that the ratio y/x is independent of the volume. In fact, $y/x = 1$ since $x = y$. Since $z = V/xy$, the ratio of the height to width of base is $z/y = V/xy^2$; thus

$$\frac{z}{y} = \frac{V}{\dfrac{3^{1/3}V^{1/3}}{2} \left(\dfrac{3^{1/3}V^{1/3}}{2}\right)^2}$$

$$= \frac{8V}{3V} = \frac{8}{3},$$

and the height should be made 8/3 the width (or length) of the base.

Example 2.   Let $f(x,y) = \dfrac{3}{2}x^2 + xy^3 - y$. Find the relative maxima and minima if any exist.

Solution:

$$f_x(x,y) = 3x + y^3$$
$$f_y(x,y) = 3xy^2 - 1$$
$$f_{xx}(x,y) = 3$$
$$f_{yy}(x,y) = 6xy$$
$$f_{xy}(x,y) = f_{yx}(x,y) = 3y^2.$$

Now solve simultaneously

$$\begin{cases} 3x + y^3 = 0 & \text{(1)} \\ 3xy^2 - 1 = 0. & \text{(2)} \end{cases}$$

From Eq. 1, $x = -y^3/3$, and substituting in Eq. 2,

$$-\frac{3y^5}{3} - 1 = 0$$

$$y^5 = -1$$

$$y = -1$$

is the only real solution for y. Substituting $y = -1$ in $x = -y^3/3$,

$$x = 1/3.$$

Thus $f(1/3, -1) = 1/6 - 1/3 + 1 = 5/6$ is the only "candidate" for a relative maximum or minimum. Since

$$f_{xx}(1/3, -1)f_{yy}(1/3, -1) - [f_{xy}(1/3, -1)]^2 = 3(-2) - (3)^2 = -8 < 0,$$

f has a saddle point at $(1/3, -1)$; f has no relative maxima or minima.

Example 3. Let the cost functions for a two-product manufacturing operation be

$$c(x_1) = x_1^2 - 2x_1 + 25$$
$$c(x_2) = x_2^2 - 2x_2 + 25,$$

where x_1 and x_2 are the respective production levels of the two products for one time period. If the selling prices are p_1 and p_2 the total profit function is given by

$$P(x_1, x_2) = p_1 x_1 + p_2 x_2 - (x_1^2 - 2x_1 + 25 + x_2^2 - 2x_2 + 25).$$

Assume the quantities that can be sold, and hence the quantities scheduled for production, are functions of the selling prices given by

$$x_1 = 30 - \frac{1}{4} p_1$$

$$x_2 = 30 - \frac{1}{4} p_2.$$

Under these conditions the profit function is

$$P(x_1, x_2) = (120 - 4x_1)x_1 + (120 - 4x_2)x_2$$
$$- (x_1^2 - 2x_1 + x_2^2 - 2x_2 + 50)$$
$$= 122x_1 - 5x_1^2 + 122x_2 - 5x_2^2 - 50.$$

Let us determine the production schedule which maximizes profit.

First Solution: We solve $\dfrac{\partial P}{\partial x_1} = 0$ and $\dfrac{\partial P}{\partial x_2} = 0$ simultaneously.

$$\begin{cases} P_{x_1}(x_1, x_2) = 122 - 10x_1 = 0 \\ P_{x_2}(x_1, x_2) = 122 - 10x_2 = 0. \end{cases}$$

The solutions are

$$x_1 = x_2 = 12.2.$$

Now

$$P_{x_1 x_1}(x_1, x_2) = -10$$
$$P_{x_2 x_2}(x_1, x_2) = -10,$$
$$P_{x_1 x_2}(x_1, x_2) = 0,$$
$$P_{x_1 x_1}(x_1, x_2) P_{x_2 x_2}(x_1, x_2) - [P_{x_1 x_2}(x_1, x_2)]^2$$
$$= (-10)(-10) - 0 = 100 > 0,$$

and $P_{x_1 x_1}(x_1, x_2) = -10 < 0$; the solution $x_1 = x_2 = 12.2$ does yield the maximum profit.

Second Solution: Although this is an example of how calculus can be used to find maximum (or minimum) values of a function of two variables, we should not lose sight of the fact that purely algebraic techniques can often be used with the same results. For example, since

$$P(x_1, x_2) = 122x_1 - 5x_1^2 + 122x_2 - 5x_2^2 - 50,$$

by "completing the square on x_1 and x_2,"

$$P(x_1, x_2) = -5\left[x_1^2 - \frac{122}{5}x_1 + \left(\frac{61}{5}\right)^2\right] - 5\left[x_2^2 - \frac{122}{5}x_2 + \left(\frac{61}{5}\right)^2\right]$$

$$- 50 + 5\left(\frac{61}{5}\right)^2 + 5\left(\frac{61}{5}\right)^2$$

$$= -5\left(x_1 - \frac{61}{5}\right)^2 - 5\left(x_2 - \frac{61}{5}\right)^2 + \frac{7192}{5}.$$

Since $5\left(x_1 - \frac{61}{5}\right)^2$ is nonnegative, $-5\left(x_1 - \frac{61}{5}\right)^2$ is nonpositive (less than or equal to zero). Thus the maximum value of $P(x_1, x_2)$ is where $x_1 = \frac{61}{5} = 12.2$ and $x_2 = \frac{61}{5} = 12.2$; the maximum value is $P(x_1, x_2) = \frac{7192}{5} = 1638.40.$

Example 4. In this example, we extend the analysis of the economic-lot-size problem to a two-product inventory. In order to avoid confusion in notation, k_1 is defined as the purchase cost of the first product, and k_2 the purchase cost of the second, and c_3, the carrying cost of one item per time period, is defined as a percentage of the purchase price rather than as an actual charge. Letting D_1 and D_2 be the respective demand for the two products we write the cost function

$$TC(q_1, q_2) = k_1 D_1 + k_2 D_2 + \frac{c_2 D_1}{q_1} + \frac{c_2 D_2}{q_2} + \frac{c_3 k_1 q_1}{2} + \frac{c_3 k_2 q_2}{2}.$$

Solving for the minimum of $TC(q_1, q_2)$,

$$\frac{\partial TC}{\partial q_1} = -\frac{c_2 D_1}{q_1^2} + \frac{c_3 k_1}{2} = 0$$

$$q_1 = \sqrt{\frac{2c_2 D_1}{c_3 k_1}}$$

$$\frac{\partial TC}{\partial q_1} = -\frac{c_2 D_2}{q_2^2} + \frac{c_3 k_2}{2} = 0$$

$$q_2 = \sqrt{\frac{2c_2 D_2}{c_3 k_2}}$$

$$TC_{q_1 q_1} = \frac{2c_2 D_1}{q_1^3}$$

$$TC_{q_2 q_2} = \frac{2c_2 D_2}{q_2^3}$$

$$TC_{q_1 q_2} = 0$$

$$TC_{q_1 q_1} TC_{q_2 q_2} - (TC_{q_1 q_2})^2 = \left(\frac{2c_2 D_1}{q_1^3}\right)\left(\frac{2c_2 D_2}{q_2^3}\right) > 0$$

and

$$TC_{q_1 q_1} > 0.$$

Thus

$$q_1 = \sqrt{\frac{2c_2 D_1}{c_3 k_1}}, \quad q_2 = \sqrt{\frac{2c_2 D_2}{c_3 k_2}}$$

yields the minimum of $TC(q_1, q_2)$.

A function f of three variables is a set of ordered pairs where the first elements are ordered triples. For example,

$$f = \{((x, y, z), w) \mid w = x^2 + 2xyz + yz^3 + 3\}.$$

Usually, f would be defined by the equation $f(x, y, z) = x^2 + 2xyz + yz^3 + 3$. Unfortunately, there is no graphical representation for functions of more than two variables; furthermore, only rather complicated sufficient conditions for maxima and minima are available. However, we still have the necessary conditions similar to the one and two variable cases which give us the "candidates" for maxima and minima points; that is, if f has a maximum (or minimum) at (a, b, c), then $f_x(a, b, c) = 0, f_y(a, b, c) = 0$, and $f_z(a, b, c) = 0$.

Since in most applications it is obvious whether the function has a maximum (or minimum), we solve simultaneously

$$f_x(x, y, z) = 0$$
$$f_y(x, y, z) = 0$$
$$f_z(x, y, z) = 0$$

to find "candidates" for our solution. Then we select which (if any) of the solutions is a tenable answer to the problem.

Example 5. Assume that f defined by

$$f(x, y, z) = \frac{(3xyz)^{1/4}}{3 + x + y + z},$$

where x, y, and z are positive numbers, has a maximum. Find the values for x, y, and z that make f a maximum and find the maximum value of f.

Solution:

$$\frac{\partial f}{\partial x} = \frac{(3 + x + y + z)(1/4)(3xyz)^{-3/4}(3yz) - (3xyz)^{1/4}}{(3 + x + y + z)^2}$$

$$= \frac{(3 + x + y + z)(3yz) - 4(3xyz)}{4(3xyz)^{3/4}(3 + x + y + z)^2}$$

$$= \frac{3yz[3 + x + y + z - 4x]}{4(3xyz)^{3/4}(3 + x + y + z)^2}.$$

Since there is complete "symmetry in the letters,"

$$\frac{\partial f}{\partial y} = \frac{3xz[3 + x + y + z - 4y]}{4(3xyz)^{3/4}(3 + x + y + z)^2}$$

and

$$\frac{\partial f}{\partial z} = \frac{3xy[3 + x + y + z - 4z]}{4(3xyz)^{3/4}(3 + x + y + z)^2}.$$

$$\frac{\partial f}{\partial x} = 0 \text{ if and only if } 3 - 3x + y + z = 0. \tag{1}$$

$$\frac{\partial f}{\partial y} = 0 \text{ if and only if } 3 + x - 3y + z = 0. \tag{2}$$

$$\frac{\partial f}{\partial z} = 0 \text{ if and only if } 3 + x + y - 3z = 0. \tag{3}$$

Solving Eqs. 1, 2, and 3, we find that $y = x$ and $z = x$. Substituting in Eq. 1,

$$3 - 3x + x + x = 0$$

$$x = 3.$$

Consequently $x = y = z = 3$ makes f a maximum. The maximum value is

$$f(3, 3, 3) = \frac{(3^4)^{1/4}}{3 + 3 + 3 + 3} = \frac{1}{4}.$$

Example 6. A soap manufacturer uses three different types of television promotion for a new product. Let A be the amount spent on one-minute commercials, B the amount for half-hour shows, and C the cost of one-hour spectaculars. It is estimated that the sales generated by a campaign composed of these three methods of advertising is given by the function

$$S(A, B, C) = A^{0.4} B^{0.6} C^{0.8}$$

The types of promotion should be allocated in such a way as to maximize the net sales; that is, we want to choose A, B, and C such that $f(A, B, C) = S - A - B - C = A^{0.4} B^{0.6} C^{0.8} - A - B - C$ is a maximum.

Solution: To determine the existence of a stationary point we solve

$$\frac{\partial f}{\partial A} = 0.4A^{-0.6}B^{0.6}C^{0.8} - 1 = 0$$

$$\frac{\partial f}{\partial B} = 0.6A^{0.4}B^{-0.4}C^{0.8} - 1 = 0$$

$$\frac{\partial f}{\partial C} = 0.8A^{0.4}B^{0.6}C^{-0.2} - 1 = 0.$$

Letting $\dfrac{\partial f}{\partial A} = \dfrac{\partial f}{\partial B}$,

$$\frac{0.4B^{0.6}C^{0.8}}{A^{0.6}} = \frac{0.6A^{0.4}C^{0.8}}{B^{0.4}}$$

$$0.4B = 0.6A$$

$$B = 1.5A.$$

Carrying out the same operation with $\dfrac{\partial f}{\partial A}$ and $\dfrac{\partial f}{\partial C}$,

$$\frac{0.4B^{0.6}C^{0.8}}{A^{0.6}} = \frac{0.8A^{0.4}B^{0.6}}{C^{0.2}}$$

$$0.4C = 0.8A$$

$$C = 2A.$$

For every dollar invested on one-minute commercials, \$1.50 should be spent on half-hour shows and \$2 should be spent on spectaculars. Since $1.00 + 1.50 + 2.00 = 4.50$ and since $100/450 \approx 0.22$, $150/450 \approx 0.33$, and $200/450 \approx 0.45$, for an established promotional budget, 22 percent should be allotted to one-minute commercials, 33 percent to half-hour shows, and 45 percent to spectaculars.

EXERCISES

Find the maxima and minima (if they exist) of each of the following functions.

1. $f(x, y) = x^2 + 2xy + y^2 + 4$.
2. $f(x, y) = 12xy - 6x^2y - 3xy^2$.
3. $f(x, y) = x^2 - 2x + xy - 1$.
4. Find the shortest distance from the point $(0, 3, 2)$ to the plane $f(x, y) = x - 3y + 2$.
5. A paneled box is to be open at the top and have volume capacity of 600 cubic inches. What are the most economical dimensions requiring the least square inches of paneling?
6. For the general polynomial function of degree two in two variables

$$f(x, y) = a_1x^2 + a_2xy + a_3y^2 + a_4x + a_5y + a_0,$$

show that if $4a_1a_3 - a_2^2 > 0$, a stationary point (b, c) is a maximum point if $a_1 < 0$ and a minimum point if $a_1 > 0$. Note that the solution of this problem provides completely general formulas for determining the maxima and minima of any function of the form shown.

7. A food packer sells two sizes of canned tomatoes, economy and jumbo size. If the contents and processing of the economy size cost 25 cents and similar costs for the jumbo are 45 cents and if the demand x_1 for the economy size and x_2 for the demand for jumbo size are given by

$$x_1 = 4p_2 - 3p_1$$
$$x_2 = 105 + p_1 - 3p_2,$$

where p_1 is the selling price of the economy size and p_2 the price of the jumbo can, find the values of p_1 and p_2 which maximize profit.

8. If the total cost of manufacturing two different products at production levels x and y per time period are

$$f(x, y) = 25x + 36y + \frac{49}{x} + \frac{64}{y},$$

find the production schedule which minimizes total cost.

7-5. MAXIMA AND MINIMA WITH CONSTRAINTS

In many maxima and minima problems the functions defined are subject to certain conditions called *constraints*. If the minimum value of the function f defined by $f(x, y) = x^2 + y^2$ is desired, the answer is trivial since $x^2 + y^2 \geq 0$ for all real numbers and since $x^2 + y^2 = 0$ if $x = 0$ and $y = 0$; that is, f has a minimum of zero at $(0, 0)$.

However, we might desire the minimum value of f subject to the condition that $g(x, y) = 0$ where $g(x, y) = 6 - 3x - 2y$. The condition that $g(x, y) = 0$ is called a *constraint for f*. If $6 - 3x - 2y = 0$, we can solve for, say, x and substitute in f; this results in an equation of one variable whose minimum value many be found by the techniques of Chapter 6.

$$x = \frac{6 - 2y}{3} \tag{1}$$

$$f\left(\frac{6 - 2y}{3}, y\right) = F(y) \left(\frac{6 - 2y}{3}\right)^2 + y^2.$$

Differentiating,

$$F'(y) = 2\left(\frac{6 - 2y}{3}\right)\left(\frac{-2}{3}\right) + 2y.$$

Setting $F'(y) = 0$,

$$-24 + 8y + 18y = 0$$
$$26y = 24$$
$$y = \frac{12}{13}.$$

Substituting,

$$x = \frac{18}{13}.$$

Thus

$$f\left(\frac{18}{13}, \frac{12}{13}\right) = \left(\frac{18}{13}\right)^2 + \left(\frac{12}{13}\right)^2$$
$$= \frac{468}{169}$$

is the minimum value of f with the given constraint on x and y,

Another method of solving such maximum or minimum problems is by use of what is called *Lagrange multipliers.* The general technique for solution of our previous example by the Lagrange multiplier technique is to define a new function F, called the *Lagrange function,* by

$$F(x, y, \lambda) = f(x, y) - \lambda g(x, y)$$

and solve simultaneously the following three equations in the three unknowns x, y, and λ:

$$(1) \quad \frac{\partial F}{\partial x} = 0$$

$$(2) \quad \frac{\partial F}{\partial y} = 0$$

$$(3) \quad \frac{\partial F}{\partial \lambda} = 0.$$

That is,

$$(1) \quad \frac{\partial F}{\partial x} = \frac{\partial f}{\partial x} - \lambda \frac{\partial g}{\partial x}$$
$$= 0$$

$$(2) \quad \frac{\partial F}{\partial y} = \frac{\partial f}{\partial y} - \lambda \frac{\partial g}{\partial y}$$
$$= 0$$

$$(3) \quad \frac{\partial F}{\partial \lambda} = g(x, y)$$
$$= 0.$$

For the example, $F(x, y, \lambda) = x^2 + y^2 - \lambda(6 - 3x - 2y)$, and we solve

    (a) $F_x = 2x + 3\lambda = 0$

    (b) $F_y = 2y + 2\lambda = 0$

    (c) $F_\lambda = -6 + 3x + 2y = 0.$

From (a) and (b), we get $x = \dfrac{3}{2}y$. Substituting in (c),

$$6 - \frac{9}{2}y - 2y = 0$$

$$13y = 12$$

$$y = \frac{12}{13}.$$

Substituting this value of y, we find $x = \dfrac{18}{13}$; this solution agrees with our previous solution.

Although Theorem 7-2 was stated for functions f and g of two variables, the technique indicated can be used for functions of more than two variables as seen in the first example below. In this example, we find the maximum value by the two methods discussed in this section so that a better comparison can be made between the two approaches.

Example 1. Find the maximum value of f defined by $f(x, y, z) = xyz$ if x, y, and z are positive and $2xy + xz + 3yz = 72$.

First Solution: Solve $2xy + xz + 3yz = 72$ for, say, z.

$$(x + 3y)z = 72 - 2xy$$

$$z = \frac{72 - 2xy}{x + 3y}.$$

Substituting in $f(x, y, z) = xyz$, we get a function F of two variables:

$$F(x, y) = xy \frac{72 - 2xy}{x + 3y}$$

$$= \frac{72xy - 2x^2y^2}{x + 3y}.$$

Finding the first partial derivatives,

$$F_x(x, y) = \frac{(x + 3y)(72y - 4xy^2) - (72xy - 2x^2y^2)}{(x + 3y)^2}$$

$$= \frac{72xy - 4x^2y^2 + 216y^2 - 12xy^3 - 72xy + 2x^2y^2}{(x + 3y)^2}$$

$$= \frac{-2x^2y^2 - 12xy^3 + 216y^2}{(x + 3y)^2}$$

$$= \frac{-2y^2(x^2 + 6xy - 108)}{(x + 3y)^2}.$$

For $F_x(x, y) = 0$, we must have

$$x^2 + 6xy - 108 = 0 \qquad (1)$$

$$F_y(x, y) = \frac{(x + 3y)(72x - 4x^2y) - (72xy - 2x^2y^2)(3)}{(x + 3y)^2}$$

$$= \frac{72x^2 - 4x^3y + 216xy - 12x^2y^2 - 216xy + 6x^2y^2}{(x + 3y)^2}$$

$$= \frac{-2x^2(3y^2 + 2xy - 36)}{(x + 3y)^2}.$$

For $F_y(x, y) = 0$, we must have

$$3y^2 + 2xy - 36 = 0. \qquad (2)$$

Multiply Eq. 2 by 3 and subtracting from Eq. 1,

$$x^2 - 9y^2 - 108 + 108 = 0$$

$$x^2 = 9y^2$$

$$x = \pm 3y.$$

Obviously $x \neq -3y$. (Why?) Substitute $x = 3y$ in Eq. 2,

$$3y^2 + 6y^2 - 36 = 0$$

$$9y^2 = 36$$

$$y = 2.$$

Since $x = 3y$,

$$x = 6.$$

Since $z = \dfrac{72 - 2xy}{x + 3y}$,

$$z = 4.$$

The maximum of f with the given constraint g is when $x = 6$, $y = 2$, $z = 4$; the maximum value is $f(6, 2, 4) = 48$.

Second Solution: Let $F(x, y, z, \lambda), = f(x, y, z) - \lambda g(x, y, z)$ where $g(x, y, z) = 2xy + xz + 3yz - 72$.

$$\frac{\partial F}{\partial x} = \frac{\partial f}{\partial x} - \lambda \frac{\partial g}{\partial x} = yz - \lambda(2y + z)$$

$$\frac{\partial F}{\partial y} = \frac{\partial f}{\partial y} - \lambda \frac{\partial g}{\partial y} = xz - \lambda(2x + 3z)$$

$$\frac{\partial F}{\partial z} = \frac{\partial f}{\partial z} - \lambda \frac{\partial g}{\partial z} = xy - \lambda(x + 3y)$$

$$\frac{\partial F}{\partial \lambda} = 2xy + xz + 3yz - 72.$$

Solving,

$$yz - \lambda(2y + z) = 0 \tag{1}$$

$$xz - \lambda(2x + 3z) = 0 \tag{2}$$

$$xy - \lambda(x + 3y) = 0 \tag{3}$$

$$2xy + xz + 3yz - 72 = 0. \tag{4}$$

Multiply Eq. 1 by x and Eq. 2 by y and subtract Eq. 2 from Eq. 1.

$$x = 3y. \tag{5}$$

Multiply Eq. 2 by y and Eq. 3 by z and subtract Eq. 3 from Eq. 2.

$$z = 2y. \tag{6}$$

Substituting Eqs. 5 and 6 in Eq. 4,

$$6y^2 + 6y^2 + 6y^2 = 72$$

$$y^2 = 4$$

$$y = 2.$$

Thus $x = 3y = 6$ and $z = 2y = 4$, the same solution previously obtained.

Example 2. Earlier in this chapter we determined the economic-lot-size formulas for a two-product problem to be

$$q_1 = \sqrt{\frac{C_2 D_1}{C_3 k_1}} \qquad q_2 = \sqrt{\frac{C_2 D_2}{C_3 k_2}}.$$

In developing this solution the assumption of instantaneous delivery was retained. Let us assume that each product requires the same amount of warehouse space but that the maximum capacity of the storage facility is 100 units. If C_2 is $4 per order and the carrying charge rate, C_3, is 10 percent, and given the following data, we search for the optimal order quantity which does not exceed the warehouse capacity.

	Product 1	Product 2
Monthly demand, D_i	2,500	2,000
Purchase price, k_i	$40.00	$12.50

Ignoring the storage restriction, we compute q_1 and q_2:

$$q_1 = \sqrt{\frac{2 \times 4 \times 2,500}{0.1 \times 40}} \approx 71$$

$$q_2 = \sqrt{\frac{2 \times 4 \times 2,000}{0.1 \times 12.50}} \approx 113.$$

However, we note this solution is not feasible because the restriction requires that

$$q_1 + q_2 \leq 100.$$

To introduce the restriction in the solution, we return to the cost function from which q_1 and q_2 were originally derived:

$$TC(q_1, q_2) = k_1 D_1 + k_2 D_2 + \frac{C_2 D_1}{q_1} + \frac{C_2 D_2}{q_2} + \frac{C_3 k_1 q_1}{2} + \frac{C_3 k_2 q_2}{2}.$$

Forming the Lagrange function,

$$\begin{aligned}
L(q_1, q_2, \lambda) &= TC(q_1, q_2) - \lambda(100 - q_1 - q_2) \\
&= 125,000 + \frac{10,000}{q_1} + \frac{8,000}{q_2} \\
&\quad + 2q_1 + 0.625q_2 - \lambda(100 - q_1 - q_2)
\end{aligned}$$

The reader should note that the inequality restriction

$$q_1 + q_2 \leq 100$$

has been treated as an equality. This may be justified by noting that the absolute minimum of $TC(q_1, q_2)$ exceeded the restriction and thus all solutions which satisfy the restriction will be more costly. We proved in Chapter 4 that the cost function increases as the absolute value of the deviation from the optimal q increases and thus we wish to minimize the difference between the solution of the Lagrange function and the solution of $TC(q_1, q_2)$. This implies that we would utilize the warehouse at its maximum capacity. Thus,

$$\frac{\partial L}{\partial q_1} = -\frac{10,000}{q_1^2} + 2 + \lambda = 0$$

$$\frac{\partial L}{\partial q_2} = -\frac{8,000}{q_2^2} + 0.625 + \lambda = 0$$

$$\frac{\partial L}{\partial \lambda} = -100 + q_1 + q_2 = 0.$$

Solving for q_1 and q_2 yields

$$q_1 = \sqrt{\frac{10,000}{2 + \lambda}} \quad \text{and} \quad q_2 = \sqrt{\frac{8,000}{0.625 + \lambda}}.$$

If we let $\lambda = 0$, we have effectively ignored the constraint and again obtain the impossible solution found earlier in the example. Even though we could solve $\partial L/\partial \lambda = 0$ for one of the variables and then reduce $\partial L/\partial q_1$ and $\partial L/\partial q_2$ to functions of q_1 and λ, the process of simultaneously solving the two resulting equations would be rather tedious. As an alternative, we shall use a common process to search for λ such that $q_1 + q_2 \leq 100$. To do this we shall guess a beginning value of λ and improve our approximation by considering other values.

λ	q_1	q_2	$q_1 + q_2$
0.1	68	106	174
0.2	67	98	165
0.5	63	84	147
1.0	58	70	128
1.5	52	61	113
2.0	50	55	105
2.1	49	54	103
2.2	48	53	101
2.25	48	53	101
2.3	48	52	100

From these calculations we conclude that the minimum total cost is achieved when q_1 is set at 48 and q_2 at 52.

Example 3. Based on its past experience, a firm believes that newspaper and television advertising lead to increases in sales S given by the function

$$S(N, T) = \frac{NT^2}{5} \times 10^{-10},$$

where N and T are amounts spent for newspaper and television advertising respectively. If the total advertising budget is \$1,000,000, find the allocation of advertising expense which maximizes the increase in sales.

Solution: Assuming the full budget is to be spent, our problem is to maximize

$$S(N, T) = \frac{NT^2}{5} \times 10^{-10}.$$

Subject to

$$N + T = 1,000,000.$$

Forming the Lagrange function, we obtain

$$L(N, T, \lambda) = \frac{NT^2}{5} \times 10^{-10} - \lambda(1,000,000 - N - T)$$

and search for the values of N, T, and λ which maximize L by solving

$$\frac{\partial L}{\partial N} = \frac{T^2}{5} \times 10^{-10} + \lambda = 0$$

$$\frac{\partial L}{\partial T} = \frac{2NT}{5} \times 10^{-10} + \lambda = 0$$

$$\frac{\partial L}{\partial \lambda} = -1,000,000 + N + T = 0.$$

Since $\dfrac{\partial L}{\partial N} = \dfrac{\partial L}{\partial T} = 0$,

$$\frac{T^2}{5} - \frac{2NT}{5} = 0,$$

which has solutions $T = 0$ and $T = 2N$. When T is zero, S is also zero, so choosing $T = 2N$, and substituting in $\partial L/\partial \lambda = 0$, we obtain $T = 667,000$, $N = 333,000$, and $\lambda = -\dfrac{2}{9}$. Thus, the maximum increase is

$$S(333,000, 667,000) = \frac{333 \times 10^3 \times (667)^2 \times 10^6}{5} \times 10^{-10}$$

$$= 2,962,960.$$

Example 4.   A study of building construction costs in a certain area show that for a single-story, light-duty warehouse floor construction costs are \$1.60/sq ft, wall construction is \$1/sq ft, and shelving which increases the height to which items may be stacked is $0.10Ah$, where A is the floor area and h is the height of the building.

If a warehouse is to contain 200,000 cu ft, we formulate the problem of determining the dimensions of the least-cost building by minimizing the function

$$f(x,y,z) = 1.60xy + 2(1.00)xz + 2(1.00)yz + 0.10xyz$$

subject to

$$xyz = 200,000,$$

where x is the length of the building, y its width, and z its height.   The Lagrange function is

$$L(x,y,z,\lambda) = 1.6xy + 2yz + 2xz + 0.1xyz - \lambda(200,000 - xyz).$$

A stationary point must satisfy

$$\frac{\partial L}{\partial x} = 1.6y + 2z + 0.1yz + \lambda yz = 0 \tag{1}$$

$$\frac{\partial L}{\partial y} = 1.6x + 2z + 0.1xz + \lambda xz = 0 \tag{2}$$

$$\frac{\partial L}{\partial z} = 2x + 2y + 0.1xy + \lambda xy = 0 \tag{3}$$

$$\frac{\partial L}{\partial \lambda} = -200,000 + xyz = 0. \tag{4}$$

From Eq. 3 we solve

$$\lambda = -\frac{2x + 2y + 0.1xy}{xy} \tag{5}$$

and from Eq. 4

$$z = \frac{200,000}{xy}. \tag{6}$$

Substituting these values into Eqs. 1 and 2,

$$1.6y + \frac{400,000}{xy} + \frac{20,000}{x} - 200,000\frac{2x + 2y + 0.1xy}{x(xy)} = 0 \qquad (7)$$

$$1.6x + \frac{400,000}{xy} + \frac{20,000}{y} - 200,000\frac{2x + 2y + 0.1xy}{y(xy)} = 0, \qquad (8)$$

which when solved simultaneously give

$$x = y.$$

Substituting this result into Eq. 7 yields

$$1.6x^4 - 400,000x = 0$$

$$x^3 = 250,000$$

$$x = y \approx 62.5.$$

Using this result in Eqs. 4 and 5 gives $z \approx 5.1$ and $\lambda \approx -0.74$. Except for round-off error these numbers satisfy Eqs. 1 through 4.

EXERCISES

1. The profit function of a process which produces two different products is

$$P(x, y) = 2xy,$$

where x and y are the production levels of the two products. If the total production must be 1,000 units, find the production schedule which maximizes $P(x, y)$.

2. The revenue produced by the sale of two models of a refrigerator is given by

$$R(x_1, x_2) = 15x_1 + 10x_2 - 2x_1^2 - x_2^2.$$

The final assembly process tends to limit the total capacity of the plant. If 4,000 hours of assembly time are available and if it requires 3 hours to assemble one unit of x_1 and 2 hours to assemble one unit of x_2, find the production schedule which maximizes total revenue.

3. Let f be defined by $f(x, y) = 4xy$ where $x > 0$, $y > 0$, and $x^2 + y^2 = 32$. (a) Find the maximum value of f using the Lagrange technique. (b) Find the maximum value of f by solving the second equation for y, substituting in the first equation, and using the techniques for determining the maximum of a function of one variable.

4. A box is to have a volume of 40 cubic inches. The material for the top and bottom costs 2 cents a square inch, the material for the front and back costs 3 cents a square inch, and the material for the sides costs 4 cents a square inch. What dimensions should the box have in order that its cost be a minimum?

5. Let x, y, and z be positive real numbers. Find the maximum value of f defined by $f(x, y, z) = xyz$ if $x + y + z = 108$.

8

Exponential, Logarithm, and Trigonometric Functions

8-1. DIFFERENTIATION OF THE INVERSE OF A FUNCTION

The inverse function g of f where $f(x) = \dfrac{3x - 7}{x + 2}$ is given by

$$g(x) = \frac{2x + 7}{3 - x}.$$

Note that $f(11) = \dfrac{33 - 7}{11 + 2} = 2$ and $g(2) = \dfrac{4 + 7}{3 - 2} = 11$; thus, $(11, 2) \in f$ and $(2, 11) \in g$. The reader should verify that in general if $(a, b) \in f$, then $(b, a) \in g$.

Often it is either difficult or impossible to find a "formula" to define the inverse function g for a given function f. Thus it is desirable to have some technique for finding the derivative of the inverse function g at some point in *its* domain in terms of the derivative of f at some point in the *domain of f*. Such a technique does exist and is exhibited by the following.

For $f(x) = \dfrac{3x - 7}{x + 2}$ and its inverse $g(x) = \dfrac{2x + 7}{3 - x}$, we can prove that since $f(11) = 2$ the derivative of g at 2 is given by $g'(2) = \dfrac{1}{f'(11)}$. Before doing this we check the validity of the statement.

$$f'(x) = \frac{(x + 2)3 - (3x - 7)}{(x + 2)^2} = \frac{13}{(x + 2)^2}$$

and

$$g'(x) = \frac{(3 - x)(2) - (2x + 7)(-1)}{(3 - x)^2} = \frac{13}{(3 - x)^2}.$$

Thus

$$f'(11) = \frac{13}{(11 + 2)^2} = \frac{13}{13^2} = \frac{1}{13}$$

and

$$g'(2) = \frac{13}{1^2} = 13.$$

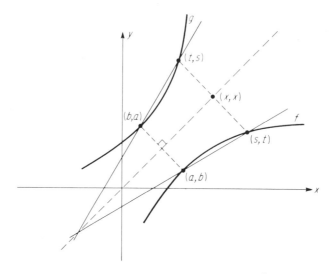

FIG. 8-1. f and g inverse functions: $g'(b) = \dfrac{1}{f'(a)}$.

Consequently,

$$g'(2) = \frac{1}{f'(11)}.$$

Let (a, b) be a given point on the graph of a function f; thus, $f(a) = b$. Let (s, t) be any other point on the graph of f; thus, $f(s) = t$. If the inverse of f is a function g, then $g(b) = a$ and $g(t) = s$. The slope of the line containing (a, b) and (s, t) is $\dfrac{t - b}{s - a}$; that is, $\dfrac{f(s) - f(a)}{s - a}$. (See Fig. 8-1.) The slope of the line containing (b, a) and (t, s) on the graph of the inverse function g is $\dfrac{s - a}{t - b}$; that is, $\dfrac{g(t) - g(b)}{t - b}$. Since

$$\frac{s - a}{t - b} = \frac{1}{\dfrac{t - b}{s - a}},$$

$$\frac{g(t) - g(b)}{t - b} = \frac{1}{\dfrac{f(s) - f(a)}{s - a}}.$$

If f is a differentiable function,

$$f'(a) = \lim_{s \to a} \frac{f(s) - f(a)}{s - a};$$

furthermore, f is continuous, so $\lim\limits_{s \to a} f(s) = f(a)$. As s "approaches" a, t "approaches" b. Thus

$$\lim_{t \to b} \frac{g(t) - g(b)}{t - b} = \frac{1}{\lim\limits_{s \to a} \dfrac{f(s) - f(a)}{s - a}},$$

and

$$g'(b) = \frac{1}{f'(a)}.$$

This asserts that the derivative of g at b is the reciprocal of the derivative of f at a where $f(a) = b$; that is, $g'(b) = \dfrac{1}{f'(g(b))}$.

Theorem 8-1. Let f and g be inverse functions. If $f'(g(b))$ exists and is not zero, then $g'(b) = 1/f'(g(b))$.

Example 1. Let $f(x) = \sqrt{3x + 1}$ and let g be the inverse of f. To find $g'(5)$, we need to know the x such that $f(x) = 5$; that is,

$$\sqrt{3x + 1} = 5.$$

Solving,

$$3x + 1 = 25$$
$$3x = 24$$
$$x = 8.$$

Thus, by Theorem 8-1,

$$g'(5) = \frac{1}{f'(8)}$$

Since

$$f'(x) = \frac{3}{2\sqrt{3x + 1}},$$

$$f'(8) = \frac{3}{2\sqrt{25}} = \frac{3}{10}.$$

Consequently,

$$g'(5) = \frac{10}{3}.$$

Check:

$$f(g(x)) = \sqrt{3g(x) + 1} = x.$$

Thus,

$$3g(x) + 1 = x^2,$$

and $g(x) = \dfrac{x^2 - 1}{3}$ is the inverse of f.

$$g'(x) = \frac{2x}{3} \qquad \text{and} \qquad g'(5) = \frac{10}{3}.$$

EXERCISES

Let g be the inverse function of f in each of the following exercises. Find $g'(5)$ by two methods: (1) using the derivative of f, and (2) finding $g'(5)$ after obtaining an equation defining g.

1. $f(x) = 3x + 6$.   **2.** $f(x) = 6x + 11$.   **3.** $f(x) = x^2 + 1$.

4. $f(x) = \sqrt{3x + 1}$.   **5.** $g(x) = \sqrt{4x - 3}$.   **6.** $f(x) = \dfrac{x}{x + 1}$.

7. $f(x) = \dfrac{3x + 7}{2x - 3}$.   **8.** $f(x) = \dfrac{4x - 3}{3x + 2}$.   **9.** $f(x) = \dfrac{4x + 2}{3x - 5}$.

10. $f(x) = x^3 - 3$.

11. $f(x) = x^2 + 2x - 3$ where $x \geq 1$.

12. $f(x) = x^2 + 2x - 3$ where $x \leq -1$.

13. $f(x) = x^2 - 4x$ where $x \geq 2$.

14. $f(x) = x^2 - 4x$ where $x \leq 2$.

8-2. EXPONENTIAL AND LOGARITHM FUNCTIONS

Let b be any real number. The student should be familiar with the fact that b^n, where n is a positive integer greater than 1, is the product of n numbers, each of which is b; furthermore, $b^1 = b$. If $b \neq 0$, negative integral exponents are defined by $b^{-n} = 1/b^n$. We complete the definition of b^n where n is an integer by defining $b^0 = 1$ if $b \neq 0$.

The following basic properties of exponents are a consequence of these definitions. For all integers m and n,

    1. $b^m b^n = b^{m+n}$.

    2. $b^m/b^n = b^{m-n}$, provided $b \neq 0$.

    3. $(b^m)^n = b^{mn}$.

These properties can be proved for positive integers by mathematical induction. Then the definitions for nonpositive integral exponents are used to prove that each property is valid for the set of all integers.

If $b > 0$, we define $b^{1/2} = \sqrt{b}$ where $\sqrt{b}$ is the positive real number x such that $x^2 = b$. In general, if $b > 0$, we define $b^{1/n}$ by $\sqrt[n]{b}$ where $\sqrt[n]{b}$ is the positive real number x such that $x^n = b$. Also, we define $b^{m/n}$ by $(b^{1/n})^m$, or $(\sqrt[n]{b})^m$. Using these definitions, the basic properties of exponents can be proved valid for the set of all rational numbers. We shall assume the student is familiar with rational exponents and the proofs of the basic theorems for rational exponents.

We now consider the problem of defining b^x where $b > 0$ and x is any real number. In attempting to define such an expression as $5^{\sqrt{2}}$, we seek affirmative answers to two questions: (1) Can irrational exponents be useful either in the further development of mathematics or in the application of mathematics to other fields? (2) Can irrational exponents be defined so that the basic properties of exponents which have been proved for rational numbers will remain valid for irrational numbers? In fact, the answer to each of these questions is "yes." It is not an easy task to give a precise definition of irrational exponents with the limited mathematical tools at our disposal, and without a precise definition of irrational exponents it is impossible for us to prove that the exponent properties for irrational numbers are valid, although this is the case.

The student should look forward to "filling in the gaps" in our discussion of exponents in his future mathematical studies. At present, we must content ourselves with the fact that if $b > 0$ then b^t can be defined precisely for any real number t and the usual properties of exponents can be proved valid for the set of real numbers.

Let f be defined by $f(x) = b^x$. If $b > 1$, the function f is continuous and increasing; if $0 < b < 1$, f is continuous and decreasing. Figure 8-2

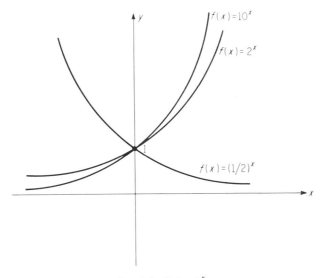

FIG. 8-2. $f(x) = b^x$.

presents the graphs of each of the functions defined by $f(x) = b^x$ where $b = 1/2$, $b = 2$, and $b = 10$. We call f an *exponential function with base b*; the exponential function with base 10 is defined by $f(x) = 10^x$.

If f is defined by $f(x) = 10^x$, then some of the ordered pairs in f are $(-1, 1/10)$, $(0, 1)$, $(1, 10)$, and $(2, 100)$. Since f is strictly increasing, it has an inverse function f^{-1} which is also strictly increasing, as indicated in Fig. 8-3. Some of the ordered pairs in f^{-1} are $(1/10, -1)$, $(1, 0)$, $(10, 1)$, and $(100, 2)$. The standard notation for the inverse function f^{-1} is $\log_{10}$ and $f^{-1}(x) = \log_{10} x$ (read "log x base 10"). The inverse function of the

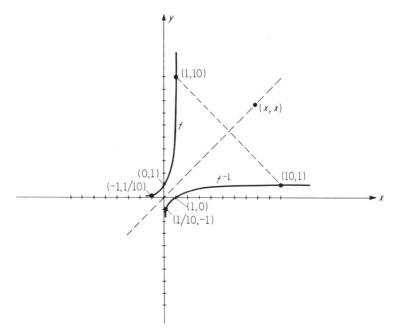

FIG. 8-3. $f(x) = 10^x$; $f^{-1}(x) = \log_{10} x$.

exponential function is called the *logarithm function*. As we have seen, $\log_{10} 10 = 1$, $\log_{10} 100 = 2$, $\log_{10} 1/10 = -1$, and $\log_{10} 1 = 0$.

Since the logarithm function is strictly increasing, and since $\log_{10} 1 = 0$ and $\log_{10} 10 = 1$, it follows that if $1 \leq x \leq 10$, then $0 \leq \log_{10} x \leq 1$. If x is any number between 1 and 10, such as 2.718, the function value $\log_{10} x$ can be found in the table on page 245. In the next section, we shall discuss a method for approximating $\log_{10} x$ for any positive real number x using the function values for numbers between 1 and 10 in the domain of the logarithm function.

In general, if $y = b^x$ where $b > 0$ and $b \neq 1$, then $x = \log_b y$. Since the range of the exponential function is the set of positive real numbers, $\log_b y$ is defined only for positive real numbers y. As a consequence of the definition of the logarithm function, it follows that $\log_b b = 1$ and $\log_b 1 = 0$.

Letting $b > 0$ and $b \neq 1$, we now state three basic logarithm theorems.

Theorem 8-2. $\text{Log}_b xy = \log_b x + \log_b y$ for positive real numbers x and y.

Theorem 8-3. $\text{Log}_b x/y = \log_b x - \log_b y$ for positive real numbers x and y.

Theorem 8-4. $\text{Log}_b x^r = r \log_b x$ for a positive real number x and any real number r.

Proof of Theorem 8-2: Let $\log_b x = u$ and $\log_b y = v$. Then, $b^u = x$ and $b^v = y$. Thus

$$b^u b^v = xy.$$

Hence

$$b^{u+v} = xy,$$

and from the definition of the logarithm function

$$\log_b xy = u + v.$$

Consequently,

$$\log_b xy = \log_b x + \log_b y.$$

The proofs of Theorems 8-3 and 8-4 are left as exercises for the student.

Now, consider determining the derivative of $f(x) = \log_b x$ at some point t in its domain. From the definition of the derivative,

$$f'(t) = \lim_{x \to t} \frac{f(x) - f(t)}{x - t}$$

$$= \lim_{x \to t} \frac{\log_b x - \log_b t}{x - t}$$

$$= \lim_{x \to t} \left[\frac{1}{x - t} \log_b\left(\frac{x}{t}\right) \right] \qquad \text{(Theorem 8-3)}$$

$$= \lim_{x \to t} \left[\log_b\left(\frac{x}{t}\right)^{1/x-t} \right] \qquad \text{(Theorem 8-4)}$$

$$= \lim_{x \to t} \frac{1}{t} \left[\log_b\left(\frac{x}{t}\right)^{t/x-t} \right] \qquad \text{(Theorem 8-4)}$$

$$= \frac{1}{t} \lim_{x \to t} \left[\log_b\left(\frac{x}{t}\right)^{t/x-t} \right] \qquad \text{(Theorem 4-3).}$$

If we let $x - t = h$, then as x "approaches" t we have h "approaches" zero. Thus

$$\lim_{x \to t} \left[\log_b\left(\frac{x}{t}\right)^{t/x-t} \right] = \lim_{h \to 0} \left[\log_b\left(\frac{t + h}{t}\right)^{t/h} \right]$$

$$= \lim_{h \to 0} \left[\log_b\left(1 + \frac{h}{t}\right)^{t/h} \right]$$

$$= \log_b\left[\lim_{h \to 0} \left(1 + \frac{h}{t}\right)^{t/h} \right].$$

It can be proved that $\lim_{h \to 0} (1 + h/t)^{t/h}$ exists and is approximately 2.71828; usually, this limit is denoted by e. Consequently,

$$f'(t) = \frac{1}{t} \log_b e.$$

Thus, if $g(x) = \log_{10} x$, then

$$g'(3) = \frac{1}{3} \log_{10} e.$$

If we choose the number e as the base of our logarithm function and let $f(x) = \log_e x$, then

$$f'(x) = \frac{1}{x} \log_e e = \frac{1}{x}.$$

Choosing e as the base of the logarithm function is standard practice. This function, which is generally denoted by $\ln x$, is called the *natural logarithm* function. Consequently, if

$$f(x) = \ln x,$$

then

$$f'(x) = \frac{1}{x}.$$

As one observes from the last equation, the natural logarithm function has the interesting property that the slope of the tangent line to the graph at any number in its domain is the reciprocal of that number.

To find the derivative of the exponential function, the inverse of the logarithm function, we use Theorem 8-1. If

$$f(x) = \log_b x,$$

then $g(x) = b^x$ and

$$g'(t) = \frac{1}{f'(g(t))}.$$

Since

$$f'(t) = \frac{1}{t} \log_b e,$$

$$f'(g(t)) = \frac{1}{b^t} \log_b e.$$

Thus

$$g'(t) = \frac{b^t}{\log_b e}.$$

Since $\dfrac{1}{\log_b e} = \log_e b$ (a fact for the reader to verify), the derivative of $g(x) = b^x$ is generally expressed as

$$g'(t) = b^t \log_e b = b^t \ln b.$$

It follows that if $g(x) = e^x$, then $g'(t) = e^t$. Geometrically, the slope of the tangent line to the graph of the exponential function with base e is the function value at that point.

Example 1. In Chapter 3 we defined the concept of interest as being the earning rate per year. Frequently the interest rate is stated as an annual rate but through a process known as compounding, the interest is computed and added to the investment more than once during the year. For example, a bank might state its interest rate as i but compound the interest on savings accounts quarterly. If an amount k is deposited in the bank at the beginning of a quarter, at the end of the first quarter the deposit is increased to $k + k\,\dfrac{i}{4}$; at the end of the second quarter,

$$\left(k + k\,\frac{i}{4}\right) + \left(k + k\,\frac{i}{4}\right)\frac{i}{4} = k\left(1 + \frac{i}{4}\right)\left(1 + \frac{i}{4}\right) = k\left(1 + \frac{i}{4}\right)^2;$$

at the end of the third quarter,

$$k\left(1 + \frac{i}{4}\right)^2 + k\left(1 + \frac{i}{4}\right)^2 \frac{i}{4} = k\left(1 + \frac{i}{4}\right)^3;$$

and, thus, the amount on deposit at the end of the year is $k\left(1 + \dfrac{i}{4}\right)^4$.

In general, if i is the stated or nominal rate per year, and the compounding process is carried out n times during the year, the effective rate of interest j can be computed by noting that if the investment k is one dollar, the value of the investment at the end of one year is

$$1 + j = \left(1 + \frac{i}{n}\right)^n$$

or

$$j = \left(1 + \frac{i}{n}\right)^n - 1.$$

By a similar development, it can be shown that the effective discount rate where discounting is carried out n times per year at a nominal rate i is

$$j = \left(1 - \frac{i}{n}\right)^n - 1.$$

In calculating earnings rate for business decisions it must be recognized that the firm does not operate in the same static time increment as does a bank. Rather, earnings occur continuously. Thus we might conclude that the firm is actually compounding a very large number of times. Mathematically, we state this by

$$1 + j = \lim_{n \to \infty} \left(1 + \frac{i}{n}\right)^n,$$

read "$1 + j$ equals the limit of $\left(1 + \dfrac{i}{n}\right)^n$ as n becomes infinite." For the limit to exist means we can find a number L and an integer N such that $\left(1 + \dfrac{i}{n}\right)^n$ can be made "arbitrarily close" to L for all $n \geq N$. (See Chapter 11 for an extended discussion of limits.) This limit is closely related to the limit encountered in the derivative of $\log_b x$. We can prove that $\lim_{n \to \infty} \left(1 + \dfrac{i}{n}\right)^n = e^i$, and thus

$$1 + j = e^i.$$

If this continuous compounding were continued for t years, the total value of an investment k is found by

$$k(1 + j) = \lim_{n \to \infty} k \left(1 + \frac{i}{n}\right)^{nt} = ke^{it}.$$

The continuous discount rate is formulated by

$$\frac{1}{1 + j} = \lim_{n \to \infty} \left(1 - \frac{i}{n}\right)^{n} = e^{-i}.$$

Frequently we are interested in the question of what continuous rate of interest is equivalent to a stated effective rate. This rate is usually indicated by δ and is sometimes referred to as the *instantaneous rate of interest* or *force of interest*. To find the number δ we note that for the two rates to be equivalent,

$$1 + j = e^{\delta};$$

thus

$$\delta = \ln(1 + j).$$

Similarly, for the discounting process,

$$\frac{1}{1 + j} = e^{-\delta},$$

$$(1 + j)^{-1} = e^{-\delta},$$

and

$$\delta = \ln(1 + j).$$

To compare the results of these two methods of calculating interest, we make a savings deposit in a bank which has a nominal interest rate of 5 percent and compounds quarterly. The effective interest rate is

$$j = \left(1 + \frac{0.05}{4}\right)^{4} - 1 = 0.051.$$

For this effective rate,

$$\delta = \ln(1 + 0.051) = 0.0488.$$

With this value of δ, the calculation of $k\left(1 + \frac{i}{n}\right)^{nt}$ and $ke^{\delta t}$ will agree at the end of each year. However, if we have picked $\delta = j = 0.051$, $ke^{\delta t}$ would always exceed $k\left(1 + \frac{i}{n}\right)^{nt}$, with the difference increasing as time passes.

Example 2. In an example of Chapter 4, we developed the learning-curve equation

$$f(x) = \frac{C(1) - C(1)a^{x}}{1 - a} = \frac{C(1)}{1 - a}(1 - a^{x}),$$

where $f(x)$ is the total cost of producing x items, $C(1)$ is the cost of producing the first item, a is the learning parameter and $0 < a < 1$. In attempting to determine the derivative of $f(x)$, we terminated the example because of our lack of knowledge at that time for computing the limit in the equation

$$f'(t) = \frac{-C(1)}{1-a} \lim_{x \to t} \frac{a^x - a^t}{x - t}.$$

We now find the derivative of f using our differentiation formula for the exponential function. The derivative is

$$\frac{d}{dx} f(x) = \frac{C(1)}{1-a} \left\{ \frac{d}{dx} (1 - a^x) \right\} = \frac{-C(1)}{1-a} [a^x \ln a].$$

Example 3. As stated in Chapter 4, the learning curve given by

$$C(i + 1) = a^i C(1)$$

is rather inaccurate in that it decreases too rapidly for "small" values of i; furthermore, as i becomes very large, $C(i + 1)$ rapidly approaches zero, which is physically impossible. What we would prefer is a learning function which decreases less rapidly in the early stages and then approaches a positive limit S called *standard cost*. One such function is

$$C(x) = S + C(1)e^{-ax}, \quad x \geq 1 \text{ and } a > 0.$$

For this function

$$\lim_{x \to \infty} C(x) = S,$$

and with a proper choice of a it possesses the other desired qualities.

The rate at which costs change is

$$C'(x) = -C(1)ae^{-ax}.$$

Since $C'(x)$ is never zero, $C(x)$ has no absolute minimum.

Example 4. The price p at which a certain commodity can be sold is a function of the amount x available for sale; it is given by

$$p = 25e^{-x/5}.$$

Find the maximum total revenue.

Solution: We first form the revenue function $R(x) = xp = 25xe^{-x/5}$. Differentiating,

$$R'(x) = 25(e^{-x/5} - \frac{1}{5} xe^{-x/5})$$
$$= 25e^{-x/5} - 5xe^{-x/5}$$
$$= 5e^{-x/5}(5 - x).$$

$R'(x) = 0$ only when $x = 5$. Finding the second derivative,

$$R''(x) = -5e^{-x/5} - 5e^{-x/5} + xe^{-x/5}$$
$$= -10e^{-x/5} + xe^{-x/5}.$$

Since $R''(5) = -5/e$ is a negative number, marketing exactly five units will maximize the revenue function.

EXERCISES

1. In certain locations in the United States competition for deposits among savings institutions is very intense. In at least one instance one such institution announced a nominal rate of 5 percent with daily compounding. Ignoring leap year, calculate the effective interest rate.

2. In Chapter 3 we derived the present-value formula

$$P(i, n) = \frac{1 - (1 + i)^{-n}}{i}.$$

Show that if the effective rate of interest is i, with continuous compounding

$$P(\delta, n) = \frac{1 - e^{-\delta n}}{\delta}.$$

Find the derivative of each of the following functions:

3. $f(x) = e^{3x}$.

4. $f(x) = \ln 3x$.

5. $f(x) = e^{x^2}$.

6. $f(x) = \ln (x^2 + 2x)$.

7. $f(x) = x \ln x$.

8. $f(x) = 2^x$.

9. $f(x) = x^2 e^{1/x}$.

10. $f(x) = 3^{x^2}$.

11. $f(x) = \dfrac{\ln x^2}{x}$.

12. $f(x) = e^x \ln x$.

13. $f(x) = x - x \ln x$.

14. $f(x) = 10^x$.

15. $f(x) = \log_{10} x^2$.

16. $f(x) = \log_{10} \left(\dfrac{x + 1}{x} \right)$.

17. In an earlier chapter we cited a study of the New York rapid transit system in which the demand q for subway service was found to be a linear function of the fare p. It was $q = a - bp$, where a and b are positive constants. The same study also proposed the following three functions as predictors of demand for different fare levels: (a) $\ln q = a - bp$, (b) $q = a - b \ln p$, and (c) $\ln q = a - b \ln p$. Assuming a and b are the same two positive constants in all three equations, find the p for each equation which maximizes the revenue function.

18. Several years ago population statisticians developed the logistic curve as a mathematical representation of population growth (see Chapter 12). This function is

$$f(t) = \frac{b}{1 + ce^{-at}},$$

where a, b, and c are positive constants, and $f(t)$ is the total population at time t. (a) Find the rate of increase of f at time t. (b) Does f have an upper limit?

19. Show that the normal probability distribution

$$f(x) = \frac{1}{\sigma\sqrt{2\pi}} e^{-\frac{1}{2}\left(\frac{x-\mu}{\sigma}\right)^2},$$

where σ and μ are constants, is maximum when $x = \mu$.

★8-3. TRIGONOMETRIC FUNCTIONS

In this section we will briefly review some of the important concepts of trigonometry. Consider the unit circle with its center at the origin of the rectangular coordinate system and radius 1. The *sine* function is the set of ordered pairs (u, y), where u is the measure of arc length measured counterclockwise from the point $(1, 0)$ on the circumference of the circle to some point P on the circle and y is the y-coordinate of P (see Fig. 8-4). Symbolically, $y = \text{sine } u$, or $y = \sin u$.

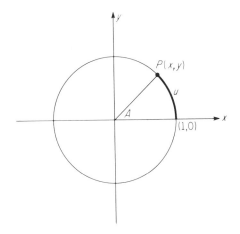

FIG. 8-4. $\sin u = y$; $\cos u = x$.

If A is the angle with the origin as vertex, the x-axis as one side, and the line containing the origin and P as the other side, then u is called the *radian measure* of angle A. For the unit circle, a straight angle subtends an arc of length π so π radians is the measure of a straight angle. We recall that in degree measure a straight angle has 180° as measure; we have the following corresponding degree measure and radian measure for special angles.

Degree Measure	Radian Measure
180	π
90	$\pi/2$
60	$\pi/3$
$180/\pi$	1
45	$\pi/4$
30	$\pi/6$
1	$\pi/180$

Since the circumference of the unit circle is 2π, it is geometrically obvious that for arc length $u + 2\pi$ the y-coordinate of P is the same as for arc length u. Thus

$$\sin (u + 2\pi) = \sin u.$$

We define $\sin 0 = 0$ and $\sin u$ where $u < 0$ by

$$\sin u = -\sin(-u).$$

Note, if $u < 0$, then $-u > 0$. The sine function is an odd function; therefore, its graph is symmetric to the origin of the coordinate system. (See Fig. 8-5.)

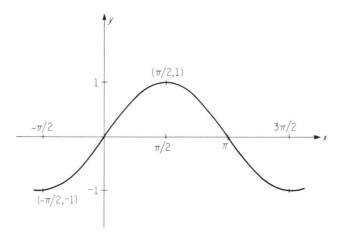

FIG. 8-5. $y = \sin x$.

The *cosine* function is the set of ordered pairs (u, x) where x is the x-coordinate of P whose counterclockwise arc length measure on the unit circle from $(1, 0)$ is u. We define $\cos 0 = 1$ and $\cos u$ where $u < 0$ by

$$\cos u = \cos(-u).$$

The cosine function is an even function; therefore, its graph is symmetric to the y-axis.

Finally, we define the tangent, cosecant, secant, and cotangent functions as follows:

$$\tan u = \frac{\sin u}{\cos u}, \quad \cos u \neq 0.$$

$$\csc u = \frac{1}{\sin u}, \quad \sin u \neq 0.$$

$$\sec u = \frac{1}{\cos u}, \quad \cos u \neq 0.$$

$$\cot u = \frac{\cos u}{\sin u}, \quad \sin u \neq 0.$$

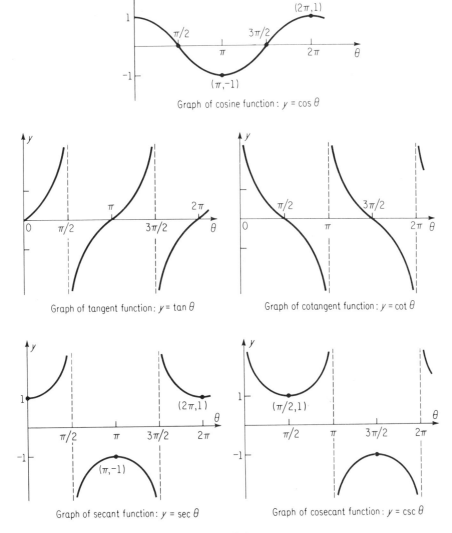

Graph of cosine function : $y = \cos \theta$

Graph of tangent function: $y = \tan \theta$

Graph of cotangent function : $y = \cot \theta$

Graph of secant function: $y = \sec \theta$

Graph of cosecant function : $y = \csc \theta$

FIG. 8-6

The function values of special angles for the trigonometric functions with which the reader should be familiar are indicated on the graphs of the functions. (See Fig. 8-6.)

We now list some of the important trigonometric identities. (An appropriate review for the reader would be to prove that each is an identity.)

1. $\sin^2 u + \cos^2 u = 1$.

2. $1 + \tan^2 u = \sec^2 u.$

3. $1 + \cot^2 u = \csc^2 u.$

4. $\sin(u + v) = \sin u \cos v + \cos u \sin v.$

5. $\sin 2u = 2 \sin u \cos u.$

6. $\cos(u + v) = \cos u \cos v - \sin u \sin v.$

7. $\cos 2u = \cos^2 u - \sin^2 u.$

8. $\sin(u - v) = \sin u \cos v - \cos u \sin v.$

9. $\cos(u - v) = \cos u \cos v + \sin u \sin v.$

10. $\tan(u + v) = \dfrac{\tan u + \tan v}{1 - \tan u \tan v}.$

11. $\tan(u - v) = \dfrac{\tan u - \tan v}{1 + \tan u \tan v}.$

12. $\sin u - \sin v = 2 \sin \dfrac{u - v}{2} \cos \dfrac{u + v}{2}.$

13. $\sin u + \sin v = 2 \dfrac{u + v}{2} \cos \dfrac{u - v}{2}.$

Let L be any nonvertical line in the coordinate system with slope m. Let L_1 be the line parallel to L containing the origin $(0,0)$. Line L_1 has slope m and intersects the unit circle at $(\cos u, \sin u)$ where u is the measure of the angle with x-axis as initial side and L_1 as terminal side. Thus, using the slope formula for the two points $(\cos u, \sin u)$ and $(0,0)$,

$$m = \frac{\sin u - 0}{\cos u - 0} = \tan u.$$

The angle with the x-axis as initial side and line L as terminal side is often called the *angle of inclination* of the line. Thus if u is the measure of the angle of inclination of a nonvertical line, then $m = \tan u$.   (See Fig. 8-7.)

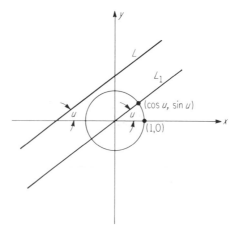

FIG. 8-7. $m = \tan u.$

*8-4. A SPECIAL LIMIT

Having reviewed some of the basic concepts of trigonometry, we now consider a limit of special importance in calculus. Geometrically, we prove that $\lim\limits_{u \to 0} \dfrac{\sin u}{u} = 1$; this type of proof is in keeping with the geometric definitions of the trigonometric functions.

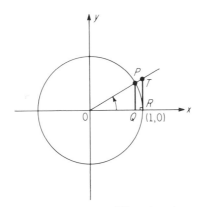

FIG. 8-8. $|PQ| < |\widehat{PR}| < |TR|$.

Assume that $0 < u < \pi/2$. (See Fig. 8-8.) By similar triangles OQP and ORT,

$$\frac{|TR|}{|PQ|} = \frac{|OR|}{|OQ|}.$$

Thus

$$\frac{|TR|}{\sin u} = \frac{1}{\cos u}$$

and

$$|TR| = \frac{\sin u}{\cos u}.$$

Furthermore,

$$0 < |PQ| < |\widehat{PR}| < |TR|;$$

thus

$$0 < \sin u < u < \frac{\sin u}{\cos u}.$$

Consequently,

$$\frac{1}{\sin u} > \frac{1}{u} > \frac{\cos u}{\sin u},$$

and

$$1 > \frac{\sin u}{u} > \cos u.$$

Now, for u "close" to 0, $\cos u$ is "close" to 1 and $\dfrac{\sin u}{u}$ is even "closer" to 1. Thus, $\dfrac{\sin u}{u}$ can be made "close" to 1 for *positive* u "close" to 0. We leave as an exercise for the reader to prove for $-\pi/2 < u < 0$ that $\dfrac{\sin u}{u}$ is "close" to 1 for u "close" to 0. Thus

$$\lim_{u \to 0} \frac{\sin u}{u} = 1.$$

EXERCISES

1. (a) Complete the accompanying table. (b) Graph the secant and cosecant functions on $[0, 2\pi]$.

Func-tion	0	$\dfrac{\pi}{6}$	$\dfrac{\pi}{4}$	$\dfrac{\pi}{3}$	$\dfrac{\pi}{2}$	$\dfrac{2\pi}{3}$	$\dfrac{3\pi}{4}$	$\dfrac{5\pi}{6}$	π	$\dfrac{7\pi}{4}$	$\dfrac{5\pi}{4}$	$\dfrac{4\pi}{3}$	$\dfrac{3\pi}{2}$	$\dfrac{5\pi}{3}$	$\dfrac{7\pi}{4}$	$\dfrac{11\pi}{6}$	2π
								Radian Measure									
$\sin \theta$									0	$\dfrac{-\sqrt{2}}{2}$							
$\cos \theta$									-1	$\dfrac{-\sqrt{2}}{2}$							
$\tan \theta$									0	1							
$\csc \theta$									$\sim$	$-\sqrt{2}$							
$\sec \theta$									-1	$-\sqrt{2}$							
$\cot \theta$									$\sim$	1							

★2. Prove that the thirteen equations on pages 167–168 are trigonometric identities.

3. Show that if $-\pi/2 < u < 0$, then $\dfrac{\sin u}{u}$ is "close" to 1 if u is "close" to 0.

4. Let L_1 and L_2 be two nonvertical intersecting lines in the rectangular coordinate plane. Let m_1 and m_2 be the slopes of L_1 to L_2, respectively. Prove that

$$\tan u = \frac{m_2 - m_1}{1 + m_1 m_2},$$

where u is the measure of the angle from L_1 to L_2.

5. Let L_1 and L_2 be two nonvertical lines in the coordinate plane with slopes m_1 and m_2, respectively. Prove that $m_1 = -1/m_2$ if and only if L_1 is perpendicular to L_2.

★8-5. DIFFERENTIATION OF THE TRIGONOMETRIC FUNCTIONS

Before deriving the derivative of the sine function, let us consider its graph to determine geometrically what might be the properties of the derived function. Since the sine function has maxima and minima at $\pm\pi/2, \pm3\pi/2, \pm5\pi/2$, etc., the value of the derivative should be zero at each of these points. Since the sine function has positive slope where $-\pi/2 < x < \pi/2, 3\pi/2 < x < 5\pi/2$, etc., the derivative should be positive in these intervals.

By the definition of the derivative, if $f(x) = \sin x$, then

$$f'(t) = \lim_{x \to t} \frac{\sin x - \sin t}{x - t}.$$

Using trigonometric identity 12, given in Sec. 8-3,

$$f'(t) = \lim_{x \to t} \frac{2 \sin \dfrac{x - t}{2} \cos \dfrac{x + t}{2}}{x - t}$$

$$= \lim_{x \to t} \frac{2 \sin\left(\dfrac{x - t}{2}\right)}{x - t} \lim_{x \to t} \cos\left(\frac{x + t}{2}\right)$$

$$= \cos t \lim_{x \to t} \frac{\sin\left(\dfrac{x - t}{2}\right)}{\dfrac{x - t}{2}}.$$

Letting $u = \dfrac{x - t}{2}$, as x approaches t, u approaches zero; thus

$$\lim_{x \to t} \frac{\sin\left(\dfrac{x - t}{2}\right)}{\dfrac{x - t}{2}} = \lim_{u \to 0} \frac{\sin u}{u} = 1.$$

Consequently,

$$f'(t) = \cos t. \tag{1}$$

We can use the fact that the derivative of the sine function is the cosine to differentiate the other trigonometric functions.

Let $f(x) = \cos x$. Then, using the trigonometric identity 8, $\sin(\pi/2 - x) = \cos x$. Thus

$$f(x) = \sin(\pi/2 - x).$$

By Eq. 1 and the composite function theorem,

$$f'(x) = [\cos(\pi/2 - x)](-1).$$
$$= -\cos(\pi/2 - x).$$

Finally, by using identity 9,

$$f'(x) = -\sin x. \tag{2}$$

Let $f(x) = \tan x$. Then $f(x) = \dfrac{\sin x}{\cos x}$. Using Eqs. 1 and 2 and the quotient theorem for differentiation,

$$\begin{aligned} f'(x) &= \frac{(\cos x)(\cos x) - (\sin x)(-\sin x)}{\cos^2 x} \\ &= \frac{\cos^2 x + \sin^2 x}{\cos^2 x} \\ &= \frac{1}{\cos^2 x} \\ &= \sec^2 x. \end{aligned} \tag{3}$$

We leave as an exercise for the reader to prove the following:

$$\frac{d}{dx}(\sec x) = \sec x \tan x. \tag{4}$$

$$\frac{d}{dx}(\csc x) = -\csc x \cot x. \tag{5}$$

$$\frac{d}{dx}(\cot x) = -\csc^2 x. \tag{6}$$

EXERCISES

Find the derivative of each function defined in the following.

1. $f(x) = \sec x$.
2. $f(x) = \csc x$.
3. $f(x) = \cot x$.
4. $f(x) = \sec^2 x + \sin 2x$.
5. $f(x) = \sin^2 x + \sqrt{1 - \sin x}$.
6. $f(x) = \dfrac{x^3}{\sin^4 x}$.
7. $f(x) = \tan 3x$.
8. $f(x) = \cot(1 - 3x) + \sec x^{1/2}$.
9. $f(x) = \cos^2 3x$.
10. $f(x) = x^2 \sin x$.
11. $f(x) = \cos(\sin x)$.
12. $f(x) = \tan(x^2 + 1)$.
13. $f(x) = \csc^2 x - \cot^2 x$.
14. $f(x) = \dfrac{\sin x + \cos x}{\tan x}$.
15. $f(x) = (\sin x)(\cos 3x)$.
16. $f(x) = (\sec 3x)(\tan 3x)$.

⋆8-6. APPLICATIONS

This section is primarily a problems section. It should give the student an opportunity to apply some of the ideas previously presented and to reinforce the learning of the various concepts involved. Let us first consider four examples.

Example 1.   Let P be the point of intersection of the graphs of the sine function and cosine function on the interval $[0, \pi/2]$. Find the measure of the angles between the tangent lines to the curves at point P.

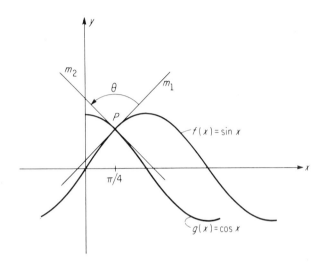

FIG. 8-9. θ = angle between tangents to sine and cosine functions at point of intersection.

Solution: For $x \in [0, \pi/2]$, $\sin x = \cos x$ when $x = \pi/4$. Thus, P has coordinates $(\pi/4, \sqrt{2}/2)$. Let m_1 be the slope of the tangent line at P to the graph of the sine function, and let m_2 be the slope of the tangent line at P to the graph of the cosine function. Thus, if $f(x) = \sin x$ and $g(x) = \cos x$, then

$$f'(x) = \cos x \qquad \text{and} \qquad g'(x) = -\sin x.$$

Furthermore, $m_1 = f'(\pi/4) = \sqrt{2}/2$ and $m_2 = g'(\pi/4) = -\sqrt{2}/2$. If θ is the measure of the angle from L_1 to L_2,

$$\tan \theta = \frac{m_2 - m_1}{1 + m_1 m_2}$$

$$= 2\sqrt{2}$$

$$\theta \approx 70°\,32'.$$

Example 2.   Find maxima, minima, and inflection points, and discuss concavity for the graph of f given by $f(x) = \sin x + \cos x$, $x \in [0, 2\pi]$.

Solution: Since $f(x) = \sin x + \cos x$,

$$f'(x) = \cos x - \sin x$$

and

$$f''(x) = -\sin x - \cos x.$$

Now, $f'(x) = 0$ where $\sin x = \cos x$. Thus, $f'(x) = 0$ for $x = \pi/4$ and $x = 5\pi/4$. Since $f'(\pi/4) = 0$ and $f''(\pi/4) < 0$, $(\pi/4, f(\pi/4))$ is a relative maximum point. Similarly, since $f'(5\pi/4) = 0$ and $f''(5\pi/4) > 0$, $(5\pi/4, f(5\pi/4))$ is a relative minimum point.

The graph of the cosine function is above the graph of the sine function in the open intervals $0 < x < \pi/4$ and $5\pi/4 < x < 2\pi$. In other words, $\cos x > \sin x$ in these intervals; thus, $f'(x) > 0$ where $x \in (0, \pi/4)$ and $x \in (5\pi/4, 2\pi)$. Consequently, f increases in these intervals. Furthermore, we conclude that the end point extremum $(0, f(0))$ is a relative minimum point and $(2\pi, f(2\pi))$ is a relative maximum point. The function decreases on the interval $\pi/4 < x < 5\pi/4$.

Since $f''(x) = 0$ where $\sin x = -\cos x$, $f''(3\pi/4) = 0$ and $f''(7\pi/4) = 0$. Furthermore, $f''(x) > 0$ for $x \in (3\pi/4, 7\pi/4)$ and $f''(x) < 0$ for $x \in (0, 3\pi/4)$ and $x \in (7\pi/4, 2\pi)$. Consequently, $(3\pi/4, f(3\pi/4))$ and $(7\pi/4, f(7\pi/4))$ are inflection points. The curve is concave upward on the interval $3\pi/4 < x < 7\pi/4$ and concave downward on the intervals $0 < x < 3\pi/4$ and $7\pi/4 < x < 2\pi$.

Example 3. Give the second-degree Taylor polynomial at $\pi/3$ to find an approximation for sin 1. (Do not give a rational approximation.) Find an upper bound on the error.

Solution: Recall that

$$f(x) = f(t) + f'(t)(x - t) + \frac{f''(t)}{2!}(x - t)^2 + \frac{f'''(c)}{3!}(x - t)^3$$

where c is between x and t. Thus, for $x = 1$, $t = \pi/3$, and $f(x) = \sin x$,

$$\sin 1 = \sin \pi/3 + f'(\pi/3)(1 - \pi/3)$$

$$+ \frac{f''(\pi/3)}{2!}(1 - \pi/3)^2 + \frac{f'''(c)}{3!}(1 - \pi/3)^3$$

where $1 < c < \pi/3$. Now, $f'(x) = \cos x$, $f''(x) = -\sin x$, and $f'''(x) = -\cos x$. Thus

$$\sin 1 = \frac{\sqrt{3}}{2} + \frac{1}{2}(1 - \pi/3) - \frac{\sqrt{3}}{4}(1 - \pi/3)^2 - \frac{\cos c}{3!}(1 - \pi/3)^3.$$

Since $|\cos c| \le 1$ for any c, the error of $\dfrac{\sqrt{3}}{2} - \dfrac{1}{2}(1 - \pi/3) - \dfrac{\sqrt{3}}{4}$.

$(1 - \pi/3)^2$ as an approximation for sin 1 is less than $\dfrac{(0.0472)^3}{6} < 1.9 \times 10^{-5}$.

EXERCISES

In Exercises 1 through 6 find maxima, minima, and inflection points; discuss the concavity of the graph of the function; and sketch the graph.

1. $f(x) = \sin x - \cos x$, $x \in [0, 2\pi]$.
2. $f(x) = \sqrt{3} \sin x + \cos x$, $x = [0, 2\pi]$.
3. $f(x) = x + \sin x$, $x \in [0, \pi]$.
4. $f(x) = \sin^2 x$, $x \in [0, 2\pi]$.
5. $f(x) = x/2 - \cos x$, $x \in [0, \pi]$.
6. $f(x) = x/2 + \sin x$, $x \in [0, \pi]$.

7. Find the angle between the tangent lines at the point of intersection of the tangent and cotangent functions.

8. Find the angles between the tangent lines at the points of intersection of the graphs of $y = \sin 2x$ and $y = \cos x$ where $-\pi < x < \pi$.

9. Find a four-place decimal approximation of $\sin 1/2$ using a Taylor polynomial at $\pi/6$ for sine function.

10. Find a four-place decimal approximation of $\tan 3/4$ using a Taylor polynomial at $\pi/4$ for the tangent function.

9

Introduction to the Definite Integral

9-1. AREA

In Euclidean plane geometry, one learns how area is assigned to polygonal figures in the plane. For example, we learn that a right triangle has area $(1/2)bh$ where b is the length of the base and h is the altitude; a rectangle has area lw where l is the length and w is the width. In general, since a polygonal figure can be considered to be made up of triangles (see Fig. 9-1), the area of plane polygonal figures can be found using only the formula for the area of a triangle.

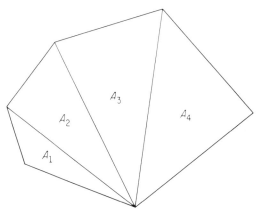

FIG. 9-1. $A = A_1 + A_2 + A_3 + A_4$.

The formula for finding the area of a circle of given radius is also discussed in geometry, but no attempt is made to discover a method to assign a number for the area of arbitrary plane regions. We now make an approach to this problem.

Suppose we wish to find the area of a plane region such as A in Fig. 9-2. If k_1 is the area of the region bounded by the graph of f, the lines $x = a, x = b$, and the x-axis and if k_2 is the area of the region bounded by the graph of g, the lines $x = a, x = b$, and the x-axis, then $(k_1 - k_2)$

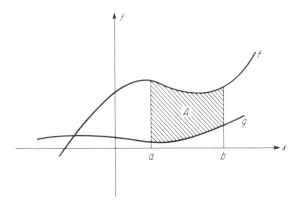

FIG. 9-2

would be the area of region A. Thus, the original problem is reduced to determining a method for assigning area to a region under the graph of a function and above the x-axis between two parallel lines perpendicular to the x-axis. Consider the following specific example.

Let f be defined by $f(x) = x^2$. We restate the problem as that of finding a method to determine the number called the *area* of the region bounded by $x = 2$, $x = 6$, the graph of f, and the x-axis. To begin, we divide the interval into four *equal* subintervals with $P = \{2, 3, 4, 5, 6\}$ as the set of end points of the subintervals. This is called a *partition* of $[2, 6]$. Since f is an increasing function on $[2, 6]$, $f(2) = 4$, $f(3) = 9$, $f(4) = 16$, and $f(5) = 25$ are the minimum values of f on each of the closed subintervals $[2, 3]$, $[3, 4]$, $[4, 5]$, and $[5, 6]$, respectively. (See Fig. 9-3.) Since the width of each subinterval is 1, the total area of the inscribed rectangles under the graph of f is

$$f(2) + f(3) + f(4) + f(5) = 54 \text{ square units.}$$

We call 54 the *lower sum* of f with respect to partition P of $[2, 6]$ and denote it by $L(P, f)$. If k is the area of the region in question, then

$$L(P, f) < k.$$

We obtain an upper approximation of the area by using circumscribed rectangles. For the given partition P, $f(3) = 9$, $f(4) = 16$, $f(5) = 25$, and $f(6) = 36$ are the maximum values of f on the closed subintervals and thus the heights of the circumscribed rectangles. The sum of the area of all of these rectangles is

$$f(3) + f(4) + f(5) + f(6) = 86 \text{ square units.}$$

We call 86 an *upper sum* of f with respect to partition P of $[2, 6]$ and denote it by $U(P, f)$. It is geometrically obvious that if k is the area of the region, then

$$L(P, f) < k < U(P, f);$$

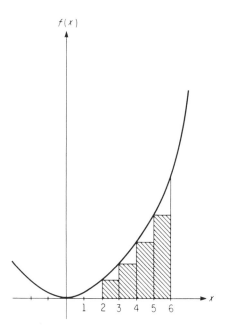

FIG. 9-3. $P = \{2, 3, 4, 5, 6\}$; $L(P, f) = f(2) + f(3) + f(4) + f(5) = 54$.

in particular,

$$54 < k < 86.$$

Knowing the area of the given region is between 54 and 86 square units is desirable information but this bound on k lacks the degree of accuracy one usually associates with area. To develop better bounds on k, we replace the original four subintervals with n equal subintervals. Now the set of partition points is

$$P = \{2 = x_0, x_1, x_2, \ldots, x_i, x_{i+1}, \ldots, x_{n-1}, x_n = 6\}$$

where $x_i < x_{i+1}$. Since the width of $[2, 6]$ is 4, the width of each of the n equal subintervals is $4/n$. Hence

$$x_0 = 2 \qquad\qquad f(x_0) = 4.$$

$$x_1 = 2 + \frac{4}{n} \qquad f(x_1) = 4 + \left(\frac{16}{n}\right) + \left(\frac{4}{n}\right)^2.$$

$$x_2 = 2 + 2\frac{4}{n} \qquad f(x_2) = 4 + 2\left(\frac{16}{n}\right) + 2^2\left(\frac{4}{n}\right)^2.$$

$$x_3 = 2 + 3\frac{4}{n} \qquad f(x_3) = 4 + 3\left(\frac{16}{n}\right) + 3^2\left(\frac{4}{n}\right)^2.$$

In general,

$$x_t = 2 + t\frac{4}{n} \qquad f(x_t) = 4 + t\left(\frac{16}{n}\right) + t^2\left(\frac{4}{n}\right)^2.$$

Notice that $f(x_0) + f(x_1) + f(x_2) + f(x_3) + \cdots + f(x_n) = 4n$

$+ \dfrac{16}{n} \cdot (1 + 2 + 3 + \cdots + n) + \left(\dfrac{4}{n}\right)^2(1^2 + 2^2 + 3^2 + \cdots + n^2).$ Re-

calling that

$$1 + 2 + 3 + \cdots + n = \frac{n(n+1)}{2}$$

and

$$1^2 + 2^2 + 3^2 + \cdots + n^2 = \frac{n(n+1)(2n+1)}{6}$$

for any integer n and using the fact that the lower sum with respect to P is given by

$$L(P,f) = \frac{4}{n}[f(x_0) + f(x_1) + \cdots + f(x_{n-1})],$$

we conclude

$$L(P,f) = \frac{4}{n}\left[4n + \frac{16(n-1)n}{2n} + \left(\frac{16}{n^2}\right)\frac{(n-1)n(2n-1)}{6}\right].$$

Thus

$$L(P,f) = 16 + 32\left(1 - \frac{1}{n}\right) + \frac{32}{3}\left(1 - \frac{1}{n}\right)\left(2 - \frac{1}{n}\right).$$

We leave as an exercise for the reader the proof that the upper sum with respect to P is given by

$$U(P,f) = 16 + 32\left(1 + \frac{1}{n}\right) + \frac{32}{3}\left(1 + \frac{1}{n}\right)\left(2 + \frac{1}{n}\right).$$

To check the derivations of $L(P,f)$ and $U(P,f)$, let $n = 4$. Then

$$L(P,f) = 16 + 32\left(\frac{3}{4}\right) + \frac{32}{3}\left(\frac{3}{4}\right)\left(\frac{7}{4}\right) = 54$$

and

$$U(P,f) = 16 + 32\left(\frac{5}{4}\right) + \frac{32}{3}\left(\frac{5}{4}\right)\left(\frac{9}{4}\right) = 86.$$

Since for "large" n both $(1 + 1/n)$ and $(1 - 1/n)$ are "close" to 1 and $(2 + 1/n)$ and $(2 - 1/n)$ are "close" to 2, both $L(P,f)$ and $U(P,f)$ are "close" to $69\frac{1}{3}$. We therefore conclude that $69\frac{1}{3}$ square units is the area of the region.

The reader should be convinced of one thing. The method discussed for assigning area to the given region is at least tedious. It should be apparent that if the function f did not have such a "well-behaved" graph the method used could prove extremely difficult. In order to show how easy the solution can be and also to give some real purpose to the next two sections, let us preview how the area can be found.

Find an antiderivative of $f(x) = x^2$; one antiderivative is $F(x) = x^3/3$. Evaluate $F(6) - F(2)$; that is, find the difference in the values of the anti-derivative at the end points of the interval.

$$F(6) - F(2) = \frac{216}{3} - \frac{8}{3}$$

$$= \frac{208}{3}$$

$$= 69\frac{1}{3}. \quad \text{(The area of the region!)}$$

In general, we assert that the area under the graph of a function f which is above the x-axis and between $x = a$ and $x = b$ is $F(b) - F(a)$ where $F'(x) = f(x)$.

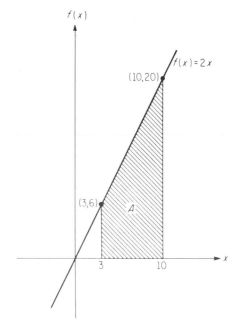

FIG. 9-4. $A = \frac{1}{2}(6 + 20)7 = 91$.

As a second illustration, consider a familiar region where area may be determined by using an established formula. The area of the trapezoid in Fig. 9-4 is

$$\frac{1}{2}(b_1 + b_2)h = \frac{1}{2}(6 + 20)7 = 91 \text{ square units.}$$

Since the trapezoid is the region bounded by $f(x) = 2x$, $x = 3$, $x = 10$, and the x-axis, we proceed as in the previous example. An antiderivative of $f(x) = 2x$ is $F(x) = x^2$, and

$$F(10) - F(3) = 100 - 9 = 91.$$

In the next two sections we develop the theory necessary to justify these procedures.

EXERCISES

1. Let f be defined by $f(x) = 2x$ with domain $[3, 10]$. (a) Find $L(P, f)$ for a partition P of 7 equal subintervals. (b) Find $U(P, f)$ for a partition P of 7 equal subintervals. (c) Find $L(P, f)$ for a partition P of n equal subintervals. (d) Find $U(P, f)$ for a partition P of n equal subintervals. (e) Show that $L(P, f)$ and $U(P, f)$ are "close" to 91 for "large" n.

2. Let f be defined by $f(x) = x^2$ with domain $[0, 5]$. (a) Find $L(P, f)$ for a partition P of 5 equal subintervals. (b) Find $U(P, f)$ for a partition P of 5 equal subintervals. (c) Find $L(P, f)$ for a partition P of n equal subintervals. (d) Find $U(P, f)$ for a partition P of n equal subintervals. (e) Show that $L(P, f)$ and $U(P, f)$ are "close" to $125/3$ for "large" n.

3. For $f(x) = x^2$, show that

$$U(P, f) = 16 + 32\left(1 + \frac{1}{n}\right) + \frac{32}{3}\left(1 + \frac{1}{n}\right)\left(2 + \frac{1}{n}\right),$$

for a partition of n equal subintervals of $[2, 6]$.

4. Let f be defined by $f(x) = x^3$ with domain $[0, 4]$. (a) Find $L(P, f)$ for a partition P of 8 equal subintervals. (b) Find $U(P, f)$ for a partition P of 8 equal subintervals. (c) Find $L(P, f)$ for a partition P of n equal subintervals. Recall that

$$1^3 + 2^3 + 3^3 + \cdots + n^3 = \frac{n^2(n + 1)^2}{4}.$$

(d) Find $U(P, f)$ for a partition P of n equal subintervals. (e) Find an antiderivative F of f. (f) Find $F(4) - F(0)$. (g) Show that both $U(P, f)$ and $L(P, f)$ can be made "close" to $F(4) - F(0)$ for "large" n.

★ 5. Let f be an increasing and continuous function on $[a, b]$. Let P be a partition of $[a, b]$ into n equal subintervals. Show that

$$U(P, f) - L(P, f) = [f(b) - f(a)]\left(\frac{b - a}{n}\right).$$

9-2. THE RIEMANN INTEGRAL

In the last section, the functions and the partitions of their domains had the following restrictions: (1) The function values of f throughout the domain $[a, b]$ were nonnegative. (2) The function was increasing through-out its domain. (3) The partitions consisted of points dividing the interval into equal subintervals. (4) The functions were continuous on $[a, b]$. In this section, we generalize the ideas of Sec. 9-1 and define what is called either the *Riemann integral* or the *definite integral of a function f from a to b*. Here, only the restriction that f be a continuous function on the closed interval $[a, b]$ is retained.

Let f be a continuous function on the closed interval $[a, b]$. Let $x_0, x_1, x_2, \ldots, x_n$ be $n + 1$ numbers in $[a, b]$ such that

$$a = x_0 < x_1 < x_2 < \cdots < x_n = b.$$

The set $P = \{x_0, x_1, x_2, \ldots, x_n\}$ is called a *partition* of $[a, b]$, and the numbers in P are the end points of n closed subintervals:

$$[x_0, x_1], [x_1, x_2], [x_2, x_3], \ldots, [x_{n-1}, x_n].$$

Since f is continuous on the closed subintervals, f attains its maximum and minimum on each subinterval; in other words, there exists

$$u_i \in [x_{i-1}, x_i], \quad i = 1, 2, 3, \ldots, n$$

such that

$$f(u_i) \leq f(x) \text{ for all } x \in [x_{i-1}, x_i].$$

Note that even though u_i need not be a unique number in the ith sub-interval since the minimum value may be attained at more than one point, the minimum value $f(u_i)$ is unique. Thus $f(u_i)(x_i - x_{i-1})$ is uniquely determined for a given partition P. Similarly there exists

$$v_i \in [x_{i-1}, x_i], \quad i = 1, 2, 3, \ldots, n$$

such that

$$f(v_i) \geq f(x) \text{ for all } x \in [x_{i-1}, x_i].$$

We define the *lower sum* of f on $[a, b]$ with respect to P by

$$L(P, f) = f(u_1)(x_1 - x_0) + f(u_2)(x_2 - x_1)$$
$$+ f(u_3)(x_3 - x_2) + \cdots + f(u_n)(x_n - x_{n-1}).$$

The *upper sum* of f on $[a, b]$ with respect to P is defined by

$$U(P, f) = f(v_1)(x_1 - x_0) + f(v_2)(x_2 - x_1)$$
$$+ f(v_3)(x_3 - x_2) + \cdots + f(v_n)(x_n - x_{n-1}).$$

Since $f(u_i) \leq f(v_i)$ in each subinterval,

$$f(u_i)(x_i - x_{i-1}) \leq f(v_i)(x_i - x_{i-1}), \quad i = 1, 2, 3, \ldots, n.$$

Thus by adding the n inequalities we conclude that

$$L(P, f) \leq U(P, f).$$

Let $f(v)$ be the absolute maximum value of f on $[a, b]$ and let $f(u)$ be the absolute minimum value of f on $[a, b]$. Thus

$$f(u) \leq f(u_i) \leq f(v_i) \leq f(v)$$

and
$$f(u_i)(x_i - x_{i-1}) \leq f(v)(x_i - x_{i-1}), \ i = 1, 2, 3, \ldots, n.$$
Consequently
$$L(P,f) \leq f(v)(x_1 - x_0 + x_2 - x_1 + x_3 - x_2 + \cdots + x_n - x_{n-1})$$
$$\leq f(v)(x_n - x_0)$$
$$\leq f(v)(b - a).$$
If the graph of f is above the x-axis, this is equivalent to stating that the sum of the areas of the inscribed rectangles is never greater than the area

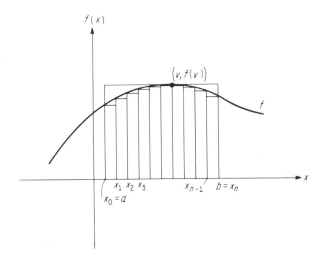

FIG. 9-5. $L(P,f) \leq f(v)(b - a)$.

of the one circumscribed rectangle (see Fig. 9-5). Similarly, since
$$f(v_i) \geq f(u)$$
and since $(x_i - x_{i-1})$ is a positive number,
$$f(v_i)(x_i - x_{i-1}) \geq f(u)(x_i - x_{i-1}).$$
We conclude that
$$L(P,f) \geq f(u)(b - a).$$
Therefore, we have the following theorem.

Theorem 9-1. Let f be continuous on $[a,b]$. Let $f(u)$ and $f(v)$, respectively, be the absolute minimum and maximum values of f on $[a,b]$. If P is any partition of $[a,b]$, then
$$f(u)(b - a) \leq L(P,f) \leq U(P,f) \leq f(v)(b - a).$$
For a continuous function f on $[a,b]$, there exists a unique number $L(P,f)$

for each partition P and thus $\{L(P,f)\}$ is a set of real numbers which (by Theorem 9-1) has $f(v)(b - a)$ as an upper bound. By the completeness property, the set of lower sums has a least upper bound. Similarly, the set of upper sums $\{U(P,f)\}$ has $f(u)(b - a)$ as a lower bound and thus has a greatest lower bound. (See Exercise 18, Sec. 1-4.) Since f is a continuous function, it can be proved that the least upper bound of the set of lower sums and the greatest lower bound of the set of upper sums is the same number. This *number* is called either the *Riemann integral* or *definite integral of f from a to b*. It is denoted by

$$\int_a^b f \qquad \text{or} \qquad \int_a^b f(x)\,dx.$$

Theorem 9-2. Let f be a continuous function on $[a, b]$. The least upper bound of $\{L(P,f)\}$ and the greatest lower bound of $\{U(P,f)\}$ exist and are equal.

For a continuous function, we know that $\int_a^b f$ exists if $a < b$. However, none of our theorems yet provide a technique for finding the Riemann integral of f from a to b. Before doing this, let us define $\int_a^b f$ for real numbers a and b where $a = b$ or $a > b$ and indicate one immediate consequence.

Definitions:

(1) $\displaystyle\int_a^a f = 0.$

(2) $\displaystyle\int_a^b f = -\int_b^a f$ if $a > b$.

Theorem 9-3. Let f be a continuous function on a closed interval containing three real numbers a, b, and c. Then

$$\int_a^b f + \int_b^c f = \int_a^c f.$$

From our usual geometric interpretation, Theorem 9-3 states that if $a < b < c$, then the area under the graph of f from a to b plus the area from b to c is the same as the area under the graph from a to c. The previous definitions make the theorem valid regardless of how a, b, and c are ordered on the number line.

9-3. FUNDAMENTAL THEOREM OF CALCULUS

Let f be a continuous function on $[a, b]$. Then, for any number t in the closed interval $[a, b]$, $\int_a^t f$ exists. Thus, we can define a new function G by

$$G(t) = \int_a^t f.$$

We now show that not only is the function G a differentiable function but that the value of the derivative of G at t is $f(t)$. That is,

$$G'(t) = f(t).$$

By the definition of the derivative of a function G at t,

$$G'(t) = \lim_{x \to t} \frac{G(x) - G(t)}{x - t},$$

provided the limit exists. Now, from the definition of G,

$$G'(t) = \lim_{x \to t} \frac{\int_a^x f - \int_a^t f}{x - t}.$$

By Theorem 9-3,

$$G'(t) = \lim_{x \to t} \frac{\int_t^x f}{x - t}.$$

If $x > t$, $\int_t^x f$ is the area under the curve in Fig. 9-6 and $(x - t)$ is the

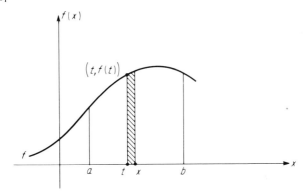

FIG. 9-6. Area $\approx f(t)(x - t)$; $f(t) \approx \dfrac{\text{area}}{x - t} = \dfrac{\int_x^t f(x)\,dx}{x - t}$.

width of the region. If x is "close" to t, then the region is nearly rectangular. Thus, the area divided by the width is "close" to the height of the "rectangle"; this is the function value of f at t. Therefore, $G'(t) = f(t)$. This geometric argument is used to justify the following theorem.

Theorem 9-4. Let f be a continuous function on $[a, b]$ and let $G(t) = \int_a^t f$. Then G is a differentiable function on $[a, b]$ and $G'(t) = f(t)$.

Let F be any antiderivative of f. Then $F'(t) = f(t)$. Since if $G(t) = \int_a^t f$, then $G'(t) = f(t)$, the function G is also an antiderivative of f. From Sec. 6-5, we know that

$$G(x) = F(x) + C,$$

where C is a constant. Since $G(a) = \int_a^a f = 0$, $F(a) + C = 0$ and $C = -F(a)$. Thus $G(b) = F(b) - F(a)$, or

$$\int_a^b f = F(b) - F(a).$$

The notation $F(x) \mid_a^b$ is sometimes used to represent the difference $F(b) - F(a)$. This completes the proof of the fundamental theorem of calculus.

Fundamental Theorem of Calculus. Let f be a function continuous on $[a, b]$. Then F, an antiderivative of f, exists and

$$\int_a^b f = F(b) - F(a).$$

Since finding a definite integral by using the fundamental theorem necessitates finding an antiderivative, we have a number of important formulas immediately available for use as a result of our work with antiderivatives in Sec. 6-5.

$$\int_a^b x^p \, dx = \frac{b^{p+1}}{p+1} - \frac{a^{p+1}}{p+1}, \quad p \neq -1. \tag{1}$$

$$\int_a^b [f(x) + g(x)] \, dx = \int_a^b f(x) \, dx + \int_a^b g(x) \, dx. \tag{2}$$

$$\int_a^b f(g(x))g'(x) \, dx = f(g(b)) - f(g(a)). \tag{3}$$

$$\int_a^b [f(x)]^p f'(x) \, dx = \frac{[f(b)]^{p+1} - [f(a)]^{p+1}}{p+1}, \quad p \neq -1. \tag{4}$$

$$\int_a^b cf(x) \, dx = c \int_a^b f(x) \, dx, \text{ where } c \text{ is a constant.} \tag{5}$$

$$\int_a^b \frac{1}{x} \, dx = \ln b - \ln a, \text{ where } a > 0 \text{ and } b > 0. \qquad (6)$$

$$\int_a^b \frac{g'(x)}{g(x)} \, dx = \ln g(b) - \ln g(a), \text{ where } g(x) > 0 \text{ for } a < x < b. \qquad (7)$$

$$\int_a^b e^x \, dx = e^b - e^a. \qquad (8)$$

$$\int_a^b e^{g(x)} g'(x) \, dx = e^{g(b)} - e^{g(a)}. \qquad (9)$$

These formulas are sufficient for the solutions of our examples.

Example 1.

$$\int_1^3 (x^2 + 2x) \, dx = \frac{x^3}{3} + x^2 \Big|_1^3 = \left(\frac{27}{3} + 9 \right) - \left(\frac{1}{3} + 1 \right) = 16\frac{2}{3}.$$

Example 2.

$$\int_0^1 (8x + 1)^{2/3} 8 \, dx = \frac{(8x + 1)^{5/3}}{5/3} \Big|_0^1 = \frac{3}{5} (9^{5/3} - 1^{5/3})$$

$$= \frac{3}{5} (9 \sqrt[3]{81} - 1).$$

NOTE: We used Formula 4 in this example and will in the next.

Example 3.

$$\int_0^{\sqrt{15}} (x^2 + 1)^{1/2} x \, dx = \frac{1}{2} \int_0^{\sqrt{15}} (x^2 + 1)^{1/2} 2x \, dx$$

$$= \frac{1}{2} \left[\frac{(x^2 + 1)^{3/2}}{3/2} \right] \Big|_0^{\sqrt{15}}$$

$$= \frac{1}{3} [(16)^{3/2} - 1^{3/2}]$$

$$= 21.$$

Example 4. Find the area of the region bounded by $y = x^2 + 1$, $x = -3$, $x = 2$ and the x-axis (see Fig. 9-7).

Solution:

$$\int_{-3}^2 (x^2 + 1) \, dx = \left(\frac{x^3}{3} + x \right) \Big|_{-3}^2$$

$$= \left(\frac{8}{3} + 2 \right) - (-9 - 3)$$

$$= \frac{50}{3} \text{ square units.}$$

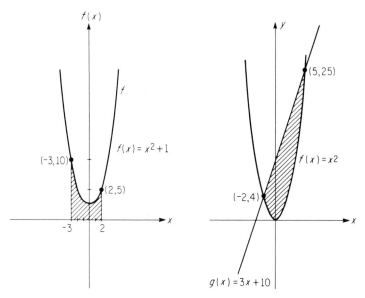

FIG. 9-7

Example 5.   Find the area of the region bounded by $y = x^2$ and $y = 3x + 10$. (See Fig. 9-7.)

Solution: The points of intersection are where

$$x^2 = 3x + 10,$$
$$x^2 - 3x - 10 = 0,$$
$$(x - 5)(x + 2) = 0,$$
$$x = 5, \quad \text{and} \quad x = -2.$$

The area of the region is the area of the trapezoid less the area above the x-axis under the graph of $y = x^2$. Using integrals,

$$A = \int_{-2}^{5} (3x + 10)\, dx - \int_{-2}^{5} x^2\, dx$$

$$= \left(\frac{3x^2}{2} + 10x\right)\Big|_{-2}^{5} - \frac{x^3}{3}\Big|_{-2}^{5}$$

$$= \left(\frac{75}{2} + 50\right) - (6 - 20) - \left(\frac{125}{3} + \frac{8}{3}\right)$$

$$= \frac{343}{6} \text{ square units.}$$

Example 6.   In Example 3 of Sec. 8-2 we proposed a learning curve where the cost of producing the xth unit was given by

$$C(x) = S + C(1)e^{-ax}. \tag{1}$$

To calculate the cost of producing the first k units we recognize this to be the sum

$$\sum_{n=1}^{k} C(n) = C(1) + C(2) + C(3) + \cdots + C(k),$$

the area of the first k rectangles shown in Fig. 9-8. Even though x is a

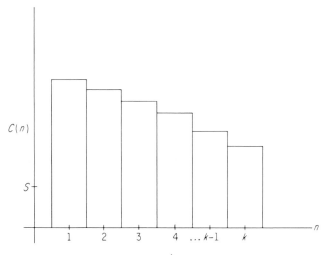

FIG. 9-8. $C(n) = \displaystyle\sum_{n=1}^{k} S + C(1)e^{-an}.$

discrete variable, we now make the familiar continuity assumption. $C(k)$ may be approximated by

$$C(k) = \int_{0}^{k} [S + C(1)e^{-ax}]\,dx.$$

Evaluating this integral,

$$\int_{0}^{k} [S + C(1)e^{-ax}]\,dx = \int_{0}^{k} S\,dx + \int_{0}^{k} C(1)e^{-ax}\,dx$$

$$= Sx \Big|_{0}^{k} - \frac{C(1)e^{-ax}}{a} \Big|_{0}^{k}$$

$$= kS - \frac{C(1)e^{-ak}}{a} + \frac{C(1)}{a}.$$

Letting $k = 2$, the total cost is

$$C(2) = 2S + \frac{C(1)}{a} - \frac{C(1)e^{-2a}}{a}.$$

However, if we evaluate $C(x)$ in Eq. 1 at $x = 1$ and $x = 2$, then

$$C(1) = S + C(1)e^{-a},$$
$$C(2) = S + C(1)e^{-2a},$$

and

$$\sum_{k=1}^{2} C(k) = 2S + C(1)e^{-a}(1 + e^{-a}).$$

The difference in the two computations results from the continuity assumption. Unless $C(1)$ is exceedingly large, the reader can verify that the amount of error introduced by the continuity assumption is negligible.

Example 7. A trucking firm has purchased an automatic loading device with which it feels it can substantially reduce costs. It is believed the yearly savings in thousands of dollars are given by $S(t) = 100 - t^2$, where the annual savings decrease due to lower operating speed and increasing damage to shipments as the machine ages. Annual operating expenses, also in thousands of dollars, are expected to be $R(t) = 12t$. The net "earnings" of the machine in year t are

$$E(t) = S(t) - R(t)$$
$$= 100 - t^2 - 12t.$$

Obviously the company will not retain the machine beyond the time period in which $S(t) = R(t)$, and to find the year in which the machine should be scrapped, we solve

$$100 - t^2 = 12t$$
$$t = 5.65.$$

For simplicity we assume the machine is retained for five years, and total net savings for the five-year period are

$$\int_{0}^{5} (100 - t^2 - 12t)\, dt = \left(100t - \frac{t^3}{3} - 6t^2\right)\Big|_{0}^{5}$$
$$= 308.333.$$

Example 8. The total earnings from the introduction of a new product are expected to be given by

$$\int_{0}^{t} (-2x + 5)\, dx = (-x^2 + 5x)\Big|_{0}^{t} = 5t - t^2.$$

To find the time period in which profit is maximum we apply the techniques of Chapter 6.

$$\frac{d}{dt}(5t - t^2) = 5 - 2t.$$

Setting the derivative equal to zero and solving, $t = 5/2$. Since the second derivative of the function is negative, $t = 5/2$ is the point in time at which profit is maximum.

Note that in this example we found the extrema by first integrating and then differentiating. We could eliminate one step in the procedure by using Theorem 9-4. Since

$$F(t) = \int_0^t (-2x + 5)\, dx,$$

$$F'(t) = -2t + 5.$$

Example 9. Differentiating "under the integral" is often useful in applications. This example pertains to what is called *Leibnitz's Rule*. Under certain conditions, if

$$F(x) = \int_{u(x)}^{v(x)} f(x, y)\, dy,$$

then

$$F'(x) = f(x, v(x))v'(x) - f(x, u(x))u'(x) + \int_{u(x)}^{v(x)} \frac{\partial}{\partial x} f(x, y)\, dy.$$

For example, let

$$F(x) = \int_x^{x^4} (x^2 + y^2)\, dy$$

and find F' by two methods.

1.

$$F(x) = \int_x^{x^4} (x^2 + y^2)\, dy = \left(x^2 y + \frac{y^3}{3}\right)\Bigg|_x^{x^4}$$

$$= \left(x^6 + \frac{x^{12}}{3}\right) - \left(x^3 + \frac{x^3}{3}\right)$$

$$= \frac{x^{12}}{3} + x^6 - \frac{4x^3}{3}.$$

Thus,

$$F'(x) = 4x^{11} + 6x^5 - 4x^2.$$

2.

$$F'(x) = f(x, x^4) \cdot 4x^3 - f(x, x) \cdot 1 + \int_x^{x^4} 2x\, dy$$

$$= (x^2 + x^8)4x^3 - (x^2 + x^2) + 2xy\Bigg|_x^{x^4}$$

$$= 4x^5 + 4x^{11} - 2x^2 + 2x^5 - 2x^2$$

$$= 4x^{11} + 6x^5 - 4x^2.$$

EXERCISES

For Exercises 1 through 12, find the specified definite integrals.

1. $\displaystyle\int_{1}^{4} (x^2 - x)\,dx.$ **2.** $\displaystyle\int_{1.}^{3} (x^2 - 2x + 7)\,dx.$

3. $\displaystyle\int_{4}^{1} x(\sqrt{x} - 1)\,dx.$ **4.** $\displaystyle\int_{1}^{2} \frac{u + 1}{u^3}\,du.$

5. $\displaystyle\int_{4}^{7} (x - 3)^{1/2}\,dx.$ **6.** $\displaystyle\int_{-1}^{-27} t(t^{1/3} - 1)\,dt.$

7. $\displaystyle\int_{0}^{1} (x^3 + 2x + 1)^4(3x^2 + 2)\,dx.$ **8.** $\displaystyle\int_{0}^{2} (4x + 1)^{3/2}\,dx.$

9. $\displaystyle\int_{0}^{1} (5x^2 + 1)^3 x\,dx.$ **10.** $\displaystyle\int_{-3}^{3} (x^3 + x)\,dx.$

11. $\displaystyle\int_{0}^{1} (x^2 + 2x + 1)^{1/2}(x + 1)\,dx.$ **12.** $\displaystyle\int_{-3}^{3} (x + 3)^3\,dx.$

13. Discuss the following:

$$\int_{-1}^{3} x^{-2}\,dx = \frac{x^{-1}}{-1}\Big|_{-1}^{3} = \left(-\frac{1}{3} + 1\right) = \frac{2}{3}.$$

Is the answer correct? Justify your answer.

★14. Assume $\displaystyle\int_{-a}^{a} f$ exists. Prove that if f is an even function,

$$\int_{-a}^{a} f = 2\int_{0}^{a} f.$$

★15. Assume $\displaystyle\int_{-a}^{a} f$ exists. Prove that if f is an odd function,

$$\int_{-a}^{a} f = 0.$$

Find the area of the regions in the plane bounded by the graphs of the given equations in Exercises 16 through 21.

16. $y = x^2 - x$ and the x-axis.
17. $y = (x - 2)(x - 5)$ and the x-axis.
18. $y = (x + 4)(x - 2)$ and the x-axis.
19. $y = x^3 + 2x$, $x = 1$, $x = 4$, and the x-axis.
20. $y = x$ and $y = x^3$.   **21.** $y = x^2$ and $y = 2x + 8$.

22. If $\displaystyle F(x) = \int_{0}^{x} e^{-2x^2 y}\,dy$, find $F'(x)$.

23. If $\displaystyle F(x) = \int_{x}^{x^2} (x^2 - y^2)^n\,dy$, find $F'(x)$.

24. If $\displaystyle F(y) = \int_{0}^{y^2} x^4(y - x)^3\,dx$, find $F'(y)$.

10
*Techniques of Integration**

10-1. SUBSTITUTION

Before discussing an integration method called the *substitution tech-nique*, we review a few facts that must be remembered since they are used throughout the remainder of this book.

If F is a function such that $F'(x) = f(x)$, then an antiderivative of f is F. That is,

$$\int f(x)\,dx = F(x) + C.$$

If a function g is continuous on the closed interval $[a, b]$, then g has an antiderivative G; the definite integral

$$\int_a^b g(x)\,dx$$

exists; and, by the fundamental theorem of calculus,

$$\int_a^b g(x) = G(b) - G(a).$$

Since in evaluating definite integrals one must first find an antiderivative, a topic of major interest in integral calculus is the techniques for finding antiderivatives of given functions.

Let us list some antiderivative formulas that have been previously derived and which should, because of their frequent use, be memorized.

$$\int [f(x) + g(x)]\,dx = \int f(x)\,dx + \int g(x)\,dx. \tag{1}$$

$$\int cf(x)\,dx = c\int f(x)\,dx, \text{ where } c \text{ is a constant.} \tag{2}$$

$$\int x^p\,dx = \frac{x^{p+1}}{p + 1} + C, \quad p \neq -1. \tag{3}$$

$$\int \frac{1}{x}\,dx = \ln x + C. \tag{4}$$

$$\int [f(x)]^p f'(x)\,dx = \frac{[f(x)]^{p+1}}{p + 1} + C, \quad p \neq -1. \tag{5}$$

*The reader should be aware that extensive tables of integrals may be found in any standard mathematical tables. However, even though the more frequently used integrals are included in such tables, it is often necessary to apply the techniques included in this chapter in order to reduce a given integral to a form which may be matched with the tables.

$$\int \frac{f'(x)}{f(x)} \, dx = \ln f(x) + C. \tag{6}$$

$$\int e^x \, dx = e^x + C. \tag{7}$$

$$\int a^x \, dx = \frac{a^x}{\ln a} + C = a^x \log_a e + C, \quad a > 0, \, a \neq 1. \tag{8}$$

$$\int e^{f(x)} f'(x) \, dx = e^{f(x)} + C. \tag{9}$$

$$\int a^{f(x)} f'(x) \, dx = \frac{a^{f(x)}}{\ln a} + C, \quad a > 0, \, a \neq 1. \tag{10}$$

As previously stated, every time one finds the derivative of a given function, an antiderivative "formula" has been established. Obviously, there is a limit to the number of these formulas that can be remembered (or put into tables) so what is needed are techniques for finding antiderivatives of particular classes of functions. Our first such technique is called *substitution*, or *change of variable*; it is illustrated in the following examples.

Example 1. Find the antiderivative $\int x \sqrt{2x + 3} \, dx$.

Solution: We first notice that the integral is not of the form of the ten "standard integrals" shown above. Since a linear expression appears under a radical, we let $u = 2x + 3$. This defines u as a function of x. Solving for x,

$$x = \frac{u - 3}{2},$$

and finding the differential dx,

$$dx = \frac{1}{2} \, du,$$

we then substitute these expressions in our original integral

$$\int x \sqrt{2x + 3} \, dx.$$

Thus

$$\int \left(\frac{u - 3}{2}\right) u^{1/2} \frac{1}{2} \, du = \frac{1}{4} \int (u^{3/2} - 3u^{1/2}) \, du$$

$$= \frac{1}{4} \int u^{3/2} \, du - \frac{3}{4} \int u^{1/2} \, du$$

$$= \frac{1}{4} \left(\frac{u^{5/2}}{5/2}\right) - \frac{3}{4} \left(\frac{u^{3/2}}{3/2}\right) + C$$

$$= \frac{1}{10} u^{5/2} - \frac{1}{2} u^{3/2} + C$$

$$= \frac{1}{10} u^{3/2} [u - 5] + C.$$

Substituting $2x + 3$ for u, we obtain

$$\int x\sqrt{2x + 3}\, dx = \frac{1}{10}(2x + 3)^{3/2}[2x + 3 - 5] + C$$

$$= \frac{1}{10}(2x + 3)^{3/2}(2x - 2) + C$$

$$= \frac{1}{5}(2x + 3)^{3/2}(x - 1) + C.$$

Check: No "answer book" is necessary to find if the answer is correct. We need only differentiate:

$$F(x) = \frac{1}{5}(2x + 3)^{3/2}(x - 1) + C.$$

$$F'(x) = \frac{1}{5}\left[\frac{3}{2}(2x + 3)^{1/2}2(x - 1) + (2x + 3)^{3/2}\right]$$

$$= \frac{(2x + 3)^{1/2}}{5}[3(x - 1) + (2x + 3)]$$

$$= \frac{(2x + 3)^{1/2}}{5}(5x)$$

$$= x\sqrt{2x + 3}.$$

Thus, the antiderivative is correct. Of course, we have only proved that the technique leads to the correct result for the given function; it is beyond the scope of our work to prove a general theorem concerning this technique.

Example 2. Evaluate $\displaystyle\int_0^8 \frac{x + 2}{\sqrt{x + 1}}\, dx$.

First Solution: We find the antiderivative of $\displaystyle\int \frac{x + 2}{\sqrt{x + 1}}\, dx$ by substitution.

Let $u = x + 1$. (This is a standard substitution to make when the integral is not a "standard form" and a linear expression appears under a radical.) Then

$$x = u - 1$$

and

$$dx = du.$$

Substituting,

$$\int \frac{(u - 1) + 2}{u^{1/2}}\, du = \int (u^{1/2} + u^{-1/2})\, du$$

$$= \int u^{1/2}\, du + \int u^{-1/2}\, du$$

$$= \frac{2}{3}u^{3/2} + 2u^{1/2} + C$$

$$= \frac{2}{3}u^{1/2}(u + 3) + C.$$

Resubstituting,

$$\int \frac{x+2}{\sqrt{x+1}}\,dx = \frac{2}{3}(x+1)^{1/2}(x+4) + C.$$

Using the fundamental theorem,

$$\int_0^8 \frac{x+2}{\sqrt{x+1}}\,dx = \frac{2}{3}(x+1)^{1/2}(x+4)\Big|_0^8$$

$$= \frac{2}{3}(3)(12) - \frac{2}{3}(1)(4)$$

$$= \frac{2}{3}(36-4)$$

$$= \frac{64}{3}.$$

Second Solution: We can avoid resubstitution in the following manner. For

$$u = x + 1,$$
$$u = 1 \text{ when } x = 0,$$

and

$$u = 9 \text{ when } x = 8.$$

Thus

$$\int_0^8 \frac{x+2}{\sqrt{x+1}}\,dx = \int_1^9 \frac{u+1}{u^{1/2}}\,du$$

$$= \int_1^9 (u^{1/2} + u^{-1/2})\,du$$

$$= \frac{2}{3}u^{3/2}\Big|_1^9 + 2u^{1/2}\Big|_1^9$$

$$= \frac{2}{3}(27-1) + 2(3-1)$$

$$= \frac{2}{3}(26) + 4$$

$$= \frac{64}{3}.$$

Example 3. Find the antiderivative $\int (x^2+1)^{-3/2}\,dx$.

First Solution: This integral is not of the form of any of ten standard formulas. [It should be noted that $\int (x^2+1)^{-3/2}\,2x\,dx$ would be of the standard form $\int f^n(x)f'(x)\,dx$.] It takes only a short time to find that the substitution $u = x^2+1$ does not work well. (One is not guaranteed that any substitution will enable us to find the antiderivative.) Occasionally, a great deal of resourcefulness is required in determining a proper substitution, but a standard one to try is $u = 1/x$. Then

$$x = \frac{1}{u}$$

and

$$dx = -\frac{1}{u^2}\, du.$$

Making this substitution in $\int (x^2 + 1)^{-3/2}\, dx$,

$$\int \left(\frac{1}{u^2} + 1\right)^{-3/2} \left(-\frac{1}{u^2}\right) du = -\int \left(\frac{1 + u^2}{u^2}\right)^{-3/2} \frac{1}{u^2}\, du$$

$$= -\int \left(\frac{u^2}{1 + u^2}\right)^{3/2} \frac{1}{u^2}\, du$$

$$= -\int (1 + u^2)^{-3/2} u\, du$$

$$= -\frac{1}{2} \int (1 + u^2)^{-3/2} 2u\, du$$

$$= -\frac{1}{2} \frac{(1 + u^2)^{-1/2}}{-1/2} + C$$

$$= (1 + u^2)^{-1/2} + C.$$

Resubstituting,

$$\int (x^2 + 1)^{-3/2}\, dx = \left(1 + \frac{1}{x^2}\right)^{-1/2} + C$$

$$= \left(\frac{x^2 + 1}{x^2}\right)^{-1/2} + C$$

$$= \left(\frac{x^2}{x^2 + 1}\right)^{1/2} + C$$

$$= \frac{x}{\sqrt{x^2 + 1}} + C.$$

*Second Solution: If one is familiar with the trigonometric functions and their derivatives, the example can be solved more simply by letting $x = \tan u$. This substitution is chosen so that $1 + x^2$ will be a perfect square. If $x = \tan u$,

$$dx = \sec^2 u\, du,$$

and

$$(1 + x^2)^{-3/2} = (1 + \tan^2 u)^{-3/2} = (\sec^2 u)^{-3/2} = (\sec u)^{-3}.$$

Substituting in

$$\int (1 + x^2)^{-3/2}\, dx,$$

$$\int \frac{\sec^2 u}{\sec^3 u}\, du = \int \frac{1}{\sec u}\, du$$

$$= \int \cos u\, du$$

$$= \sin u + C.$$

If $x = \tan u$, then

$$x^2 = \tan^2 u,$$

$$1 + x^2 = 1 + \tan^2 u = \sec^2 u,$$

and

$$\sec u = \sqrt{1 + x^2}.$$

Since $\tan u = \dfrac{\sin u}{\cos u}$ and $\sec u = \dfrac{1}{\cos u}$,

$$\sin u = \frac{\tan u}{\sec u}.$$

Thus

$$\int (1 + x^2)^{-3/2} \, dx = \frac{x}{\sqrt{1 + x^2}} + C.$$

EXERCISES

Find the antiderivatives and check your answers by differentiation.

1. $\int \sqrt{3x + 1} \, dx.$ 2. $\int x \sqrt{2x + 5} \, dx.$

3. $\int x \sqrt{3x - 6} \, dx.$ 4. $\int \dfrac{e^x}{e^x + 1} \, dx.$

5. $\int (x^2 - 2x)^6 (x - 1) \, dx.$ 6. $\int (3x + 1)^{12} \, dx.$

7. $\int x(3x + 1)^{2/3} \, dx.$ 8. $\int x e^{x^2} \, dx.$

9. $\int \dfrac{dx}{x \ln x}.$ $\left[\text{HINT: Consider } \dfrac{1/x \, dx}{\ln x} \text{ where } f(x) = \ln x.\right]$

10. $\int 6^x \, dx.$ 11. $\int x(1 + \sqrt{x + 1}) \, dx.$

12. $\int (1 - x^2)^{-3/2} \, dx.$ 13. $\int 2^{x^3} x^2 \, dx.$

14. $\int (2x^2 + 1)^{1/2} x \, dx.$ 15. $\int \dfrac{x}{\sqrt{x + 1}} \, dx.$

10-2. INTEGRATION BY PARTS

Recall that the derivative of the product of two functions is given by $(fg)' = fg' + f'g$. Since antiderivatives of a given function differ only by a constant,

$$\int (fg)' = fg + C$$

and

$$fg + C = \int (fg' + f'g),$$

where C is a constant. Since the antiderivative of a sum is the sum of the antiderivatives, except for a possible constant, $fg + C = \int fg' + \int f'g$, and

$$\int fg' = fg - \int f'g + C,$$

where C is some constant. This expression is called the *integration by parts formula*. It may also be expressed by

$$\int f(x)g'(x)\,dx = f(x)g(x) - \int f'(x)g(x)\,dx.$$

This formula facilitates determining the antiderivative of many functions because the integral on the right-hand side may be simpler than the original integral.

Example 1. Find $\int x^2 \ln x \, dx$.

Solution: Let $f(x) = \ln x$ and $g'(x) = x^2$. Then

$$f'(x) = \frac{1}{x} \quad \text{and} \quad g(x) = \frac{x^3}{3}.$$

Thus

$$\int x^2 \ln x \, dx = \frac{x^3}{3} \ln x - \int \frac{1}{x} \cdot \frac{x^3}{3} dx$$

$$= \frac{x^3}{3} \ln x - \frac{1}{3} \int x^2 \, dx$$

$$= \frac{x^3}{3} \ln x - \frac{x^3}{9} + C.$$

We verify our answer by letting

$$F(x) = \frac{x^3}{3} \ln x - \frac{x^3}{9} + C,$$

and then differentiating F:

$$F'(x) = \frac{x^3}{3} \cdot \frac{1}{x} + (\ln x)x^2 - \frac{3x^2}{9}$$

$$= \frac{x^2}{3} + x^2 \ln x - \frac{x^2}{3}$$

$$= x^2 \ln x.$$

We should make some things clear about the technique of integration by parts.

1. To find $\int F(x)\,dx$, we must choose f and g' such that $f(x)g'(x) = F(x)$.

2. Since it is necessary to find g, an antiderivative of g', it is important to let g' be a function we can integrate. Thus we tend to choose g' first.

3. If there is no clear indication how g' should be chosen, then we choose f so that f' will simplify integrating $\int f'g$. This frequently is accomplished by picking f such that f' is a simpler function.

4. As we shall discover, it not only may be necessary to make "unobvious" choices for f' and g but also may be necessary to repeat the

integration by parts process two or more times before finding the anti-derivative of a given function.

5. Last, but not least, the technique may not "work."

Since we are studying a technique, it is essential that the reader care-fully consider the examples and then work the exercises that follow to develop some facility in finding antiderivatives by this technique.

Example 2. Find $\int xe^x\,dx$.

Solution: Let $f(x) = x$ and $g'(x) = e^x$. Then

$$f'(x) = 1 \qquad \text{and} \qquad g(x) = e^x.$$

Thus, by integration by parts formula,

$$\int xe^x\,dx = xe^x - \int e^x\,dx$$
$$= xe^x - e^x + C.$$

Example 3. Find $\int x^2\,e^x\,dx$.

Solution: Let $f(x) = x^2$ and $g'(x) = e^x$. Then

$$f'(x) = 2x \qquad \text{and} \qquad g(x) = e^x.$$

Thus, by integration by parts formula,

$$\int x^2\,e^x\,dx = x^2\,e^x - 2\int xe^x\,dx.$$

Using the solution of Example 1,

$$\int x^2 e^x\,dx = x^2 e^x - 2xe^x + 2e^x + C.$$

Example 4. Find $\displaystyle\int \frac{x}{\sqrt{x+1}}\,dx$.

Solution: (Note that this example is Exercise 15 of Sec. 10-1 and can also be solved by the change of variable technique.) Let $f(x) = x$ and $g'(x) = (x + 1)^{-1/2}$.

$$f'(x) = 1 \qquad \text{and} \qquad g(x) = 2(x + 1)^{1/2}.$$

Thus

$$\int \frac{x}{\sqrt{x+1}}\,dx = 2x(x + 1)^{1/2} - 2\int (x + 1)^{1/2}\,dx$$

$$= 2x(x + 1)^{1/2} - \frac{4}{3}(x + 1)^{3/2} + C$$

$$= \frac{6x(x + 1)^{1/2} - 4(x + 1)^{3/2}}{3} + C$$

$$= \frac{2}{3}(x + 1)^{1/2}[3x - 2x - 2] + C$$

$$= \frac{2}{3}(x + 1)^{1/2}(x - 2) + C.$$

Example 5. Find $\int x(x - 4)^7 \, dx$.

Solution: Let $f(x) = x$ and $g'(x) = (x - 4)^7$. Then

$$f'(x) = 1 \quad \text{and} \quad g(x) = \frac{(x - 4)^8}{8}.$$

Thus

$$\int x(x - 4)^7 \, dx = \frac{x(x - 4)^8}{8} - \int \frac{(x - 4)^8}{8} \, dx$$

$$= \frac{x(x - 4)^8}{8} - \frac{(x - 4)^9}{72} + C$$

$$= \frac{(x - 4)^8}{72}(8x + 4) + C$$

$$= \frac{(x - 4)^8}{18}(2x + 1) + C.$$

Example 6. Find $\int \ln x \, dx$.

Solution: Let $f(x) = \ln x$ and $g'(x) = 1$. Then

$$f'(x) = \frac{1}{x} \quad \text{and} \quad g(x) = x.$$

Thus

$$\int \ln x \, dx = x \ln x - \int \frac{1}{x} \cdot x \, dx$$

$$= x \ln x - \int 1 \, dx$$

$$= x \ln x - x + C.$$

Example 7. Find $\int \frac{\ln x}{x} \, dx$.

Solution: Let $f(x) = \ln x$ and $g'(x) = \frac{1}{x}$. Then

$$f'(x) = \frac{1}{x} \quad \text{and} \quad g(x) = \ln x.$$

Now

$$\int \frac{\ln x}{x} \, dx = (\ln x)(\ln x) - \int \frac{\ln x}{x} \, dx + C$$

$$= (\ln x)^2 - \int \frac{\ln x}{x} \, dx + C.$$

In the last equation, $\int \frac{\ln x}{x} \, dx$ appears on both sides. Transposing,

$$2 \int \frac{\ln x}{x} \, dx = (\ln x)^2 + C.$$

Thus

$$\int \frac{\ln x}{x} dx = \frac{1}{2}(\ln x)^2 + C_1,$$

where $C_1 = C/2$.

EXERCISES

Find the antiderivatives.

1. $\int \dfrac{x}{\sqrt{3x + 1}} dx.$ 2. $\int \dfrac{x}{\sqrt{5x + 2}} dx.$

3. $\int x(x - 4)^5 dx.$ 4. $\int x(2x - 3)^6 dx.$

5. $\int x \ln x \, dx.$ 6. $\int xe^{-x} dx.$

7. $\int x^2 e^{-x} dx.$ 8. $\int x^3 e^{x^2} dx.$

9. $\int (\ln x)^2 dx.$

10. Show that $\int x^n \ln x \, dx = \dfrac{x^{n+1}}{n + 1}\left(\ln x - \dfrac{1}{n + 1}\right) + C, n \neq -1.$

$\star$11. $\int x \cos x \, dx.$ $\star$12. $\int x^2 \sin x \, dx.$

$\star$13. $\int e^x \cos x \, dx.$ $\star$14. $\int x \sec x \tan x \, dx.$

$\star$15. $\int e^x \sin x \, dx.$ $\star$16. $\int x^2 \cos x \, dx.$

10-3. PARTIAL FRACTIONS

We next consider a method of determining antiderivatives for rational expressions of the form $\int \dfrac{f(x)}{g(x)} dx$, where f and g are polynomial functions. If the degree of the numerator f is greater than or equal to the degree of the denominator g, by using the ordinary division algorithm for dividing polynomials, $f(x)/g(x)$ can be written as

$$\frac{f(x)}{g(x)} = q(x) + \frac{r(x)}{g(x)},$$

where the degree of $r(x)$ is less than the degree of the divisor $g(x)$. That is, $\dfrac{r(x)}{g(x)}$ is a proper fraction. For example,

$$\frac{x^3 + 3x^2 + 5x + 1}{x^2 - 2x} = (x + 5) + \frac{15x + 1}{x^2 - 2x}.$$

Since the polynomial $q(x)$ can be integrated term by term, we need only consider a technique for determining the indefinite integrals of the form $\int \dfrac{f(x)}{g(x)} dx$ where the degree of f is less than the degree of g.

Any polynomial (with integers as coefficients) can be written as the product of linear and irreducible quadratic factors. A quadratic polynomial $ax^2 + bx + c$ with real coefficients is irreducible if the roots of $ax^2 + bx + c = 0$ are not real numbers. For example,

$$x^2 - 9 = (x + 3)(x - 3)$$

and

$$x^3 - 1 = (x - 1)(x^2 + x + 1),$$

but $x^2 + x + 1$ is an irreducible quadratic factor. Thus, we need techniques for finding antiderivatives of rational functions f/g where the degree of f is less than the degree of g and g is the product of linear and irreducible quadratic factors.

The following rules enable us to express the quotient f/g where the degree of f is less than the degree of g as the sum of several rational functions for which we can find the antiderivatives by earlier techniques.

Rule 1. *The denominator g has only linear factors none of which is repeated.*

If $g(x) = (a_1 x + b_1)(a_2 x + b_2) \cdots (a_n x + b_n)$, then f/g can be written as

$$\frac{f(x)}{g(x)} = \frac{A_1}{a_1 x + b_1} + \frac{A_2}{a_2 x + b_2} + \cdots + \frac{A_n}{a_n x + b_n},$$

where $A_1, A_2, A_3, \ldots, A_n$ are constants whose values can be determined by the method shown in the following example.

Example 1. Express $\dfrac{3}{(x + 2)(2x - 5)}$ in the form $\dfrac{A}{x + 2} + \dfrac{B}{2x - 5}$.

First Solution: If the equality

$$\frac{3}{(x + 2)(2x - 5)} = \frac{A}{x + 2} + \frac{B}{2x - 5}$$

is to hold for *all* x except $x = -2$ and $x = 5/2$, then it follows that

$$\frac{3}{(x + 2)(2x - 5)} = \frac{A(2x - 5) + B(x + 2)}{(x + 2)(2x - 5)}$$

and

$$\frac{3}{(x + 2)(2x - 5)} = \frac{(2A + B)x + (-5A + 2B)}{(x + 2)(2x - 5)}.$$

For the last equation to be an identity, it must be true that

$$(2A + B)x + (-5A + 2B) = 3.$$

Since the coefficient of x on the left-hand side is zero, it must be true that $2A + B = 0$; likewise, the constant term on the left-hand side is 3 and thus $-5A + 2B = 3$.

Here we used the fact that if two polynomials are equal for all x in the domain of the functions then their coefficients must be equal.

Solving the pair of equations for A and B,

$$\begin{cases} 4A + 2B = 0 \\ -5A + 2B = 3 \end{cases}$$
$$A = -1/3$$
$$B = 2/3.$$

Thus

$$\frac{3}{(x + 2)(2x - 5)} = \frac{-1/3}{x + 2} + \frac{2/3}{2x - 5}.$$

(The student should check this result.)

Second Solution: Suppose we want to make

$$\frac{3}{(x + 2)(2x - 5)} = \frac{A}{x + 2} + \frac{B}{2x - 5}$$

for all x except $x = -2$ and $x = 5/2$. Then we must have

$$\frac{3}{(x + 2)(2x - 5)} = \frac{A(2x - 5) + B(x + 2)}{(x + 2)(2x - 5)}.$$

If $A(2x - 5) + B(x + 2) = 3$ for *every* x, then this is an identity for any x we wish to substitute. If we let $x = -2$, we get

$$A(-4 - 5) = 3$$
$$-9A = 3$$
$$A = -1/3;$$

if we let $x = 5/2$, we get

$$B\left(\frac{5}{2} + 2\right) = 3$$
$$\frac{9}{2}B = 3$$
$$B = 2/3.$$

Rule 2.   *The denominator g has only a linear factor which is repeated k times.*

If $g(x) = (ax + b)^k$, then f/g can be written as

$$\frac{f(x)}{g(x)} = \frac{A_1}{ax + b} + \frac{A_2}{(ax + b)^2} + \frac{A_3}{(ax + b)^3} + \cdots + \frac{A_k}{(ax + b)^k},$$

where the constants $A_1, A_2, A_3, \ldots, A_k$ can be determined as follows. [Of course, if $f(x) = C$, then $A_k = C$ and $A_1, A_2, A_3, \ldots, A_{k-1}$ are all zero.]

Example 2.   Express $\dfrac{7x + 1}{(x + 2)^3}$ in the form $\dfrac{A}{x + 2} + \dfrac{B}{(x + 2)^2} + \dfrac{C}{(x + 2)^3}.$

Solution: Assume

$$\frac{7x + 1}{(x + 2)^3} = \frac{A}{x + 2} + \frac{B}{(x + 2)^2} + \frac{C}{(x + 2)^3}$$

for all $x \neq -2$. Then

$$\frac{7x + 1}{(x + 2)^3} = \frac{A(x + 2)^2 + B(x + 2) + C}{(x + 2)^3}$$

$$= \frac{Ax^2 + 4Ax + 4A + Bx + 2B + C}{(x + 2)^3}$$

$$= \frac{Ax^2 + (4A + B)x + (4A + 2B + C)}{(x + 2)^3}.$$

Equating coefficients in the numerators,

$$\left\{ \begin{array}{r} A = 0 \\ 4A + B = 7 \\ 4A + 2B + C = 1. \end{array} \right.$$

Solving,

$$B = 7$$
$$C = -13.$$

Thus

$$\frac{7x + 1}{(x + 2)^3} = \frac{7}{(x + 2)^2} + \frac{-13}{(x + 2)^3}.$$

We note in this example that some of the constants may be zero.

Rule 3.   *The denominator g has only irreducible quadratic factors none of which is repeated.*

If $g(x) = (a_1 x^2 + b_1 x + c_1)(a_2 x^2 + b_2 x + c_2)$, then f/g can be written as

$$\frac{f(x)}{g(x)} = \frac{A_1 x + B_1}{a_1 x^2 + b_1 x + c_1} + \frac{A_2 x + B_2}{a_2 x^2 + b_2 x + c_2},$$

where the coefficients can be determined as follows.

Example 3.   Express $\dfrac{2x + 1}{(x^2 + 4)(x^2 + 1)}$ in the form $\dfrac{Ax + B}{x^2 + 4} + \dfrac{Cx + D}{x^2 + 1}$.

Solution: If

$$\frac{2x + 1}{(x^2 + 4)(x^2 + 1)} = \frac{Ax + B}{x^2 + 4} + \frac{Cx + D}{x^2 + 1}$$

for all x, then

$$\frac{2x + 1}{(x^2 + 4)(x^2 + 1)} = \frac{(Ax + B)(x^2 + 1) + (Cx + D)(x^2 + 4)}{(x^2 + 4)(x^2 + 1)}$$

and

$$\frac{2x + 1}{(x^2 + 4)(x^2 + 1)} = \frac{Ax^3 + Bx^2 + Ax + B + Cx^3 + Dx^2 + 4Cx + 4D}{(x^2 + 4)(x^2 + 1)}.$$

Equating coefficients in the numerators,

$$\begin{cases} A + C = 0 \\ B + D = 0 \\ A + 4C = 2 \\ B + 4D = 1. \end{cases}$$

From the first two equations,

$$A = -C$$
$$B = -D.$$

Substituting in the last two equations, we get

$$A - 4A = 2$$

and

$$B - 4B = 1.$$

Hence

$$A = -2/3$$
$$C = 2/3$$
$$B = -1/3$$
$$D = 1/3.$$

Thus

$$\frac{2x + 1}{(x^2 + 4)(x^2 + 1)} = \frac{-2/3 x - 1/3}{x^2 + 4} + \frac{2/3 x + 1/3}{x^2 + 1}.$$

Rule 4. *The denominator g has only one repeated irreducible quadratic factor.*

If $g(x) = (ax^2 + bx + c)^k$, then f/g can be written as

$$\frac{f(x)}{g(x)} = \frac{A_1 x + B_1}{ax^2 + bx + c} + \frac{A_2 x + B_2}{(ax^2 + bx + c)^2} + \cdots + \frac{A_k x + B_k}{(ax^2 + bx + c)^k},$$

where the coefficients can be determined in a manner similar to the preceding examples.

Rule 5. *If g has several linear and several quadratic factors, a suitable expression is found by a combination of the preceding rules.*

Example 4. Find $\displaystyle\int \frac{x + 5}{(2x - 1)(x + 3)}\,dx.$

Solution: Let $\dfrac{x + 5}{(2x - 1)(x + 3)} = \dfrac{A}{2x - 1} + \dfrac{B}{x + 3}.$ Thus

$$\frac{x + 5}{(2x - 1)(x + 3)} = \frac{(A + 2B)x + (3A - B)}{(2x - 1)(x + 3)}.$$

Equating coefficients in the numerators, we get

$$\begin{cases} A + 2B = 1 \\ 3A - B = 5. \end{cases}$$

Solving, we find

$$A = \frac{11}{7} \quad \text{and} \quad B = -\frac{2}{7}.$$

Hence

$$\int \frac{x + 5}{(2x - 1)(x + 3)} dx = \frac{11}{7} \int \frac{dx}{2x - 1} - \frac{2}{7} \int \frac{dx}{x + 3}$$

$$= \frac{11}{14} \int \frac{2dx}{2x - 1} - \frac{2}{7} \int \frac{dx}{x + 3}$$

$$= \frac{11}{14} \ln (2x - 1) - \frac{2}{7} \ln (x + 3) + C.$$

Example 5. Find $\int \dfrac{5x^2 - x + 3}{(2x - 1)(x^2 + 1)} dx$.

Solution: Let $\dfrac{5x^2 - x + 3}{(2x - 1)(x^2 + 1)} = \dfrac{A}{2x - 1} + \dfrac{Bx + C}{x^2 + 1}$. Thus

$$\frac{5x^2 - x + 3}{(2x - 1)(x^2 + 1)} = \frac{(A + 2B)x^2 + (2C - B)x + (A - C)}{(2x - 1)(x^2 + 1)}.$$

Equating coefficients in the numerators,

$$\begin{cases} A + 2B = 5 \\ 2C - B = -1 \\ A - C = 3. \end{cases}$$

Solving,

$$B = 1 \qquad A = 3 \qquad C = 0.$$

Hence

$$\int \frac{5x^2 - x + 3}{(2x - 1)(x^2 + 1)} dx = \int \frac{3}{2x - 1} dx + \int \frac{x}{x^2 + 1} dx$$

$$= \frac{3}{2} \int \frac{2}{2x - 1} dx + \frac{1}{2} \int \frac{2x}{x^2 + 1} dx$$

$$= \frac{3}{2} \ln (2x - 1) + \frac{1}{2} \ln (x^2 + 1) + C.$$

EXERCISES

1. $\int \dfrac{2}{(x + 5)(x - 3)} dx.$ 2. $\int \dfrac{1}{(2x + 1)(x + 4)} dx.$

3. $\int \dfrac{3x - 5}{(3x + 7)(2x - 3)} dx.$ **4.** $\int \dfrac{x^4 - 37x^2 - 24x + 181}{x^2 + 3x - 10} dx.$

5. $\int \dfrac{5x^2 + 14x + 8}{(x + 5)(x^2 + x + 1)} dx.$ **6.** $\int \dfrac{dx}{(x - 3)^2}.$

7. $\int \dfrac{dx}{(2x + 5)^3}.$ **8.** $\int \dfrac{3x + 1}{(x + 2)(x - 4)^2} dx.$

★10-4. INVERSE TANGENT FUNCTION

In Sec. 8-5 we defined the tangent function and proved that if $F(x) = \tan x$, then $F'(x) = \sec^2 x$. It is easy to prove that the tangent function is an increasing function for every number in its domain.

If $F(x) = \tan x$, where x is any real number different from $\pi/2 + k\pi$ ($k = 0, \pm 1, \pm 2, \pm 3, \ldots$), then F does not have an inverse since, for example, $\tan \pi/4 = \tan 5\pi/4$. However, if we restrict the domain and define a function f by $f(x) = \tan x$ where $-\pi/2 < x < \pi/2$, then f is increasing and continuous in its domain and has an inverse function g which is also increasing and continuous. The function g is called the *inverse tangent* and is denoted by $tan^{-1}x$, or $arc\ tan\ x$.

Since f and g are inverses, $f(g(t)) = t$ for all t; that is,

$$\tan(\text{arc tan } t) = t.$$

Differentiating both sides and using the composite function theorem,

$$[\sec^2 (\text{arc tan } t)] \frac{d}{dt} (\text{arc tan } t) = 1$$

$$\frac{d}{dt} (\text{arc tan } t) = \frac{1}{\sec^2 (\text{arc tan } t)}.$$

Since $1 + \tan^2 x = \sec^2 x$,

$$\sec^2 (\text{arc tan } t) = 1 + \tan^2 (\text{arc tan } t);$$

thus

$$\sec^2 (\text{arc tan } t) = 1 + t^2.$$

Consequently,

$$\frac{d}{dt} (\text{arc tan } t) = \frac{1}{1 + t^2}.$$

In addition to deriving the derivative of the inverse tangent function, we have obtained an important antiderivative formula:

$$\int \frac{dt}{1 + t^2} = \text{arc tan } t + C.$$

In the preceding section it was necessary to avoid certain irreducible quadratic functions in the denominator of integrals of the form $\int \dfrac{f(x)}{g(x)} dx$ since this antiderivative formula had not been discussed.

Example 1. Find $\int \dfrac{dx}{4 + x^2}$.

Solution:

$$\int \frac{dx}{4 + x^2} = \frac{1}{4} \int \frac{dx}{1 + \left(\dfrac{x}{2}\right)^2}.$$

Let $t = x/2$; then $dx = 2\, dt$. Substituting,

$$\frac{1}{4} \int \frac{2}{1 + t^2} dt = \frac{1}{2} \int \frac{dt}{1 + t^2}$$

$$= \frac{1}{2} \arctan t + C.$$

Resubstituting,

$$\int \frac{dx}{4 + x^2} = \frac{1}{2} \arctan \frac{x}{2} + C.$$

Example 2. Find $\int \dfrac{dx}{(x^2 + 1)(x + 3)}$.

Solution:

$$\frac{1}{(x^2 + 1)(x + 3)} = \frac{Ax + B}{x^2 + 1} + \frac{C}{x + 1}$$

$$= \frac{(A + C)x^2 + (A + B)x + (B + C)}{(x^2 + 1)(x + 1)}.$$

Equating numerators,

$$1 = (A + C)x^2 + (A + B)x + (B + C).$$

Letting $x = -1$,

$$1 = A + C - A - B + B + C.$$

Thus, $C = 1/2$. Solving,

$$\begin{cases} A + C = 0 \\ A + B = 0 \\ B + C = 1. \end{cases}$$

$A = -1/2$, $B = 1/2$, and $C = 1/2$. Consequently,

$$\int \frac{dx}{(x^2 + 1)(x + 3)} = \frac{1}{2} \int \frac{-x + 1}{x^2 + 1} \, dx + \frac{1}{2} \int \frac{dx}{x + 1}$$

$$= \frac{1}{2} \int \frac{-x}{x^2 + 1} \, dx + \frac{1}{2} \int \frac{dx}{x^2 + 1} + \frac{1}{2} \int \frac{dx}{x + 1}$$

$$= -\frac{1}{4} \ln (x^2 + 1) + \frac{1}{2} \arctan x + \frac{1}{2} \ln (x + 1) + C.$$

EXERCISES

Find the indicated antiderivatives.

1. $\displaystyle\int \frac{dx}{(x^2 + 4)(2x + 1)}$.

2. $\displaystyle\int \frac{2x + 1}{(x^2 + 1)(x + 3)} \, dx$.

3. $\displaystyle\int \frac{dx}{x^2 + 9}$.

4. $\displaystyle\int \frac{dx}{x^2 + a^2}$, $a > 0$.

11

More on Limits

11-1. L'HÔPITAL'S RULE

An important theorem used for finding limits is a consequence of the extended law of the mean called L'Hôpital's first rule. This technique first appeared in a text written in 1696 by the Marquis de L'Hôpital (1661–1704).

L'Hôpital's First Rule. Let f and g be functions with the following properties:

$$\lim_{x \to c} f(x) = 0 \text{ and } \lim_{x \to c} g(x) = 0 \text{ for some } c \in (a, b). \tag{1}$$

$$f' \text{ and } g' \text{ exist on } [a, b] \text{ and } g'(x) \neq 0 \text{ for all } x \neq c. \tag{2}$$

$$\lim_{x \to c} \frac{f'(x)}{g'(x)} = L. \tag{3}$$

Conclusion:

$$\lim_{x \to c} \frac{f(x)}{g(x)} = L.$$

We shall only outline how this theorem is proved. Since f and g are differentiable functions, they are continuous; thus, from hypothesis 1 we conclude that $f(c) = g(c) = 0$. If $x \in [a, b]$ and $x \neq c$, then by the extended law of the mean there exists a t between x and c such that

$$\frac{f(x) - f(c)}{g(x) - g(c)} = \frac{f'(t)}{g'(t)};$$

that is,

$$\frac{f(x)}{g(x)} = \frac{f'(t)}{g'(t)}.$$

Since t is between x and c, as x approaches c we conclude that t approaches c. Since $\lim_{x \to c} \dfrac{f'(t)}{g'(t)} = L$ and since $\dfrac{f(x)}{g(x)} = \dfrac{f'(t)}{g'(t)}$,

$$\lim_{x \to c} \frac{f(x)}{g(x)} = L.$$

Example 1. Find $\lim_{x \to 3} \dfrac{x^3 - 27}{x - 3}$.

211

Solution: Let $f(x) = x^3 - 27$ and $g(x) = x - 3$. Then

$$\lim_{x \to 3} f(x) = \lim_{x \to 3} g(x) = 0,$$

f' and g' exist, and $g'(x) \neq 0$ for all x. Now,

$$\lim_{x \to 3} \frac{f'(x)}{g'(x)} = \lim_{x \to 3} \frac{3x^2}{1} = 27.$$

Therefore,

$$\lim_{x \to 3} \frac{x^3 - 27}{x - 3} = 27.$$

Example 2.   Find $\lim_{x \to 2} \dfrac{x^3 + x^2 - 5x - 2}{x^3 + 2x^2 - 6x - 4}$.

Solution: Let $f(x) = x^3 + x^2 - 5x - 2$ and $g(x) = x^3 + 2x^2 - 6x - 4$. Then

$$\lim_{x \to 2} f(x) = \lim_{x \to 2} g(x) = 0,$$

f' and g' exist, $g'(x) = 3x^2 + 4x - 6$, and $g'(x) \neq 0$ in some neighborhood of 2 where $x \neq 2$; this is called a *deleted neighborhood* of 2. Now

$$\lim_{x \to 2} \frac{f'(x)}{g'(x)} = \lim_{x \to 2} \frac{3x^2 + 2x - 5}{3x^2 + 4x - 6} = \frac{11}{14}.$$

Therefore,

$$\lim_{x \to 2} \frac{x^3 + x^2 - 5x - 2}{x^3 + 2x^2 - 6x - 4} = \frac{11}{14}.$$

Example 3.   Find $\lim_{x \to 1} \dfrac{x^{19} - 2x^{18} + x^{17} + 3x^2 - 6x + 3}{x^4 - 2x^3 + 2x^2 - 2x + 1}$.

Solution: Let $f(x) = x^{19} - 2x^{18} + x^{17} + 3x^2 - 6x + 3$ and $g(x) = x^4 - 2x^3 + 2x^2 - 2x + 1$. Then

$$\lim_{x \to 1} f(x) = 0 \text{ and } \lim_{x \to 1} g(x) = 0.$$

Furthermore,

$$f'(x) = 19x^{18} - 36x^{17} + 17x^{16} + 6x - 6,$$
$$g'(x) = 4x^3 - 6x^2 + 4x - 2,$$

and $g'(x) \neq 0$ in some deleted neighborhood of 1. Thus we need to find

$$\lim_{x \to 1} \frac{f'(x)}{g'(x)}.$$

But

$$\lim_{x \to 1} f'(x) = 0$$

and

$$\lim_{x \to 1} g'(x) = 0$$

and f' and g' have the L'Hôpital properties since f'' and g'' exist and $g''(x) \neq 0$ in some deleted neighborhood of 1 as seen by the following:

$$f''(x) = 342x^{17} - 612x^{16} + 272x^{15} + 6$$
$$g''(x) = 12x^2 - 12x + 4.$$

Since

$$\lim_{x \to 1} \frac{f''(x)}{g''(x)} = \frac{342 - 612 + 27 + 6}{12 - 12 + 4} = \frac{8}{4} = 2,$$

$\lim_{x \to 1} \dfrac{f'(x)}{g'(x)} = 2$ by L'Hôpital's rule. By a second application of the rule,

$$\lim_{x \to 1} \frac{f(x)}{g(x)} = 2.$$

The student is cautioned to be certain when using L'Hôpital's first rule to find limits that each of the hypotheses of the theorem is satisfied.

EXERCISES

Find the limits, if they exist, in each Exercise.

1. $\lim_{x \to 1} \dfrac{2x^6 - 5x^5 + 3x^4 - 2x^2 + 3x - 1}{x - 1}.$

2. $\lim_{x \to 2} \dfrac{3x^3 - 7x^2 + x + 2}{x^2 - 4}.$

3. $\lim_{x \to 2} \dfrac{3x + 2}{x^2 - 4}.$

4. $\lim_{x \to -3} \dfrac{7x + 21}{2x + 3}.$

5. $\lim_{x \to 4} \dfrac{x^2 - 2x - 8}{x^2 - 16}.$

6. $\lim_{x \to 5} \dfrac{x^4 - 625}{x^2 - 25}.$

7. $\lim_{x \to 2} \dfrac{3x^3 - 5x^2 - 2x}{x^4 - x^3 + 2x^2 - 16}.$

8. $\lim_{x \to 1} \dfrac{7x^6 - 6x^2 - 1}{x^2 - 1}.$

9. $\lim_{x \to -1} \dfrac{4x^4 - 11x^3 - x^2 - x - 15}{3x^4 + x^3 - 6x^2 - 3x + 1}.$

10. $\lim_{x \to 3} \dfrac{2x^2 + 1}{3x - 1}.$

11-2. INFINITE LIMITS

If a number a is a limit point of the domain of a function f and if for any positive number M (no matter how large) we can find an interval containing a such that $f(x) > M$ for every x in the interval other than a, then f is said to become positively infinite at a; symbolically,

$$\lim_{x \to a} f(x) = +\infty \qquad \text{or} \qquad f(x) \to +\infty \text{ as } x \to a.$$

For example,

$$\lim_{x \to 3} \frac{1}{(x - 3)^2} = +\infty.$$

If for any negative number N we can find an interval containing a such that $f(x) < N$ for every x in the interval other than a, then f is said to become negatively infinite at a; symbolically,

$$\lim_{x \to a} f(x) = -\infty \qquad \text{or} \qquad f(x) \to -\infty \text{ as } x \to a.$$

For example,

$$\lim_{x \to 2} \frac{-1}{(x - 2)^2} = -\infty.$$

We have discussed what are often called *infinite limits.* This gives us information about the behavior of the function (the function values) near certain limit points of the domain of a function; the reader should not get the mistaken idea that ∞ is a real number.

Another important limit pertains to the behavior of the function (the function values) for "large" numbers in the domain. For example, it is important to know that the function $f(x) = \dfrac{3x + 2}{2x - 5}$ has values near 3/2 for "large" values of x. Geometrically, if we graphed this function, the line $y = 3/2$ would approximate the graph of f for "large" values of x; that is, $y = 3/2$ is an asymptote for the graph. Since

$$\frac{3x + 2}{2x - 5} = \frac{3 + 2/x}{2 - 5/x}$$

for all x different from zero or 5/2, it is obvious $\dfrac{3x + 2}{2x - 5}$ is "near" 3/2 for "large" x since $2/x$ and $5/x$ are then "near" zero. Symbolically,

$$\lim_{x \to +\infty} \frac{3x + 2}{2x - 5} = \frac{3}{2}.$$

More precisely, if for any positive number ϵ there exists a real number L and a positive number M such that

$$|f(x) - L| < \epsilon$$

for all $x > M$, then f is said to have limit L as x becomes positively infinite; symbolically,

$$\lim_{x \to +\infty} f(x) = L \qquad \text{or} \qquad f(x) \to L \text{ as } x \to +\infty.$$

Similarly, $\lim_{x \to -\infty} f(x) = L$ means there exists a negative number N such that

$$|f(x) - L| < \epsilon$$

for all $x < N$. For example, $\lim_{x \to -\infty} \dfrac{1}{x} = 0$. Sometimes we say that these are examples of "limits at infinity."

If for any positive number N there exists a positive number M such that

$$f(x) > N \text{ for all } x > M,$$

then f is said to become positively infinite as x becomes positively infinite; symbolically, $\lim\limits_{x \to +\infty} f(x) = +\infty$. For example,

$$\lim_{x \to +\infty} (3x + 1) = +\infty.$$

We define $\lim\limits_{x \to -\infty} f(x) = +\infty$, $\lim\limits_{x \to +\infty} f(x) = -\infty$, and $\lim\limits_{x \to -\infty} f(x) = -\infty$ in a similar fashion.

Fortunately, there exist various extensions and variations of L'Hôpital's first rule. Two of them are as follows.

L'Hôpital's Second Rule. Let f and g be functions with the following properties:

$$\lim_{x \to c} f(x) = +\infty \text{ and } \lim_{x \to c} g(x) = +\infty \text{ for } c \in (a, b). \tag{1}$$

$$f' \text{ and } g' \text{ exist and } g'(c) \neq 0. \tag{2}$$

$$\lim_{x \to c} \frac{f'(x)}{g'(x)} = L. \tag{3}$$

Conclusion:

$$\lim_{x \to c} \frac{f(x)}{g(x)} = L.$$

Extended L'Hôpital's Rule. Let f and g be functions with the following properties:

$$\lim_{x \to +\infty} f(x) = 0, +\infty, \text{ or } -\infty \text{ and } \lim_{x \to +\infty} g(x) = 0, +\infty, \text{ or } -\infty,$$

respectively. $\tag{1}$

$$f' \text{ and } g' \text{ exist and } g'(x) \neq 0 \text{ for } x > M. \tag{2}$$

$$\lim_{x \to +\infty} \frac{f'(x)}{g'(x)} = L. \tag{3}$$

Conclusion:

$$\lim_{x \to +\infty} \frac{f(x)}{g(x)} = L.$$

Example 1. Find $\lim\limits_{x \to +\infty} \dfrac{\log x}{x}$.

Solution: $\lim\limits_{x \to +\infty} \log x = +\infty$, $\lim\limits_{x \to +\infty} x = +\infty$, and $g'(x) = 1$ where $g(x) = x$. Furthermore, $f'(x) = \dfrac{1}{x}$ where $f(x) = \log x$. Thus

$$\lim_{x \to +\infty} \frac{f'(x)}{g'(x)} = \lim_{x \to +\infty} \frac{1/x}{1} = \lim_{x \to +\infty} \frac{1}{x} = 0.$$

Consequently,

$$\lim_{x \to +\infty} \frac{\log x}{x} = 0.$$

Often it is necessary to find limits of functions to which L'Hôpital's rule does not directly apply. For example, consider $\lim\limits_{x \to +\infty} x^{1/x}$. This is said to have the *indeterminate form* ∞^0; $x^{1/x}$ can be modified by algebraic manipulation so that one of the rules apply. To understand why this limit has the indeterminate form ∞^0, notice that if $f(x) = x$ and $g(x) = \dfrac{1}{x}$, then $\lim\limits_{x \to +\infty} f(x) = +\infty$, $\lim\limits_{x \to +\infty} \dfrac{1}{x} = 0$, and $x^{1/x} = [f(x)]^{g(x)}$. Since

$$x^{1/x} = e^{(1/x)\log x}$$

and since

$$\lim_{x \to +\infty} \frac{\log x}{x} = 0, \ \lim_{x \to +\infty} e^{(\log x)/x} = e^0 = 1;$$

thus,

$$\lim_{x \to +\infty} x^{1/x} = 1.$$

Other similar indeterminate forms for which L'Hôpital's rules can be tried after suitable algebraic manipulation are $0 \cdot \infty$, $\infty - \infty$, 0^0, 1^∞, and 0^∞.

EXERCISES

Find the indicated limits.

1. $\lim\limits_{x \to +\infty} \dfrac{2x^2 + 3x - 5}{5x^3 + 7x + 6}$.

2. $\lim\limits_{x \to +\infty} \dfrac{3x^2 + 5x - 7}{2x^2 + 7x - 1}$.

3. $\lim\limits_{x \to +\infty} \dfrac{x^3 + 3x^2 + 6}{2x + 11}$.

4. $\lim\limits_{x \to -1} \dfrac{x^2 + 2}{x + 1}$.

5. $\lim\limits_{x \to -1} \dfrac{-3}{(x + 1)^2}$.

6. $\lim\limits_{x \to -\infty} \dfrac{1}{x}$.

7. $\lim\limits_{x \to -\infty} \dfrac{1}{x^2}$.

8. $\lim\limits_{x \to 0} \dfrac{\ln |x|}{1/x}$.

9. $\lim\limits_{x \to +\infty} \dfrac{x}{e^x}$.

10. $\lim\limits_{x \to +\infty} \dfrac{1 + \ln x}{x \ln x}$.

11. $\lim\limits_{x \to +\infty} \dfrac{\ln (\ln x)}{\ln x}$.

12. $\lim\limits_{x \to +\infty} \dfrac{e^x + 1}{e^x + x}$.

13. $\lim\limits_{x \to 0} (1 - x)^{1/x}$.

14. $\lim\limits_{x \to +\infty} \dfrac{\ln x + x}{x}$.

11-3. IMPROPER INTEGRALS

Consider the integrals

$$\int_1^t \frac{1}{x} \, dx \quad \text{and} \quad \int_1^t \frac{1}{x^2} \, dx$$

where $t > 1$. Each represents the area of the region bounded by $x = 1$, $x = t$, the graph of the function, and the x-axis. (See Fig. 11-1.) Note that

$$\int_1^t \frac{1}{x}\, dx = \ln x \Big|_1^t = \ln t \qquad (1)$$

and

$$\int_1^t \frac{1}{x^2}\, dx = \frac{-1}{x}\Big|_1^t = 1 - \frac{1}{t}. \qquad (2)$$

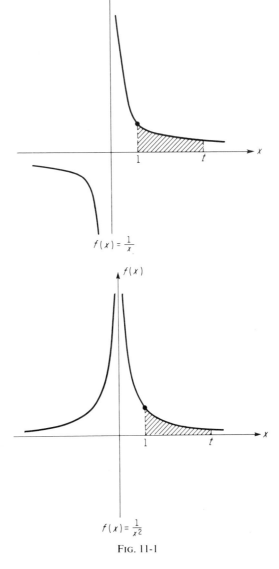

$$f(x) = \frac{1}{x}$$

$$f(x) = \frac{1}{x^2}$$

Fig. 11-1

Thus, the area of region 1 (Eq. 1) is unbounded but the area of region 2 (Eq. 2) is always less than 1. In fact, area 2 can be made "arbitrarily close" to 1 for "large" t. In other words, if

$$F(t) = \int_1^t \frac{1}{x} \, dx \qquad \text{and} \qquad G(t) = \int_1^t \frac{1}{x^2} \, dx,$$

then

$$\lim_{t \to +\infty} F(t) = +\infty \qquad \text{and} \qquad \lim_{t \to +\infty} G(t) = 1.$$

If f is an integrable function on the closed interval $[a, t]$, where t is any real number greater than a, then we call $\int_a^\infty f(x) \, dx$ an *improper integral* and make the following definition.

I. $$\int_a^\infty f(x) \, dx = \lim_{t \to +\infty} \int_a^t f(x) \, dx.$$

When the limit exists and is some real number, the improper integral is said to be *convergent*; otherwise the improper integral is said to be *divergent*.

Two other improper integrals are defined as follows.

II. $$\int_{-\infty}^a f(x) \, dx = \lim_{t \to -\infty} \int_t^a f(x) \, dx.$$

III. $$\int_{-\infty}^\infty f(x) \, dx = \int_{-\infty}^a f(x) \, dx + \int_a^\infty f(x) \, dx, \text{provided each integral}$$

on the right-hand side is convergent.

Example 1. Find $\int_2^\infty e^{-x} \, dx$.

Solution: Since $\int e^{-x} \, dx = -e^{-x} + C$,

$$\int_2^t e^{-x} \, dx = -e^{-t} + e^{-2} = \frac{1}{e^2} - \frac{1}{e^t}.$$

Thus,

$$\int_2^\infty e^{-x} \, dx = \lim_{t \to +\infty} \left(\frac{1}{e^2} - \frac{1}{e^t} \right) = \frac{1}{e^2}.$$

Example 2. A model from economics states that the sale value of land which can be rented is given by

$$\text{Land value} = \frac{\text{annual rent}}{i},$$

where i is the prevailing interest rate. To derive this model we first assume that land is indestructible and can be rented in all time periods t, $0 < t < +\infty$. Thus the problem is that of finding the present value of an infinite stream of rental payments R.

Solution: The reader will recall that the present value of a future benefit can be found by continuously discounting with the factor e^{-it}. Consequently, the present value of the stream of rental payments is given by

$$P(R) = \int_0^\infty Re^{-it} \, dt$$

$$= \lim_{V \to +\infty} \int_0^V Re^{-it} \, dt$$

$$= \lim_{V \to +\infty} \left[\frac{-Re^{-iv}}{i} + \frac{Re^0}{i} \right]$$

$$= \frac{R}{i}.$$

Example 3. In statistics, the function which represents the way in which the relative frequency of individual events, belonging to a universe of events, is distributed is known as a probability distribution. Since the function is concerned with the relative frequency of the different, disjoint events, if we consider all the possible events in the universe, the relative frequency must be 1. Thus for a continuous function f with (a, b) as domain to be a probability distribution function it must be true that

$$\int_a^b f(x) \, dx = 1.$$

As an example, consider the exponential probability function

$$f(x) = \lambda e^{-\lambda x} \quad \text{for } x > 0 \text{ and } \lambda > 0.$$

To show that f is a valid probability distribution function on the set of positive real numbers we must show that

$$\int_0^\infty \lambda e^{-\lambda x} \, dx = 1.$$

Now

$$\int_0^\infty \lambda e^{-\lambda x} \, dx = \lim_{t \to +\infty} \int_0^t \lambda e^{-\lambda x} \, dx$$

$$= \lim_{t \to +\infty} (-e^{-\lambda x}) \Big|_0^t$$

$$= \lim_{t \to +\infty} (-e^{-\lambda t} + e^0)$$

$$= \lim_{t \to +\infty} \left(\frac{-1}{e^{\lambda t}} + 1 \right)$$

$$= 1.$$

EXERCISES

For Exercises 1 through 4, determine if the improper integral converges, and, if so, find the value of the integral.

1. $\displaystyle\int_{1}^{\infty} \frac{1}{x^{3/2}}\, dx.$

2. $\displaystyle\int_{0}^{\infty} xe^{-x^2}\, dx.$

3. $\displaystyle\int_{0}^{\infty} \frac{x}{1 + x^2}\, dx.$

4. $\displaystyle\int_{-\infty}^{\infty} \frac{e^x}{e^x + 1}\, dx.$

★5. Give an example to show that $\displaystyle\lim_{t \to +\infty} \int_{-t}^{t} f(x)\, dx$ can exist even though $\displaystyle\int_{-\infty}^{\infty} f(x)\, dx$ does not exist.

12

Differential Equations

12-1. INTRODUCTION

In the study of algebra and trigonometry, we learn to solve various types of equations such as
  (a) $3x^2 + 5x - 6 = 0$ (algebraic equation);
  (b) $\log x^2 + \log x = 3$ (logarithmic equation);
  (c) $2 \sin^2 x + \sin x - 1 = 0$ (trigonometric equation).
For each of these equations, the solution set consists of those numbers that when substituted for x make the equality a true statement. Many applications of calculus lead to equations involving derivatives; these are called *differential equations*. For example,

$$\frac{d^2y}{dx^2} - 2\frac{dy}{dx} = 3y \tag{1}$$

is such an equation. The equation $y = e^{3x}$ is called a *solution* of the given differential equation; if

$$y = e^{3x},$$

then

$$\frac{dy}{dx} = 3e^{3x}$$

and

$$\frac{d^2y}{dx^2} = 9e^{3x}.$$

Substituting each of these expressions in Eq. 1 reduces it to an identity. More precisely, $G(x, y, y', y'', \ldots, y^{(n)}) = 0$ is called an *ordinary differential equation of order n* and a function f is called a *solution* if $G(x, f(x), f'(x), f''(x), \ldots, f^{(n)}(x)) = 0$ is a true statement for every x in the domain of f. It should be noted that every time we find the antiderivative of a given function this is equivalent to finding the solution of a first-order differential equation. For example, since $\int x^3\, dx = x^4/4 + C$, the equation $y = x^4/4 + C$ is the solution of the differential equation

$$\frac{dy}{dx} = x^3.$$

The following are further examples of differential equations.

221

$$\frac{dy}{dx} = 6. \tag{1}$$

$$\frac{dy}{dx} = 3x^2. \tag{2}$$

$$\frac{dy}{dx} = -\frac{y}{x}. \tag{3}$$

$$x + y\frac{dy}{dx} = 0. \tag{4}$$

$$y\frac{dy}{dx} = \sin x + x. \tag{5}$$

$$\left(\frac{d^2y}{dx^2}\right)^3 + 4y = 0. \tag{6}$$

$$\frac{d^2y}{dx^2} - 2\frac{dy}{dx} + y = 0. \tag{7}$$

$$y - x\frac{dy}{dx} + \left(\frac{dy}{dx}\right)^2 = 0. \tag{8}$$

In the examples, each equation, except Eqs. 6 and 7, is an ordinary differential equation of order one (first order). Equations 6 and 7 are second-order ordinary differential equations, since the highest order of derivatives in each equation is two. An equation such as $\frac{\partial^2 f}{\partial x^2} - \frac{\partial^2 f}{\partial y^2} = 0$ is a differential equation but it is not an ordinary differential equation; it is called a *partial differential* equation. In general, we shall restrict our study to first-order ordinary differential equations.

Three questions arise immediately. (1) For a given differential equation, does a solution exist? (2) If so, is there more than one? (3) How does one determine the solution if one exists? In general, the answer to these questions are not easily obtained, and thus we shall limit our investigation to a few simple but important types of differential equations.

Under certain conditions an nth order differential equation has a unique solution containing n arbitrary constants. For example, as the reader should verify,

$$y = c_1 e^{3x} + c_2 e^{-x}$$

is a solution of the second-order differential equation

$$\frac{d^2y}{dx^2} - 2\frac{dy}{dx} = 3y,$$

where c_1 and c_2 are arbitrary constants. It can be proved that all other solutions to this differential equation can be obtained by assigning particular values to the arbitrary constants. A solution of an nth order differential equation containing n arbitrary constants will be referred to as the *general solution*; solutions obtained by assigning values to the arbitrary constants are called *particular solutions*.

In applications of differential equations, the arbitrary constants in the general solutions are determined by supplementary conditions called *initial conditions*, or *boundary conditions*. For example, it is known that the acceleration of a free-falling body is approximately 32 feet per second per second. Since acceleration is the rate of change of velocity v with respect to time t, it follows that $dv/dt = 32$. Now, $v(t) = 32t + c$ is the general solution of $dv/dt = 32$. If a body falls from rest, then its velocity at time zero is zero; that is, $v(0) = 0$. Thus, in this case $c = 0$ and the velocity of a free-falling body falling from rest is $32t$ feet per second at time t seconds. If we had assumed that a body was thrown downward at an initial velocity of v_0 feet per second, then $v(0) = v_0$ would have been the initial condition. In this latter case, $c = v_0$ and $v(t) = 32t + v_0$.

Some differential equations have what are called *singular solutions*; these are solutions not obtainable by assigning values to the arbitrary constants in the general solution. Although we shall not be concerned with singular solutions, the reader should show that $y = cx - c^2$ is the general solution of the first-order differential equation $y - x\dfrac{dy}{dx} + \left(\dfrac{dy}{dx}\right)^2 = 0$ and that $y = x^2/4$ is a singular solution.

EXERCISES

1. Prove that $y = c_1 e^{3x} + c_2 e^{-x}$ is the general solution of the second-order differential equation $\dfrac{d^2y}{dx^2} - 2\dfrac{dy}{dx} = 3y$.

2. Prove that $y = cx - c^2$ is the general solution of the first-order differential equation $y - x\dfrac{dy}{dx} + \left(\dfrac{dy}{dx}\right)^2 = 0$. Show that $y = x^2/4$ is a singular solution.

In each of the following problems, verify that the defined function is a solution of the given differential equation.

3. Equation: $y'' = 3x^2$. Solution: $y = x^4/4 + cx + c$.

4. Equation: $\dfrac{dy}{dx} = -\dfrac{y}{x}$. Solution: $y = c/x$.

5. Equation: $x + y\dfrac{dy}{dx} = 0$. Solution: $y = \sqrt{c - x^2}$.

6. Equation: $\dfrac{d^2y}{dx^2} - 2\dfrac{dy}{dx} + y = 0$. Solution: $y = c_1 e^x + c_2 x e^x$.

★7. Equation: $y\dfrac{dy}{dx} = \sin x + x$. Solution: $y = \sqrt{x^2 - 2\cos x + c}$.

12-2. SEPARABLE EQUATIONS

Consider a differential equation of the form

$$M(x) + N(y) \frac{dy}{dx} = 0$$

where y is a function of x. It can be proved that

$$\int M(x)dx + \int N(y)dy = c$$

is the general solution of this first-order differential equation. As an example, consider the equation

$$y \frac{dy}{dx} = e^x + x.$$

This may be written in the form

$$M(x) + N(y) \frac{dy}{dx} = 0$$

by

$$(-e^x - x) + y \frac{dy}{dx} = 0$$

where $M(x) = -e^x - x$ and $N(y) = y$. Hence,

$$\int (-e^x - x)dx + \int y\, dy = c$$

$$-e^x - \frac{x^2}{2} + \frac{y^2}{2} = c$$

is the general solution. Since this solution equation defines a function implicitly, one of the easiest ways to verify that it is correct is by implicit differentiation.

It should be noted that $y \dfrac{dy}{dx} = e^x + x$ can be written in what is called the differential form:

$$y\, dy = (e^x + x)dx.$$

If we integrate both sides of the equality,

$$\int y\, dy = \int (e^x + x)\, dx$$

$$\frac{y^2}{2} = e^x + \frac{x^2}{2} + c,$$

which is the general solution. This procedure is called *separating the variables*. Essentially, algebraic manipulation is performed on the original equation until (if possible) it is in the form $M(x)dx = N(y)dy$ and then both sides of the equality are integrated.

Example 1. Solve $\dfrac{dy}{dx} = \dfrac{x^2}{y^2}$.

Solution:

$$y^2 dy = x^2 dx$$

$$\int y^2 dy = \int x^2 dx$$

$$\frac{y^3}{3} = \frac{x^3}{3} + c$$

$$y^3 - x^3 = 3c,$$

or

$$y^3 - x^3 = c_1,$$

where $c_1 = 3c$.

Example 2. Solve $3xy^2 + \sqrt{1 + x^2}\,\dfrac{dy}{dx} = 0$.

Solution:

$$3xy^2 = -\sqrt{1 + x^2}\,\frac{dy}{dx}$$

$$\frac{3x}{\sqrt{1 + x^2}}\,dx = -\frac{dy}{y^2}$$

$$3(1 + x^2)^{-1/2} x\,dx = -y^{-2}\,dy$$

$$\frac{3}{2} \int (1 + x^2)^{-1/2} 2x\,dx = -\int y^{-2}\,dy$$

$$\frac{3}{2}\,\frac{(1 + x^2)^{1/2}}{1/2} = y^{-1} + c$$

$$3\sqrt{1 + x^2} = \frac{1}{y} + c$$

$$3y\sqrt{1 + x^2} = 1 + cy.$$

Example 3. Solve $f'(x) = \dfrac{xy + y}{x + xy}$.

Solution:

$$\frac{dy}{dx} = \frac{y(x + 1)}{x(y + 1)}$$

$$\frac{y + 1}{y}\,dy = \frac{x + 1}{x}\,dx$$

$$\int \left(1 + \frac{1}{y}\right) dy = \int \left(1 + \frac{1}{x}\right) dx$$

$$y + \ln y = x + \ln x + c$$

$$\ln \frac{y}{x} = x - y + c$$

$$\frac{y}{x} = e^{x-y+c} = e^{x-y}e^c = c_1 e^{x-y},$$

where $c_1 = e^c$. Thus $y = c_1 x e^{x-y}$ is the general solution.

Example 4.   Solve $\dfrac{dy}{dx} = xe^y$.

Solution:

$$e^{-y}\,dy = x\,dx$$
$$-\int e^{-y}(-1)dy = \int x\,dx$$
$$c - e^{-y} = \frac{x^2}{2}.$$

Other forms of the solution are:

$$e^{-y} = c - \frac{x^2}{2},$$

$$\ln e^{-y} = \ln\left(c - \frac{x^2}{2}\right),$$

$$-y = \ln\left(\frac{2c - x^2}{2}\right),$$

$$y = \ln\left(\frac{2}{2c - x^2}\right).$$

EXERCISES

Solve each of the following differential equations.

1. $3xy' - y = 0$.   **2.** $x^2 + e^x - y\dfrac{dy}{dx} = 0$.

3. $xy + e^x\dfrac{dy}{dx} = 0$.   **4.** $(y^2 + 4) - (xy + 3y)\dfrac{dy}{dx} = 0$.

5. $x\dfrac{dy}{dx} + y = y^2$.   **6.** $(2x + 3x^2 - 1)\dfrac{dy}{dx} + (6xy + 2y) = 0$.

12-3. HOMOGENEOUS EQUATIONS

A function f of two variables is called *homogeneous of degree n* if

$$f(tx, ty) = t^n f(x, y)$$

for every real number t. For example, $f(x, y) = x^3 + x^2 y - 2xy^2$ is a homogeneous function of degree three, since

$$f(ty, tx) = (tx)^3 + (tx)^2(ty) - 2(tx)(ty)^2$$
$$= t^3x^3 + t^3x^2y - 2t^3xy^2$$
$$= t^3(x^3 + x^2y - 2xy^2)$$
$$= t^3f(x, y).$$

In other words, f is homogeneous if the degree of each term in x and y is the same. The functions $F(x, y) = x^4 + 2x^2y^2$ and $G(x, y) = xy + x^2$ are homogeneous, but $g(x, y) = x^2 + 2xy^3$ and $h(x, y) = x^2 + y^2 + 7$ are not homogeneous functions.

If $M(x, y)$ and $N(x, y)$ are both homogeneous functions of degree n, then

$$M(x, y) + N(x, y)\frac{dy}{dx} = 0,$$

or

$$M(x, y)\, dx + N(x, y)\, dy = 0,$$

is called a first-order *homogeneous differential equation*. We will show that every equation of this form can be made separable by an appropriate substitution. Before doing this, let us exhibit the general procedure by an example.

Example 1. Solve $2xy + (x^2 + y^2)\dfrac{dy}{dx} = 0.$

Solution: Let $y = xv$ where v is a function of x. Differentiating by the product rule,

$$\frac{dy}{dx} = x\frac{dv}{dx} + v.$$

Substituting in the original equation,

$$2x(xv) + [x^2 + (xv)^2]\left(x\frac{dv}{dx} + v\right) = 0$$

$$2x^2v + x^2(1 + v^2)\left(x\frac{dv}{dx} + v\right) = 0.$$

Assuming $x \neq 0$ and dividing by x^2,

$$2v + (1 + v^2)\left(x\frac{dv}{dx} + v\right) = 0$$

$$2v + x\frac{dv}{dx} + v + xv^2\frac{dv}{dx} + v^3 = 0$$

$$3v + v^3 + x(1 + v^2)\frac{dv}{dx} = 0$$

$$(3v + v^3) = -x(1 + v^2) \frac{dv}{dx}$$

$$-\frac{dx}{x} = \frac{(1 + v^2)}{3v + v^3} dv.$$

The original equation has been made separable by the substitution so we integrate both sides of the equality.

$$\int -\frac{dx}{x} = \int \frac{1 + v^2}{3v + v^3} dv$$

$$\int \frac{dx}{x} = -\frac{1}{3} \int \frac{3 + 3v^2}{3v + v^3} dv$$

$$\ln x = -\frac{1}{3} \ln(3v + v^3) + c.$$

Letting $c = \ln c_1$ and substituting $v = \frac{y}{x}$,

$$\ln x = -\frac{1}{3} \ln\left(\frac{3y}{x} + \frac{y^3}{x^3}\right) + \ln c_1$$

$$3 \ln x = -\ln \frac{3x^2y + y^3}{x^3} + 3 \ln c_1$$

$$\ln \frac{3x^2y + y^3}{x^3} + \ln x^3 + \ln c_1^3 = 0.$$

Using the fact that $\ln M + \ln N = \ln(MN)$,

$$\ln\left[\frac{3x^2y + y^3}{x^3} (x^3)(c_1^3)\right] = 0,$$

thus

$$(3x^2y + y^3)c_1^3 = 1$$

$$3x^2y + y^3 = \frac{1}{c_1^3}.$$

Letting $c_2 = 1/c_1^3$, the general solution is

$$3x^2y + y^3 = c_2.$$

Check: Differentiate implicitly the solution $3x^2y + y^3 = c_2$.

$$3(x^2y' + 2xy) + 3y^2y' = 0$$

$$x^2y' + 2xy + y^2y' = 0$$

$$2xy + (x^2 + y^2)y' = 0.$$

Since the original equation is obtained, the solution is correct.

Now let us derive the general solution to any homogeneous differential equation of the form

$$M(x, y) + N(x, y) \frac{dy}{dx} = 0,$$

using the method of solution in our example.

If $M(x, y)$ is homogeneous of degree n, then

$$M(tx, ty) = t^n M(x, y).$$

Letting $t = 1/x$,

$$M\left(1, \frac{y}{x}\right) = \frac{1}{x^n} M(x, y),$$

or

$$M(x, y) = x^n M\left(1, \frac{y}{x}\right).$$

Similarly, if $N(x, y)$ is homogeneous of degree n, then

$$N(x, y) = x^n N\left(1, \frac{y}{x}\right).$$

Letting $y = xv$, we have

$$\frac{dy}{dx} = x \frac{dv}{dx} + v.$$

Substituting in the equation

$$M(x, y) + N(x, y) \frac{dy}{dx} = 0,$$

we get

$$x^n M\left(1, \frac{y}{x}\right) + x^n N\left(1, \frac{y}{x}\right) \frac{dy}{dx} = 0$$

$$x^n M(1, v) + x^n N(1, v)\left(x \frac{dv}{dx} + v\right) = 0.$$

Dividing by x^n and then simplifying,

$$M(1, v) + xN(1, v) \frac{dv}{dx} + vN(1, v) = 0$$

$$M(1, v) + vN(1, v) = -xN(1, v) \frac{dv}{dx}$$

$$\frac{dx}{x} = \frac{-N(1, v)dv}{M(1, v) + vN(1, v)}.$$

Integrating both sides of the equation,

$$\int \frac{dx}{x} = -\int \frac{N(1, v)}{M(1, v) + vN(1, v)} dv.$$

Thus,

$$\ln x = -\int \frac{N(1, v)}{M(1, v) + vN(1, v)} \, dv + c,$$

where $v = y/x$, is the *general solution* of the first-order homogeneous equation.

Let us verify this formal solution with the previous example $2xy + (x^2 + y^2) \dfrac{dy}{dx} = 0$. Since $M(x, y) = 2xy$ and $N(x, y) = x^2 + y^2$,

$$M(1, v) = 2v \qquad \text{and} \qquad N(1, v) = 1 + v^2.$$

Thus

$$-\int \frac{N(1, v)}{M(1, v) + vN(1, v)} \, dv = -\int \frac{1 + v^2}{2v + v(1 + v^2)} \, dv$$

$$= -\int \frac{1 + v^2}{3v + v^3} \, dv.$$

By our formal solution,

$$\ln x = -\int \frac{1 + v^2}{3v + v^3} \, dv + c,$$

where $v = y/x$; this agrees with our previous solution.

EXERCISES

Solve the following differential equations.

1. $(x + y) + 2x \dfrac{dy}{dx} = 0.$ **2.** $(x^2 + xy) \dfrac{dy}{dx} + y^2 = 0.$

3. $(x^3 + xy^2) + 2x^3 \dfrac{dy}{dx} = 0.$ **4.** $(2x^2 - y^2) + x^2 \dfrac{dy}{dx} = 0.$

5. $x \dfrac{dy}{dx} = x + y.$ **6.** $y \sqrt{x^2 - y^2} - xy + x^2 \dfrac{dy}{dx} = 0.$

12-4. EXACT EQUATIONS

A differential equation of the form $M(x, y)\, dx + N(x, y)\, dy = 0$ is called *exact* if there exists a function f such that its total differential $df = \dfrac{\partial f}{\partial x} \, dx + \dfrac{\partial f}{\partial y} \, dy = M(x, y)\, dx + N(x, y)\, dy$. For example, consider the differential equation $2xy \, dx + (x^2 + y^2)\, dy = 0$ discussed in the preceding section as an example of a homogeneous equation. If

$$f(x, y) = \frac{y^3}{3} + x^2 y,$$

then

$$df = 2xy \, dx + (x^2 + y^2)\, dy,$$

and the differential equation $2xy\,dx + (x^2 + y^2)\,dy = 0$ is exact. We can prove that $f(x, y) = c$, that is, $y^3/3 + x^2y = c$ is the general solution.

Two questions arise immediately: (1) How can one determine if a differential equation of the form $M(x, y)\,dx + N(x, y)\,dy = 0$ is exact? (2) How does one find a function f such that $df = M(x, y)\,dx + N(x, y)\,dy$? Though it is not exceptionally difficult to prove, we state without proof that $M(x, y)\,dx + N(x, y)\,dy = 0$ is exact if and only if $\partial M/\partial y = \partial N/\partial x$. Furthermore, if the equation is exact, then

$$f(x, y) = \int M(x, y)\,dx + \int \left[N(x, y) - \frac{\partial}{\partial y} \int M(x, y)\,dx \right] dy.$$

In the example,

$$f(x, y) = \int 2xy\,dx + \int \left[(x^2 + y^2) - \frac{\partial}{\partial y} \int 2xy\,dx \right] dy$$

$$= 2y \int x\,dx + \int \left[x^2 + y^2 - \frac{\partial}{\partial y} (x^2y) \right] dy$$

$$= yx^2 + \int [x^2 + y^2 - x^2]\,dy$$

$$= yx^2 + \int y^2\,dy$$

$$= x^2y + y^3/3.$$

The usual technique to solve this type of equation employs the following steps:

1. Verify the equation is exact by showing that $\partial M/\partial y = \partial N/\partial x$.
2. Integrate $\int M(x, y)\,dx$ treating y as a constant.
3. Integrate $\int G(y)\,dy$ where $G(y)$ are those terms in $N(x, y)$ "free of x."
4. Add steps 2 and 3 and equate to a constant.
5. The solution should be checked.

Example 1. Solve $(x^2 + y)dx + (x + e^y)\,dy = 0$.

Solution:

$$M(x, y) = x^2 + y, \quad \partial M/\partial y = 1 \tag{1}$$
$$N(x, y) = x + e^y, \quad \partial N/\partial x = 1.$$

Since $\partial M/\partial y = \partial N/\partial x$, the equation is exact.

$$\int (x^2 + y)\,dx = x^3/3 + yx. \tag{2}$$
$$\int e^y\,dy = e^y. \tag{3}$$
$$x^3/3 + xy + e^y = c. \tag{4}$$

Check: By implicit differentiation,

$$x^2 + x\frac{dy}{dx} + y + e^y\frac{dy}{dx} = 0,$$

$$(x^2 + y) + (x + e^y)\frac{dy}{dx} = 0,$$

or

$$(x^2 + y)dx + (x + e^y)dy = 0.$$

EXERCISES

Solve the following differential equations.
1. $(e^x y + x) dx + (e^x + 6) dy = 0.$
2. $(3x^2 y^2 - 4y) dx + (2y - 4x + 2x^3 y) dy = 0.$
3. $(3x^2 y + y^2) dx + (x^3 + 2xy) dy = 0.$
4. $(2x + y) dx + (y^2 + x + 1) dy = 0.$

12-5. LINEAR EQUATIONS

Let P and Q be functions of one variable. Then, a differential equation of the form

$$\frac{dy}{dx} + P(x)y = Q(x)$$

is called a *first-order linear differential equation*. For example, $x\,\frac{dy}{dx} + 2y = 6x$ is first-order linear equation since it can be written as

$$\frac{dy}{dx} + \frac{2}{x}\,y = 6.$$

To solve the equation $\frac{dy}{dx} + \frac{2}{x}\,y = 6$, we multiply both sides of the equality by

$$
\begin{aligned}
e^{\int P(x)\,dx} &= e^{\int (2/x)\,dx}\\
&= e^{2\int (1/x)\,dx}\\
&= e^{2\ln x}\\
&= e^{\ln x^2}\\
&= x^2.
\end{aligned}
$$

[Recall that $e^{\ln f(x)} = f(x)$.] Multiplying by x^2,

$$x^2\,\frac{dy}{dx} + 2xy = 6x^2,$$

or

$$(2xy - 6x^2)\,dx + x^2\,dy = 0.$$

If $M(x, y) = 2xy - 6x^2$ and $N(x, y) = x^2$, then

$$\frac{\partial M}{\partial y} = 2x \quad \text{and} \quad \frac{\partial N}{\partial x} = 2x.$$

Consequently, the equation is exact and can be solved by methods discussed in the preceding section.

A function, such as $f(x) = e^{\int P(x)\,dx}$, which is multiplied in an equation to make it exact is called an *integrating factor*. Although an integrating factor may not be easy to determine (even if it exists) for a general differential equation, we can prove that $e^{\int P(x)\,dx}$ is an integrating factor for any first-order linear differential equation. In fact, we can give an explicit solution for y in terms of x.

We begin by writing $dy/dx + P(x)y = Q(x)$ in the form

$$[P(x)y - Q(x)]\,dx + dy = 0.$$

Multiplying by $e^{\int P(x)\,dx}$,

$$e^{\int P(x)\,dx}[P(x)y - Q(x)]\,dx + e^{\int P(x)\,dx}\,dy = 0. \tag{1}$$

Letting $M(x, y) = e^{\int P(x)\,dx}[P(x)y - Q(x)]$ and $N(x, y) = e^{\int P(x)\,dx}$,

$$\frac{\partial M}{\partial y} = e^{\int P(x)\,dx} \cdot P(x)$$

and

$$\frac{\partial N}{\partial x} = e^{\int P(x)\,dx} \cdot \frac{d}{dx}\int P(x)\,dx = e^{\int P(x)\,dx} \cdot P(x).$$

Since $\partial M/\partial y = \partial N/\partial x$, the equation is exact.

The reader can verify that

$$ye^{\int P(x)\,dx} = \int Q(x)e^{\int P(x)\,dx}\,dx + C$$

is the *general solution* of Eq. 1 and hence of the equation

$$\frac{dy}{dx} + P(x)y = Q(x).$$

In our example $\dfrac{dy}{dx} + \dfrac{2}{x}y = 6$, $P(x) = 2/x$, and $Q(x) = 6$; the solution is

$$ye^{\int (2/x)\,dx} = \int 6e^{\int (2/x)\,dx}\,dx + C$$
$$ye^{\ln x^2} = \int 6e^{\ln x^2}\,dx + C$$
$$x^2y = 2x^3 + C.$$

EXERCISES

1. $\dfrac{dy}{dx} + \dfrac{y}{x} = x^2$.

2. $\dfrac{dy}{dx} + y = e^x$.

3. $\dfrac{dy}{dx} + x^2y = x^2$.

4. $x^2\dfrac{dy}{dx} + xy = 1$.

5. $x\dfrac{dy}{dx} + y = x^2 + 2$.

6. $\dfrac{dy}{dx} - \dfrac{y}{x} = 4x^2$.

12-6. APPLICATIONS OF DIFFERENTIAL EQUATIONS

In the preceding sections we have established methods for finding solution equations for certain types of first-order differential equations. We now consider some applications of differential equations. The most common application is in dynamic processes where the independent variable is time. Thus an equation such as

$$\frac{dy}{dt} = bqt + bI_0$$

which may be written as

$$dy = (bqt + bI_0)\, dt$$

represents the rate at which some phenomenon y is changing with respect to time t. In our examples the equations will always be presented or developed in the context of rate of change with respect to time.

Before considering the examples, one point should be clarified. In all dynamic applications, the time variable t represents non-negative integers. When we select some measurable period of time such as a minute, day, or year, it is customary to let zero be the initial time and the positive integers represent the end of each of the respective time periods. It would be more appropriate to use difference equations rather than differential equations for these applications. However, since an assumption of continuity is essential to applying calculus to most business problems, we shall make this assumption in the examples which follow. (The reader would find that the techniques for solving difference equations are very similar to those for solving differential equations, although the basic theory is quite different.)

Example 1. In 1944, E. Domar advanced a national debt model which still bears his name. One hypothesis of the model is that national income I increases by a constant increment, say q dollars, per year. Thus the rate of change is

$$\frac{dI}{dt} = q.$$

Domar further concluded that the annual increase in the national debt D is directly proportional to the national income. If we let b be the constant of proportionality,

$$\frac{dD}{dt} = bI.$$

The first equation is separable, and solving we obtain

$$dI = qdt$$
$$I = qt + C_1.$$

If national income at time zero is I_0, we evaluate C_1 by letting $I = I_0$ and $t = 0$.

$$I_0 = q(0) + C_1.$$

Therefore

$$I = qt + I_0.$$

The reader should realize that the equation $I = qt + I_0$ could be derived without calculus. If I_0 is the present national income and if it increases yearly by an amount q, at the end of one year it would be $I_0 + q$, at the end of two years it would be $I_0 + 2q$ and at the end of t years it would be $I_0 + tq$.

Substituting this solution in the differential equation $dD/dt = bI$ and solving,

$$\frac{dD}{dt} = b(qt + I_0)$$

$$dD = bqt\,dt + bI_0\,dt$$

$$D = \frac{bqt^2}{2} + bI_0 t + C_2.$$

To evaluate C_2, let $D = D_0$ at $t = 0$:

$$D_0 = C_2.$$

Thus

$$D = \frac{bqt^2}{2} + bI_0 t + D_0.$$

Though Domar's model is an example of an application of differential equations to economic analysis, the accuracy of the model as a predictor is open to serious question.

Example 2. In Exercise 18 of Sec. 8-2 we cited the logistic curve as a model of population growth. We now show that the function

$$f(t) = \frac{b}{1 + ce^{-at}}$$

is the solution of a separable differential equation. Letting x be the population size at time t, we assume the population increases at a rate directly proportional to the product of birth factor and a death factor as follows:

$$\frac{dx}{dt} = ax\left(1 - \frac{x}{b}\right),$$

where a and b are positive constants. The variables may be separated by

$$\frac{b\,dx}{x(b - x)} = a\,dt.$$

The left-hand side may be simplified by using partial fractions:

$$\frac{dx}{x} + \frac{dx}{b - x} = a\,dt.$$

Integrating,

$$\int \frac{dx}{x} + \int \frac{dx}{b-x} = a \int dt$$

$$\ln x - \ln(b-x) = at + c_1$$

$$-\ln \frac{b-x}{x} = at + c_1.$$

Taking powers of e on both sides,

$$\frac{b-x}{x} = e^{-at-c_1} = e^{-at}e^{-c_1}.$$

Since e^{-c_1} is also a positive constant, we let c be this constant. Thus

$$b - x = xce^{-at},$$

or

$$x = \frac{b}{1 + ce^{-at}}.$$

If we let $x = x_0$ when $t = 0$, c is determined by

$$x_0 = \frac{b}{1+c}$$

$$c = \frac{b - x_0}{x_0}.$$

Substituting this result,

$$x = \frac{b}{1 + \left(\dfrac{b - x_0}{x_0}\right)e^{-at}}.$$

Thus the constant c that appears in the denominator of the logistic model is $\dfrac{b - x_0}{x_0}$ where b and x_0 are also constants.

Example 3. Many elementary applications of differential equations in business decision processes are concerned with growth or decay models derived from a general equation describing the diffusion process. The diffusion process was originally concerned with certain physical applications but received one important application in the study of the transmission of epidemics.

Assume among a population of fixed size n, some m individuals are infected but circulate freely among the remaining $n - m$ individuals. Assume that during a time period t each infected individual makes c contacts and that each contact with an uninfected person results in transmission of the epidemic.

The rate of change in the number of infected is given by

$$\frac{dm}{dt} = cm\left(1 - \frac{m}{n}\right).$$

The student will note that this equation is the same as the equation used to derive the logistic curve in Example 2, even though the environment of the diffusion model differs radically from that of the logistic curve.

To explain how this equation was formed and to give some insight into how differential equations in general are established, we return to the hypotheses of the process. Since the numbers m and n are positive integers we avoid a continuity assumption by directing our attention to the proportion of the population infected rather than the number infected. Since the number uninfected is $n - m$, the proportion uninfected is $(n - m)/n = 1 - m/n$. By the hypotheses, each of the m infected individuals makes c contacts in some time increment which we shall denote by Δt. Thus the total contacts in Δt is $cm(\Delta t)$. Since transmission of the epidemic can only occur among the uninfected, we eliminate all contacts with the previously infected by multiplying by the proportion uninfected, $1 - m/n$. Thus the incremental change in the number infected, Δm, is given by

$$\Delta m = cm(\Delta t)(1 - m/n)$$

which, if we let $\Delta t = dt$ and $\Delta m = dm$, will be recognized as the original differential equation.

This equation is separable:

$$\frac{dm}{m} + \frac{1}{n}\left(\frac{dm}{1 - m/n}\right) = cdt$$

$$\ln m - \ln(1 - m/n) = ct + c_1$$

$$\ln\left(\frac{m}{1 - m/n}\right) = ct + c_1$$

$$\frac{m}{1 - m/n} = e^{ct+c_1} = c_2 e^{ct} \ .$$

If $m = m_0$ when $t = 0$,

$$\frac{m_0}{1 - m_0/n} = c_2 \ .$$

Hence,

$$m = \frac{m_0}{n - m_0}(n - m)e^{ct} \ .$$

$$= \frac{nm_0 e^{ct}}{m_0 e^{ct} + n - m_0} \ .$$

We note that if the solution is rewritten as a proportion,

$$\frac{m}{n} = \frac{1}{1 + (n/m_0 - 1)e^{-ct}},$$

one may conclude that the entire population becomes infected as t becomes very large.

A frequently used analogy to relate the diffusion process to a business environment is that of considering the diffusion of knowledge about a product. In the simplest case, we again assume a population of fixed size n, m of whom possess knowledge of the product, and these m communicate c times with uninformed persons during a time period t. Again converting to proportions, the rate at which the number informed is changing is

$$dm = cm \, dt \left(1 - \frac{m}{n}\right), \quad \text{or} \quad \frac{dm}{dt} = cm \left(1 - \frac{m}{n}\right),$$

which yields the same solution as before.

Even the most naïve recognize that person-to-person communication is not a very effective method, from the seller's point of view, to transmit product knowledge. Thus he resorts to promotion to increase the rate of contact. Assume his plan produces a additional contacts by each informed person during each time increment. Now

$$dm = cmdt \left(1 - \frac{m}{n}\right) + amdt \left(1 - \frac{m}{n}\right)$$

$$\frac{dm}{dt} = (c + a)m \left(1 - \frac{m}{n}\right)$$

$$\frac{dm}{m \left(1 - \frac{m}{n}\right)} = (c + a)dt.$$

Expanding the left-hand side by partial fractions and integrating yields

$$\ln m - \ln \frac{n - m}{n} = (c + a)t + c_1$$

$$\ln \frac{m}{1 - \frac{m}{n}} = (c + a)t + c_1$$

$$\frac{m}{1 - \frac{m}{n}} = e^{(c+a)t} e^{c_1} = c_2 e^{(c+a)t}$$

To evaluate c_2, we again let $m = m_0$ when $t = 0$, and thus

$$c_2 = \frac{m_0}{1 - \frac{m_0}{n}}$$

$$\frac{m}{1 - \frac{m}{n}} = \frac{m_0 e^{(c+a)t}}{1 - \frac{m_0}{n}}.$$

To find the number of informed people m at some time t, we solve for m:

$$\frac{mn}{n-m} = \frac{nm_0}{n-m_0} e^{(c+a)t}$$

$$m = \frac{nm_0 e^{(c+a)t}}{n-m_0+m_0 e^{(c+a)t}} .$$

Though a promotion scheme which increases contact by the informed is fairly realistic, a more likely plan would be regular advertising by which the seller obtains an additional k contacts per time period, but where these contacts are independent of the informed individuals. Again assuming each of the k contacts succeeds in transmitting information, the rate of change in m as a result of advertising alone is given by

$$\frac{dm}{dt} = k\left(1 - \frac{m}{n}\right).$$

Solving,

$$\frac{dm}{1 - \frac{m}{n}} = k\, dt$$

$$-n \ln\left(1 - \frac{m}{n}\right) = kt + c_1$$

$$\left(1 - \frac{m}{n}\right)^{-n} = e^{kt} e^{c_1}.$$

If when $t = 0, m = m_0$,

$$\left(1 - \frac{m}{n}\right)^{-n} = e^{kt}\left(1 - \frac{m_0}{n}\right)^{-n}$$

$$\frac{1}{n-m} = \frac{e^{kt/n}}{n-m_0}$$

$$m = m_0 e^{-kt/n} + n(1 - e^{-kt/n}).$$

Combining the three contact methods and their associated coefficients $c, a,$ and k into a single model becomes rather tedious, but the reader who feels fairly confident of his ability should attempt to solve the problem.

Up to this point we have assumed the population was fixed at some number n, an assumption which is rather far from reality. Instead, a population of buyers experiences new arrivals (people move, income increases) and departures (deaths, removals, loss of income). Defining the arrival rate as g and the removal rate as r and, to avoid confusion, subscripting m and n as m_t and n_t to indicate, respectively, the number of informed people and the population size at time t, we revise the second model. Assuming the entry rate to the population is exponential and letting $n = n_0$ when $t = 0$,

$$n_t = n_0 e^{gt}.$$

Recognizing that the removals from the population will contain some who are informed, the model becomes

$$\frac{dm}{dt} = (c + a)m\left(1 - \frac{m}{n_0 e^{gt}}\right) - rm,$$

with solution

$$m_t = \frac{c + a - (g + r)}{-\dfrac{(c + a)m_0 + [c + a - (g + r)]n_0}{m_0 n_0} e^{-t(c+a-r)} + \dfrac{c + a}{n_0} e^{-gt}}.$$

Example 4. As an example of the application of diffusion models we summarize the results of an advertising study published by Vidale and Wolfe in 1957. Suppose there exists a single-product market of fixed size m. Advertising is at a constant rate indicated by A and the effectiveness of the advertising is indicated by a positive constant c. Thus the effect of advertising upon sales S is given by

$$\frac{dS}{dt} = cA\left(\frac{M - S}{M}\right),$$

where $(M - S)/M$ represents the proportion of the market which is not currently possessed by the firm. Note that the right-hand side of this differential equation is never negative, which would be interpreted as meaning that with continuous advertising the firm would eventually capture the entire market and could then cease advertising without any ill effect on sales. However, one knows that customers do switch brands, often as a result of advertising by competitors, and cease buying a product when they either reach saturation or find a substitute product. Let us assume that when no advertising is being used sales decline in proportion to a constant decay rate r. Thus in this situation

$$\frac{dS_t}{dt} = -rS_t,$$

where S_t is the level of sales at time t. Solving this equation,

$$\ln S_t = -rt + c_1.$$

Letting $S_t = S_0$ when $t = 0$,

$$c_1 = \ln S_0$$
$$S_t = S_0 e^{-rt}.$$

Combining the effects of advertising and competitive losses,

$$\frac{dS_t}{dt} = cA\left(\frac{M - S_t}{M}\right) - rS_t,$$

which we rewrite in the form of a general linear equation

$$\frac{dS_t}{dt} + \left(r + \frac{cA}{M}\right)S_t = cA.$$

Letting $g = r + \dfrac{cA}{M}$,

$$
\begin{aligned}
S_t &= e^{-\int g\,dt}\left(\int cA\,e^{\int g\,dt}\,dt + c_1\right)\\
&= e^{-gt}\left(\int cA\,e^{gt}\,dt + c_1\right)\\
&= \frac{e^{-gt}\,cA\,e^{gt}}{g} + c_1 e^{-gt}\\
&= \frac{cA}{g} + c_1 e^{-gt}.
\end{aligned}
$$

Again letting $S_t = S_0$ when $t = 0$,

$$S_0 = \frac{cA}{g} + c_1$$

$$c_1 = S_0 - \frac{cA}{g}.$$

Substituting the value of c_1 and g, we find the solution

$$S_t = \frac{cA}{r + \dfrac{cA}{M}} + \left(S_0 - \frac{cA}{r + \dfrac{cA}{M}}\right)e^{-t\left(r + \frac{cA}{M}\right)}.$$

The same study also investigated the effect on sales, of one shot, intensive promotion such as a television spectacular or widespread distribution of samples. To develop this solution we assume the total advertising budget for T time periods is a. Thus, assuming uniform advertising in each time period t, the advertising rate A is

$$A = \frac{a}{T},$$

which we substitute in the previous solution

$$S_t = \frac{cMa}{rTM + ca} + \left(S_0 - \frac{cMa}{rTM + ca}\right)e^{-t\left(r + \frac{ca}{Tm}\right)}.$$

In the intensive form of promotion the length of the advertising period will be relatively short and can be well approximated by finding $\lim_{T\to 0} S_t = S_{0^+}$ where S_{0^+} is the immediate change in the sales level as a result of the promotion. Thus

$$S_{0^+} = M + (S_0 - M)e^{-ca/m}.$$

To show that

$$\lim_{T\to 0} -t\left(r + \frac{ca}{TM}\right) = -\frac{ca}{M},$$

we note that t is bounded by $0 \le t \le T$, and as $T \to 0, t \to T$. Thus

$$\lim_{T \to 0} \; - \; t\left(r + \frac{ca}{TM}\right) = \lim_{T \to 0} \; - \; T\left(\frac{rTM + ca}{TM}\right) = - \frac{ca}{M}.$$

To find the immediate net result of the promotion,

$$S_{0^+} - S_0 = M - S_0 + (S_0 - M)e^{-ca/M}$$
$$= (M - S_0)(1 - e^{-ca/M}).$$

Tables

The tables in this section are from the *Handbook of Chemistry and Physics*, 46th ed. (Cleveland, Ohio: The Chemical Rubber Company), 1965. Permission to reproduce these tables was granted by The Chemical Rubber Company.

TABLE 1
Four Place Logarithms

N	0	1	2	3	4	5	6	7	8	9	1 2 3	4 5 6	7 8 9
10	0000	0043	0086	0128	0170	0212	0253	0294	0334	0374	4 8 12	17 21 25	29 33 37
11	0414	0453	0492	0531	0569	0607	0645	0682	0719	0755	4 8 11	15 19 23	26 30 34
12	0792	0828	0864	0899	0934	0969	1004	1038	1072	1106	3 7 10	14 17 21	24 28 31
13	1139	1173	1206	1239	1271	1303	1335	1367	1399	1430	3 6 10	13 16 19	23 26 29
14	1461	1492	1523	1553	1584	1614	1644	1673	1703	1732	3 6 9	12 15 18	21 24 27
15	1761	1790	1818	1847	1875	1903	1931	1959	1987	2014	3 6 8	11 14 17	20 22 25
16	2041	2068	2095	2122	2148	2175	2201	2227	2253	2279	3 5 8	11 13 16	18 21 24
17	2304	2330	2355	2380	2405	2430	2455	2480	2504	2529	2 5 7	10 12 15	17 20 22
18	2553	2577	2601	2625	2648	2672	2695	2718	2742	2765	2 5 7	9 12 14	16 19 21
19	2788	2810	2833	2856	2878	2900	2923	2945	2967	2989	2 4 7	9 11 13	16 18 20
20	3010	3032	3054	3075	3096	3118	3139	3160	3181	3201	2 4 6	8 11 13	15 17 19
21	3222	3243	3263	3284	3304	3324	3345	3365	3385	3404	2 4 6	8 10 12	14 16 18
22	3424	3444	3464	3483	3502	3522	3541	3560	3579	3598	2 4 6	8 10 12	14 16 17
23	3617	3636	3655	3674	3692	3711	3729	3747	3766	3784	2 4 6	7 9 11	13 15 17
24	3802	3820	3838	3856	3874	3892	3909	3927	3945	3962	2 4 5	7 9 11	12 14 16
25	3979	3997	4014	4031	4048	4065	4082	4099	4116	4133	2 4 5	7 9 10	12 14 16
26	4150	4166	4183	4200	4216	4232	4249	4265	4281	4298	2 3 5	7 8 10	11 13 15
27	4314	4330	4346	4362	4378	4393	4409	4425	4440	4456	2 3 5	6 8 9	11 12 14
28	4472	4487	4502	4518	4533	4548	4564	4579	4594	4609	2 3 5	6 8 9	11 12 14
29	4624	4639	4654	4669	4683	4698	4713	4728	4742	4757	1 3 4	6 7 9	10 12 13
30	4771	4786	4800	4814	4829	4843	4857	4871	4886	4900	1 3 4	6 7 9	10 11 13
31	4914	4928	4942	4955	4969	4983	4997	5011	5024	5038	1 3 4	5 7 8	10 11 12
32	5051	5065	5079	5092	5105	5119	5132	5145	5159	5172	1 3 4	5 7 8	9 11 12
33	5185	5198	5211	5224	5237	5250	5263	5276	5289	5302	1 3 4	5 7 8	9 11 12
34	5315	5328	5340	5353	5366	5378	5391	5403	5416	5428	1 2 4	5 6 8	9 10 11
35	5441	5453	5465	5478	5490	5502	5514	5527	5539	5551	1 2 4	5 6 7	9 10 11
36	5563	5575	5587	5599	5611	5623	5635	5647	5658	5670	1 2 4	5 6 7	8 10 11
37	5682	5694	5705	5717	5729	5740	5752	5763	5775	5786	1 2 4	5 6 7	8 9 11
38	5798	5809	5821	5832	5843	5855	5866	5877	5888	5899	1 2 3	5 6 7	8 9 10
39	5911	5922	5933	5944	5955	5966	5977	5988	5999	6010	1 2 3	4 5 7	8 9 10
40	6021	6031	6042	6053	6064	6075	6085	6096	6107	6117	1 2 3	4 5 6	8 9 10
41	6128	6138	6149	6160	6170	6180	6191	6201	6212	6222	1 2 3	4 5 6	7 8 9
42	6232	6243	6253	6263	6274	6284	6294	6304	6314	6325	1 2 3	4 5 6	7 8 9
43	6335	6345	6355	6365	6375	6385	6395	6405	6415	6425	1 2 3	4 5 6	7 8 9
44	6435	6444	6454	6464	6474	6484	6493	6503	6513	6522	1 2 3	4 5 6	7 8 9
45	6532	6542	6551	6561	6571	6580	6590	6599	6609	6618	1 2 3	4 5 6	7 8 9
46	6628	6637	6646	6656	6665	6675	6684	6693	6702	6712	1 2 3	4 5 6	7 7 8
47	6721	6730	6739	6749	6758	6767	6776	6785	6794	6803	1 2 3	4 5 6	7 7 8
48	6812	6821	6830	6839	6848	6857	6866	6875	6884	6893	1 2 3	4 5 6	7 7 8
49	6902	6911	6920	6928	6937	6946	6955	6964	6972	6981	1 2 3	4 4 5	6 7 8
50	6990	6998	7007	7016	7024	7033	7042	7050	7059	7067	1 2 3	3 4 5	6 7 8
51	7076	7084	7093	7101	7110	7118	7126	7135	7143	7152	1 2 3	3 4 5	6 7 8
52	7160	7168	7177	7185	7193	7202	7210	7218	7226	7235	1 2 3	3 4 5	6 7 7
53	7243	7251	7259	7267	7275	7284	7292	7300	7308	7316	1 2 2	3 4 5	6 6 7
54	7324	7332	7340	7348	7356	7364	7372	7380	7388	7396	1 2 2	3 4 5	6 6 7
N	0	1	2	3	4	5	6	7	8	9	1 2 3	4 5 6	7 8 9

TABLE 1 (*Continued*)

N	0	1	2	3	4	5	6	7	8	9	1 2 3	4 5 6	7 8 9
				Mantissas								**Proportional Parts**	
55	7404	7412	7419	7427	7435	7443	7451	7459	7466	7474	1 2 2	3 4 5	5 6 7
56	7482	7490	7497	7505	7513	7520	7528	7536	7543	7551	1 2 2	3 4 5	5 6 7
57	7559	7566	7574	7582	7589	7597	7604	7612	7619	7627	1 1 2	3 4 5	5 6 7
58	7634	7642	7649	7657	7664	7672	7679	7686	7694	7701	1 1 2	3 4 4	5 6 7
59	7709	7716	7723	7731	7738	7745	7752	7760	7767	7774	1 1 2	3 4 4	5 6 7
60	7782	7789	7796	7803	7810	7818	7825	7832	7839	7846	1 1 2	3 4 4	5 6 6
61	7853	7860	7868	7875	7882	7889	7896	7903	7910	7917	1 1 2	3 3 4	5 6 6
62	7924	7931	7938	7945	7952	7959	7966	7973	7980	7987	1 1 2	3 3 4	5 5 6
63	7993	8000	8007	8014	8021	8028	8035	8041	8048	8055	1 1 2	3 3 4	5 5 6
64	8062	8069	8075	8082	8089	8096	8102	8109	8116	8122	1 1 2	3 3 4	5 5 6
65	8129	8136	8142	8149	8156	8162	8169	8176	8182	8189	1 1 2	3 3 4	5 5 6
66	8195	8202	8209	8215	8222	8228	8235	8241	8248	8254	1 1 2	3 3 4	5 5 6
67	8261	8267	8274	8280	8287	8293	8299	8306	8312	8319	1 1 2	3 3 4	5 5 6
68	8325	8331	8338	8344	8351	8357	8363	8370	8376	8382	1 1 2	3 3 4	4 5 6
69	8388	8395	8401	8407	8414	8420	8426	8432	8439	8445	1 1 2	3 3 4	4 5 6
70	8451	8457	8463	8470	8476	8482	8488	8494	8500	8506	1 1 2	3 3 4	4 5 6
71	8513	8519	8525	8531	8537	8543	8549	8555	8561	8567	1 1 2	3 3 4	4 5 6
72	8573	8579	8585	8591	8597	8603	8609	8615	8621	8627	1 1 2	3 3 4	4 5 6
73	8633	8639	8645	8651	8657	8663	8669	8675	8681	8686	1 1 2	2 3 4	4 5 5
74	8692	8698	8704	8710	8716	8722	8727	8733	8739	8745	1 1 2	2 3 4	4 5 5
75	8751	8756	8762	8768	8774	8779	8785	8791	8797	8802	1 1 2	2 3 3	4 5 5
76	8808	8814	8820	8825	8831	8837	8842	8848	8854	8859	1 1 2	2 3 3	4 4 5
77	8865	8871	8876	8882	8887	8893	8899	8904	8910	8915	1 1 2	2 3 3	4 4 5
78	8921	8927	8932	8938	8943	8949	8954	8960	8965	8971	1 1 2	2 3 3	4 4 5
79	8976	8982	8987	8993	8998	9004	9009	9015	9020	9025	1 1 2	2 3 3	4 4 5
80	9031	9036	9042	9047	9053	9058	9063	9069	9074	9079	1 1 2	2 3 3	4 4 5
81	9085	9090	9096	9101	9106	9112	9117	9122	9128	9133	1 1 2	2 3 3	4 4 5
82	9138	9143	9149	9154	9159	9165	9170	9175	9180	9186	1 1 2	2 3 3	4 4 5
83	9191	9196	9201	9206	9212	9217	9222	9227	9232	9238	1 1 2	2 3 3	4 4 5
84	9243	9248	9253	9258	9263	9269	9274	9279	9284	9289	1 1 2	2 3 3	4 4 5
85	9294	9299	9304	9309	9315	9320	9325	9330	9335	9340	1 1 2	2 3 3	4 4 5
86	9345	9350	9355	9360	9365	9370	9375	9380	9385	9390	1 1 2	2 3 3	4 4 5
87	9395	9400	9405	9410	9415	9420	9425	9430	9435	9440	1 1 2	2 3 3	4 4 5
88	9445	9450	9455	9460	9465	9469	9474	9479	9484	9489	0 1 1	2 2 3	3 4 4
89	9494	9499	9504	9509	9513	9518	9523	9528	9533	9538	0 1 1	2 2 3	3 4 4
90	9542	9547	9552	9557	9562	9566	9571	9576	9581	9586	0 1 1	2 2 3	3 4 4
91	9590	9595	9600	9605	9609	9614	9619	9624	9628	9633	0 1 1	2 2 3	3 4 4
92	9638	9643	9647	9652	9657	9661	9666	9671	9675	9680	0 1 1	2 2 3	3 4 4
93	9685	9689	9694	9699	9703	9708	9713	9717	9722	9727	0 1 1	2 2 3	3 4 4
94	9731	9736	9741	9745	9750	9754	9759	9763	9768	9773	0 1 1	2 2 3	3 4 4
95	9777	9782	9786	9791	9795	9800	9805	9809	9814	9818	0 1 1	2 2 3	3 4 4
96	9823	9827	9832	9836	9841	9845	9850	9854	9859	9863	0 1 1	2 2 3	3 4 4
97	9868	9872	9877	9881	9886	9890	9894	9899	9903	9908	0 1 1	2 2 3	3 4 4
98	9912	9917	9921	9926	9930	9934	9939	9943	9948	9952	0 1 1	2 2 3	3 3 4
99	9956	9961	9965	9969	9974	9978	9983	9987	9991	9996	0 1 1	2 2 3	3 3 4
N	0	1	2	3	4	5	6	7	8	9	1 2 3	4 5 6	7 8 9

TABLE 2
Trig and Log Trig
[Subtract 10 from logs $= n.xxxx$ if $n = 7, 8,$ or 9]

Radians	Degrees	Sine Value	Sine Log	Tangent Value	Tangent Log	Cotangent Value	Cotangent Log	Cosine Value	Cosine Log		
.0000	0° 00′	.0000	—	.0000	—	—	—	1.0000	0.0000	90° 00′	1.5708
.0029	10	.0029	7.4637	.0029	7.4637	343.77	2.5363	1.0000	.0000	50	1.5679
.0058	20	.0058	.7648	.0058	.7648	171.89	.2352	1.0000	.0000	40	1.5650
.0087	30	.0087	7.9408	.0087	7.9409	114.59	2.0591	1.0000	.0000	30	1.5621
.0116	40	.0116	8.0658	.0116	8.0658	85.940	1.9342	.9999	.0000	20	1.5592
.0145	50	.0145	.1627	.0145	.1627	68.750	.8373	.9999	0.0000	10	1.5563
.0175	1° 00′	.0175	8.2419	.0175	8.2419	57.290	1.7581	.9998	9.9999	89° 00′	1.5533
.0204	10	.0204	.3088	.0204	.3089	49.104	.6911	.9998	.9999	50	1.5504
.0233	20	.0233	.3668	.0233	.3669	42.964	.6331	.9997	.9999	40	1.5475
.0262	30	.0262	.4179	.0262	.4181	38.188	.5819	.9997	.9999	30	1.5446
.0291	40	.0291	.4637	.0291	.4638	34.368	.5362	.9996	.9998	20	1.5417
.0320	50	.0320	.5050	.0320	.5053	31.242	.4947	.9995	.9998	10	1.5388
.0349	2° 00′	.0349	8.5428	.0349	8.5431	28.636	1.4569	.9994	9.9997	88° 00′	1.5359
.0378	10	.0378	.5776	.0378	.5779	26.432	.4221	.9993	.9997	50	1.5330
.0407	20	.0407	.6097	.0407	.6101	24.542	.3899	.9992	.9996	40	1.5301
.0436	30	.0436	.6397	.0437	.6401	22.904	.3599	.9990	.9996	30	1.5272
.0465	40	.0465	.6677	.0466	.6682	21.470	.3318	.9989	.9995	20	1.5243
.0495	50	.0494	.6940	.0495	.6945	20.206	.3055	.9988	9.9995	10	1.5213
.0524	3° 00′	.0523	8.7188	.0524	8.7194	19.081	1.2806	.9986	.9994	87° 00′	1.5184
.0553	10	.0552	.7423	.0553	.7429	18.075	.2571	.9985	.9993	50	1.5155
.0582	20	.0581	.7645	.0582	.7652	17.169	.2348	.9983	.9993	40	1.5126
.0611	30	.0610	.7857	.0612	.7865	16.350	.2135	.9981	.9992	30	1.5097
.0640	40	.0640	.8059	.0641	.8067	15.605	.1933	.9980	.9991	20	1.5068
.0669	50	.0669	.8251	.0670	.8261	14.924	.1739	.9978	.9990	10	1.5039
.0698	4° 00′	.0698	8.8436	.0699	8.8446	14.301	1.1554	.9976	9.9989	86° 00′	1.5010
.0727	10	.0727	.8613	.0729	.8624	13.727	.1376	.9974	.9989	50	1.4981
.0756	20	.0756	.8783	.0758	.8795	13.197	.1205	.9971	.9988	40	1.4952
.0785	30	.0785	.8946	.0787	.8960	12.706	.1040	.9969	.9987	30	1.4923
.0814	40	.0814	.9104	.0816	.9118	12.251	.0882	.9967	.9986	20	1.4893
.0844	50	.0843	.9256	.0846	.9272	11.826	.0728	.9964	.9985	10	1.4864
.0873	5° 00′	.0872	8.9403	.0875	8.9420	11.430	1.0580	.9962	9.9983	85° 00′	1.4835
.0902	10	.0901	.9545	.0904	.9563	11.059	.0437	.9959	.9982	50	1.4806
.0931	20	.0929	.9682	.0934	.9701	10.712	.0299	.9957	.9981	40	1.4777
.0960	30	.0958	.9816	.0963	.9836	10.385	.0164	.9954	.9980	30	1.4748
.0989	40	.0987	8.9945	.0992	8.9966	10.078	1.0034	.9951	.9979	20	1.4719
.1018	50	.1016	9.0070	.1022	9.0093	9.7882	0.9907	.9948	.9977	10	1.4690
.1047	6° 00′	.1045	9.0192	.1051	9.0216	9.5144	0.9784	.9945	9.9976	84° 00′	1.4661
.1076	10	.1074	.0311	.1080	.0336	9.2553	.9664	.9942	.9975	50	1.4632
.1105	20	.1103	.0426	.1110	.0453	9.0098	.9547	.9939	.9973	40	1.4603
.1134	30	.1132	.0539	.1139	.0567	8.7769	.9433	.9936	.9972	30	1.4573
.1164	40	.1161	.0648	.1169	.0678	8.5555	.9322	.9932	.9971	20	1.4544
.1193	50	.1190	.0755	.1198	.0786	8.3450	.9214	.9929	.9969	10	1.4515
.1222	7° 00′	.1219	9.0859	.1228	9.0891	8.1443	0.9109	.9925	9.9968	83° 00′	1.4486
.1251	10	.1248	.0961	.1257	.0995	7.9530	.9005	.9922	.9966	50	1.4457
.1280	20	.1276	.1060	.1287	.1096	7.7704	.8904	.9918	.9964	40	1.4428
.1309	30	.1305	.1157	.1317	.1194	7.5958	.8806	.9914	.9963	30	1.4399
.1338	40	.1334	.1252	.1346	.1291	7.4287	.8709	.9911	.9961	20	1.4370
.1367	50	.1363	.1345	.1376	.1385	7.2687	.8615	.9907	.9959	10	1.4341
.1396	8° 00′	.1392	9.1436	.1405	9.1478	7.1154	0.8522	.9903	9.9958	82° 00′	1.4312
.1425	10	.1421	.1525	.1435	.1569	6.9682	.8431	.9899	.9956	50	1.4283
.1454	20	.1449	.1612	.1465	.1658	6.8269	.8342	.9894	.9954	40	1.4254
.1484	30	.1478	.1697	.1495	.1745	6.6912	.8255	.9890	.9952	30	1.4224
.1513	40	.1507	.1781	.1524	.1831	6.5606	.8169	.9886	.9950	20	1.4195
.1542	50	.1536	.1863	.1554	.1915	6.4348	.8085	.9881	.9948	10	1.4166
.1571	9° 00′	.1564	9.1943	.1584	9.1997	6.3138	0.8003	.9877	9.9946	81° 00′	1.4137
		Value Cosine	Log	Value Cotangent	Log	Value Tangent	Log	Value Sine	Log	Degrees	Radians

TABLE 2 (*Continued*)

Radians	Degrees	Sine Value	Sine Log	Tangent Value	Tangent Log	Cotangent Value	Cotangent Log	Cosine Value	Cosine Log		
.1571	9° 00′	.1564	9.1943	.1584	9.1997	6.3138	0.8003	.9877	9.9946	81° 00′	1.4137
.1600	10	.1593	.2022	.1614	.2078	6.1970	.7922	.9872	.9944	50	1.4108
1629	20	.1622	.2100	.1644	.2158	6.0844	.7842	.9868	.9942	40	1.4079
.1658	30	.1650	.2176	.1673	.2236	5.9758	.7764	.9863	.9940	30	1.4050
.1687	40	.1679	.2251	.1703	.2313	5.8708	.7687	.9858	.9938	20	1.4021
.1716	50	.1708	.2324	.1733	.2389	5.7694	.7611	.9853	.9936	10	1.3992
.1745	10° 00′	.1736	9.2397	.1763	9.2463	5.6713	0.7537	.9848	9.9934	80° 00′	1.3963
.1774	10	.1765	.2468	.1793	.2536	5.5764	.7464	.9843	.9931	50	1.3934
.1804	20	.1794	.2538	.1823	.2609	5.4845	.7391	.9838	.9929	40	1.3904
.1833	30	.1822	.2606	.1853	.2680	5.3955	.7320	.9833	.9927	30	1.3875
.1862	40	.1851	.2674	.1883	.2750	5.3093	.7250	.9827	.9924	20	1.3846
.1891	50	.1880	.2740	.1914	.2819	5.2257	.7181	.9822	.9922	10	1.3817
.1920	11° 00′	.1908	9.2806	.1944	9.2887	5.1446	0.7113	.9816	9.9919	79° 00′	1.3788
.1949	10	.1937	.2870	.1974	.2953	5.0658	.7047	.9811	.9917	50	1.3759
.1978	20	.1965	.2934	.2004	.3020	4.9894	.6980	.9805	.9914	40	1.3730
.2007	30	.1994	.2997	.2035	.3085	4.9152	.6915	.9799	.9912	30	1.3701
.2036	40	.2022	.3058	.2065	.3149	4.8430	.6851	.9793	.9909	20	1.3672
.2065	50	.2051	.3119	.2095	.3212	4.7729	.6788	.9787	.9907	10	1.3643
.2094	12° 00′	.2079	9.3179	.2126	9.3275	4.7046	0.6725	.9781	9.9904	78° 00′	1.3614
.2123	10	.2108	.3238	.2156	.3336	4.6382	.6664	.9775	.9901	50	1.3584
.2153	20	.2136	.3296	.2186	.3397	4.5736	.6603	.9769	.9899	40	1.3555
.2182	30	.2164	.3353	.2217	.3458	4.5107	.6542	.9763	.9896	30	1.3526
.2211	40	.2193	.3410	.2247	.3517	4.4494	.6483	.9757	.9893	20	1.3497
.2240	50	.2221	.3466	.2278	.3576	4.3897	.6424	.9750	.9890	10	1.3468
.2269	13° 00′	.2250	9.3521	.2309	9.3634	4.3315	0.6366	.9744	9.9887	77° 00′	1.3439
.2298	10	.2278	.3575	.2339	.3691	4.2747	.6309	.9737	.9884	50	1.3410
.2327	20	.2306	.3629	.2370	.3748	4.2193	.6252	.9730	.9881	40	1.3381
.2356	30	.2334	.3682	.2401	.3804	4.1653	.6196	.9724	.9878	30	1.3352
.2385	40	.2363	.3734	.2432	.3859	4.1126	.6141	.9717	.9875	20	1.3323
.2414	50	.2391	.3786	.2462	.3914	4.0611	.6086	.9710	.9872	10	1.3294
.2443	14° 00′	.2419	9.3837	.2493	9.3968	4.0108	0.6032	.9703	9.9869	76° 00′	1.3265
.2473	10	.2447	.3887	.2524	.4021	3.9617	.5979	.9696	.9866	50	1.3235
.2502	20	.2476	.3937	.2555	.4074	3.9136	.5926	.9689	.9863	40	1.3206
.2531	30	.2504	.3986	.2586	.4127	3.8667	.5873	.9681	.9859	30	1.3177
.2560	40	.2532	.4035	.2617	.4178	3.8208	.5822	.9674	.9856	20	1.3148
.2589	50	.2560	.4083	.2648	.4230	3.7760	.5770	.9667	.9853	10	1.3119
.2618	15° 00′	.2588	9.4130	.2679	9.4281	3.7321	0.5719	.9659	9.9849	75° 00′	1.3090
.2647	10	.2616	.4177	.2711	.4331	3.6891	.5669	.9652	.9846	50	1.3061
.2676	20	.2644	.4223	.2742	.4381	3.6470	.5619	.9644	.9843	40	1.3032
.2705	30	.2672	.4269	.2773	.4430	3.6059	.5570	.9636	.9839	30	1.3003
.2734	40	.2700	.4314	.2805	.4479	3.5656	.5521	.9628	.9836	20	1.2974
.2763	50	.2728	.4359	.2836	.4527	3.5261	.5473	.9621	.9832	10	1.2945
.2793	16° 00′	.2756	9.4403	.2867	9.4575	3.4874	0.5425	.9613	9.9828	74° 00′	1.2915
.2822	10	.2784	.4447	.2899	.4622	3.4495	.5378	.9605	.9825	50	1.2886
.2851	20	.2812	.4491	.2931	.4669	3.4124	.5331	.9596	.9821	40	1.2857
.2880	30	.2840	.4533	.2962	.4716	3.3759	.5284	.9588	.9817	30	1.2828
.2909	40	.2868	.4576	.2994	.4762	3.3402	.5238	.9580	.9814	20	1.2799
.2938	50	.2896	.4618	.3026	.4808	3.3052	.5192	.9572	.9810	10	1.2770
.2967	17° 00′	.2924	9.4659	.3057	9.4853	3.2709	0.5147	.9563	9.9806	73° 00′	1.2741
.2996	10	.2952	.4700	.3089	.4898	3.2371	.5102	.9555	.9802	50	1.2712
.3025	20	.2979	.4741	.3121	.4943	3.2041	.5057	.9546	.9798	40	1.2683
.3054	30	.3007	.4781	.3153	.4987	3.1716	.5013	.9537	.9794	30	1.2654
.3083	40	.3035	.4821	.3185	.5031	3.1397	.4969	.9528	.9790	20	1.2625
.3113	50	.3062	.4861	.3217	.5075	3.1084	.4925	.9520	.9786	10	1.2595
.3142	18° 00′	.3090	9.4900	.3249	9.5118	3.0777	0.4882	.9511	9.9782	72° 00′	1.2566
		Value	Log Cosine	Value	Log Cotangent	Value	Log Tangent	Value	Log Sine	Degrees	Radians

TABLE 2 (*Continued*)

Radians	Degrees	Sine Value	Log	Tangent Value	Log	Cotangent Value	Log	Cosine Value	Log		
.3142	18° 00′	.3090	9.4900	.3249	9.5118	3.0777	0.4882	.9511	9.9782	72° 00′	1.2566
.3171	10	.3118	.4939	.3281	.5161	3.0475	.4839	.9502	.9778	50	1.2537
.3200	20	.3145	.4977	.3314	.5203	3.0178	.4797	.9492	.9774	40	1.2508
.3229	30	.3173	.5015	.3346	.5245	2.9887	.4755	.9483	.9770	30	1.2479
.3258	40	.3201	.5052	.3378	.5287	2.9600	.4713	.9474	.9765	20	1.2450
.3287	50	.3228	.5090	.3411	.5329	2.9319	.4671	.9465	.9761	10	1.2421
.3316	19° 00′	.3256	9.5126	.3443	9.5370	2.9042	0.4630	.9455	9.9757	71° 00′	1.2392
.3345	10	.3283	.5163	.3476	.5411	2.8770	.4589	.9446	.9752	50	1.2363
.3374	20	.3311	.5199	.3508	.5451	2.8502	.4549	.9436	.9748	40	1.2334
.3403	30	.3338	.5235	.3541	.5491	2.8239	.4509	.9426	.9743	30	1.2305
.3432	40	.3365	.5270	.3574	.5531	2.7980	.4469	.9417	.9739	20	1.2275
.3462	50	.3393	.5306	.3607	.5571	2.7725	.4429	.9407	.9734	10	1.2246
.3491	20° 00′	.3420	9.5341	.3640	9.5611	2.7475	0.4389	.9397	9.9730	70° 00′	1.2217
.3520	10	.3448	.5375	.3673	.5650	2.7228	.4350	.9387	.9725	50	1.2188
.3549	20	.3475	.5409	.3706	.5689	2.6985	.4311	.9377	.9721	40	1.2159
.3578	30	.3502	.5443	.3739	.5727	2.6746	.4273	.9367	.9716	30	1.2130
.3607	40	.3529	.5477	.3772	.5766	2.6511	.4234	.9356	.9711	20	1.2101
.3636	50	.3557	.5510	.3805	.5804	2.6279	.4196	.9346	.9706	10	1.2072
.3665	21° 00′	.3584	9.5543	.3839	9.5842	2.6051	0.4158	.9336	9.9702	69° 00′	1.2043
.3694	10	.3611	.5576	.3872	.5879	2.5826	.4121	.9325	.9697	50	1.2014
.3723	20	.3638	.5609	.3906	.5917	2.5605	.4083	.9315	.9692	40	1.1985
.3752	30	.3665	.5641	.3939	.5954	2.5386	.4046	.9304	.9687	30	1.1956
.3782	40	.3692	.5673	.3973	.5991	2.5172	.4009	.9293	.9682	20	1.1926
.3811	50	.3719	.5704	.4006	.6028	2.4960	.3972	.9283	.9677	10	1.1897
.3840	22° 00′	.3746	9.5736	.4040	9.6064	2.4751	0.3936	.9272	9.9672	68° 00′	1.1868
.3869	10	.3773	.5767	.4074	.6100	2.4545	.3900	.9261	.9667	50	1.1839
.3898	20	.3800	.5798	.4108	.6136	2.4342	.3864	.9250	.9661	40	1.1810
.3927	30	.3827	.5828	.4142	.6172	2.4142	.3828	.9239	.9656	30	1.1781
.3956	40	.3854	.5859	.4176	.6208	2.3945	.3792	.9228	.9651	20	1.1752
.3985	50	.3881	.5889	.4210	.6243	2.3750	.3757	.9216	.9646	10	1.1723
.4014	23° 00′	.3907	9.5919	.4245	9.6279	2.3559	0.3721	.9205	9.9640	67° 00′	1.1694
.4043	10	.3934	.5948	.4279	.6314	2.3369	.3686	.9194	.9635	50	1.1665
.4072	20	.3961	.5978	.4314	.6348	2.3183	.3652	.9182	.9629	40	1.1636
.4102	30	.3987	.6007	.4348	.6383	2.2998	.3617	.9171	.9624	30	1.1606
.4131	40	.4014	.6036	.4383	.6417	2.2817	.3583	.9159	.9618	20	1.1577
.4160	50	.4041	.6065	.4417	.6452	2.2637	.3548	.9147	.9613	10	1.1548
.4189	24° 00′	.4067	9.6093	.4452	9.6486	2.2460	0.3514	.9135	9.9607	66° 00′	1.1519
.4218	10	.4094	.6121	.4487	.6520	2.2286	.3480	.9124	.9602	50	1.1490
.4247	20	.4120	.6149	.4522	.6553	2.2113	.3447	.9112	.9596	40	1.1461
.4276	30	.4147	.6177	.4557	.6587	2.1943	.3413	.9100	.9590	30	1.1432
.4305	40	.4173	.6205	.4592	.6620	2.1775	.3380	.9088	.9584	20	1.1403
.4334	50	.4200	.6232	.4628	.6654	2.1609	.3346	.9075	.9579	10	1.1374
.4363	25° 00′	.4226	9.6259	.4663	9.6687	2.1445	0.3313	.9063	9.9573	65° 00′	1.1345
.4392	10	.4253	.6286	.4699	.6720	2.1283	.3280	.9051	.9567	50	1.1316
.4422	20	.4279	.6313	.4734	.6752	2.1123	.3248	.9038	.9561	40	1.1286
.4451	30	.4305	.6340	.4770	.6785	2.0965	.3215	.9026	.9555	30	1.1257
.4480	40	.4331	.6366	.4806	.6817	2.0809	.3183	.9013	.9549	20	1.1228
.4509	50	.4358	.6392	.4841	.6850	2.0655	.3150	.9001	.9543	10	1.1199
.4538	26° 00′	.4384	9.6418	.4877	9.6882	2.0503	0.3118	.8988	9.9537	64° 00′	1.1170
.4567	10	.4410	.6444	.4913	.6914	2.0353	.3086	.8975	.9530	50	1.1141
.4596	20	.4436	.6470	.4950	.6946	2.0204	.3054	.8962	.9524	40	1.1112
.4625	30	.4462	.6495	.4986	.6977	2.0057	.3023	.8949	.9518	30	1.1083
.4654	40	.4488	.6521	.5022	.7009	1.9912	.2991	.8936	.9512	20	1.1054
.4683	50	.4514	.6546	.5059	.7040	1.9768	.2960	.8923	.9505	10	1.1025
.4712	27° 00′	.4540	9.6570	.5095	9.7072	1.9626	0.2928	.8910	9.9499	63° 00′	1.0996
		Value	Log Cosine	Value	Log Cotangent	Value	Log Tangent	Value	Log Sine	Degrees	Radians

TABLE 2 (*Continued*)

Radians	Degrees	Sine Value	Log	Tangent Value	Log	Cotangent Value	Log	Cosine Value	Log		
.4712	27° 00′	.4540	9.6570	.5095	9.7072	1.9626	0.2928	.8910	9.9499	63° 00′	1.0996
.4741	10	.4566	.6595	.5132	.7103	1.9486	.2897	.8897	.9492	50	1.0966
.4771	20	.4592	.6620	.5169	.7134	1.9347	.2866	.8884	.9486	40	1.0937
.4800	30	.4617	.6644	.5206	.7165	1.9210	.2835	.8870	.9479	30	1.0908
.4829	40	.4643	.6668	.5243	.7196	1.9074	.2804	.8857	.9473	20	1.0879
.4858	50	.4669	.6692	.5280	.7226	1.8940	.2774	.8843	.9466	10	1.0850
.4887	28° 00′	.4695	9.6716	.5317	9.7257	1.8807	0.2743	.8829	9.9459	62° 00′	1.0821
.4916	10	.4720	.6740	.5354	.7287	1.8676	.2713	.8816	.9453	50	1.0792
.4945	20	.4746	.6763	.5392	.7317	1.8546	.2683	.8802	.9446	40	1.0763
.4974	30	.4772	.6787	.5430	.7348	1.8418	.2652	.8788	.9439	30	1.0734
.5003	40	.4797	.6810	.5467	.7378	1.8291	.2622	.8774	.9432	20	1.0705
.5032	50	.4823	.6833	.5505	.7408	1.8165	.2592	.8760	.9425	10	1.0676
.5061	29° 00′	.4848	9.6856	.5543	9.7438	1.8040	0.2562	.8746	9.9418	61° 00′	1.0647
.5091	10	.4874	.6878	.5581	.7467	1.7917	.2533	.8732	.9411	50	1.0617
.5120	20	.4899	.6901	.5619	.7497	1.7796	.2503	.8718	.9404	40	1.0588
.5149	30	.4924	.6923	.5658	.7526	1.7675	.2474	.8704	.9397	30	1.0559
.5178	40	.4950	.6946	.5696	.7556	1.7556	.2444	.8689	.9390	20	1.0530
.5207	50	.4975	.6968	.5735	.7585	1.7437	.2415	.8675	.9383	10	1.0501
.5236	30° 00′	.5000	9.6990	.5774	9.7614	1.7321	0.2386	.8660	9.9375	60° 00′	1.0472
.5265	10	.5025	.7012	.5812	.7644	1.7205	.2356	.8646	.9368	50	1.0443
.5294	20	.5050	.7033	.5851	.7673	1.7090	.2327	.8631	.9361	40	1.0414
.5323	30	.5075	.7055	.5890	.7701	1.6977	.2299	.8616	.9353	30	1.0385
.5352	40	.5100	.7076	.5930	.7730	1.6864	.2270	.8601	.9346	20	1.0356
.5381	50	.5125	.7097	.5969	.7759	1.6753	.2241	.8587	.9338	10	1.0327
.5411	31° 00′	.5150	9.7118	.6009	9.7788	1.6643	0.2212	.8572	9.9331	59° 00′	1.0297
.5440	10	.5175	.7139	.6048	.7816	1.6534	.2184	.8557	.9323	50	1.0268
.5469	20	.5200	.7160	.6088	.7845	1.6426	.2155	.8542	.9315	40	1.0239
.5498	30	.5225	.7181	.6128	.7873	1.6319	.2127	.8526	.9308	30	1.0210
.5527	40	.5250	.7201	.6168	.7902	1.6212	.2098	.8511	.9300	20	1.0181
.5556	50	.5275	.7222	.6208	.7930	1.6107	.2070	.8496	.9292	10	1.0152
.5585	32° 00′	.5299	9.7242	.6249	9.7958	1.6003	0.2042	.8480	9.9284	58° 00′	1.0123
.5614	10	.5324	.7262	.6289	.7986	1.5900	.2014	.8465	.9276	50	1.0094
.5643	20	.5348	.7282	.6330	.8014	1.5798	.1986	.8450	.9268	40	1.0065
.5672	30	.5373	.7302	.6371	.8042	1.5697	.1958	.8434	.9260	30	1.0036
.5701	40	.5398	.7322	.6412	.8070	1.5597	.1930	.8418	.9252	20	1.0007
.5730	50	.5422	.7342	.6453	.8097	1.5497	.1903	.8403	.9244	10	.9977
.5760	33° 00′	.5446	9.7361	.6494	9.8125	1.5399	0.1875	.8387	9.9236	57° 00′	.9948
.5789	10	.5471	.7380	.6536	.8153	1.5301	.1847	.8371	.9228	50	.9919
.5818	20	.5495	.7400	.6577	.8180	1.5204	.1820	.8355	.9219	40	.9890
.5847	30	.5519	.7419	.6619	.8208	1.5108	.1792	.8339	.9211	30	.9861
.5876	40	.5544	.7438	.6661	.8235	1.5013	.1765	.8323	.9203	20	.9832
.5905	50	.5568	.7457	.6703	.8263	1.4919	.1737	.8307	.9194	10	.9803
.5934	34° 00′	.5592	9.7476	.6745	9.8290	1.4826	0.1710	.8290	9.9186	56° 00′	.9774
.5963	10	.5616	.7494	.6787	.8317	1.4733	.1683	.8274	.9177	50	.9745
.5992	20	.5640	.7513	.6830	.8344	1.4641	.1656	.8258	.9169	40	.9716
.6021	30	.5664	.7531	.6873	.8371	1.4550	.1629	.8241	.9160	30	.9687
.6050	40	.5688	.7550	.6916	.8398	1.4460	.1602	.8225	.9151	20	.9657
.6080	50	.5712	.7568	.6959	.8425	1.4370	.1575	.8208	.9142	10	.9628
.6109	35° 00′	.5736	9.7586	.7002	9.8452	1.4281	0.1548	.8192	9.9134	55° 00′	.9599
.6138	10	.5760	.7604	.7046	.8479	1.4193	.1521	.8175	.9125	50	.9570
.6167	20	.5783	.7622	.7089	.8506	1.4106	.1494	.8158	.9116	40	.9541
.6196	30	.5807	.7640	.7133	.8533	1.4019	.1467	.8141	.9107	30	.9512
.6225	40	.5831	.7657	.7177	.8559	1.3934	.1441	.8124	.9098	20	.9483
.6254	50	.5854	.7675	.7221	.8586	1.3848	.1414	.8107	.9089	10	.9454
.6283	36° 00′	.5878	9.7692	.7265	9.8613	1.3764	0.1387	.8090	9.9080	54° 00′	.9425
		Value Cosine	Log	Value Cotangent	Log	Value Tangent	Log	Value Sine	Log	Degrees	Radians

TABLE 2 (*Continued*)

Radians	Degrees	Sine Value	Log	Tangent Value	Log	Cotangent Value	Log	Cosine Value	Log		
.6283	36° 00'	.5878	9.7692	.7265	9.8613	1.3764	0.1387	.8090	9.9080	54° 00'	.9425
.6312	10	.5901	.7710	.7310	.8639	1.3680	.1361	.8073	.9070	50	.9396
.6341	20	.5925	.7727	.7355	.8666	1.3597	.1334	.8056	.9061	40	.9367
.6370	30	.5948	.7744	.7400	.8692	1.3514	.1308	.8039	.9052	30	.9338
.6400	40	.5972	.7761	.7445	.8718	1.3432	.1282	.8021	.9042	20	.9308
.6429	50	.5995	.7778	.7490	.8745	1.3351	.1255	.8004	.9033	10	.9279
.6458	37° 00'	.6018	9.7795	.7536	9.8771	1.3270	0.1229	.7986	9.9023	53° 00'	.9250
.6487	10	.6041	.7811	.7581	.8797	1.3190	.1203	.7969	.9014	50	.9221
.6516	20	.6065	.7828	.7627	.8824	1.3111	.1176	.7951	.9004	40	.9192
.6545	30	.6088	.7844	.7673	.8850	1.3032	.1150	.7934	.8995	30	.9163
.6574	40	.6111	.7861	.7720	.8876	1.2954	.1124	.7916	.8985	20	.9134
.6603	50	.6134	.7877	.7766	.8902	1.2876	.1098	.7898	.8975	10	.9105
.6632	38° 00'	.6157	9.7893	.7813	9.8928	1.2799	0.1072	.7880	9.8965	52° 00'	.9076
.6661	10	.6180	.7910	.7860	.8954	1.2723	.1046	.7862	.8955	50	.9047
.6690	20	.6202	.7926	.7907	.8980	1.2647	.1020	.7844	.8945	40	.9018
.6720	30	.6225	.7941	.7954	.9006	1.2572	.0994	.7826	.8935	30	.8988
.6749	40	.6248	.7957	.8002	.9032	1.2497	.0968	.7808	.8925	20	.8959
.6778	50	.6271	.7973	.8050	.9058	1.2423	.0942	.7790	.8915	10	.8930
.6807	39° 00'	.6293	9.7989	.8098	9.9084	1.2349	0.0916	.7771	9.8905	51° 00'	.8901
.6836	10	.6316	.8004	.8146	.9110	1.2276	.0890	.7753	.8895	50	.8872
.6865	20	.6338	.8020	.8195	.9135	1 2203	.0865	.7735	.8884	40	.8843
.6894	30	.6361	.8035	.8243	.9161	1.2131	.0839	.7716	.8874	30	.8814
.6923	40	.6383	.8050	.8292	.9187	1.2059	.0813	.7698	.8864	20	.8785
.6952	50	.6406	.8066	.8342	.9212	1.1988	.0788	.7679	.8853	10	.8756
.6981	40° 00'	.6428	9.8081	.8391	9.9238	1.1918	0.0762	.7660	9.8843	50° 00'	.8727
.7010	10	.6450	.8096	.8441	.9264	1.1847	.0736	.7642	.8832	50	.8698
.7039	20	.6472	.8111	.8491	.9289	1.1778	.0711	.7623	.8821	40	.8668
.7069	30	.6494	.8125	.8541	.9315	1.1708	.0685	.7604	.8810	30	.8639
.7098	40	.6517	.8140	.8591	.9341	1.1640	.0659	.7585	.8800	20	.8610
.7127	50	.6539	.8155	.8642	.9366	1.1571	.0634	.7566	.8789	10	.8581
.7156	41° 00'	.6561	9.8169	.8693	9.9392	1.1504	0.0608	.7547	9.8778	49° 00'	.8552
.7185	10	.6583	.8184	.8744	.9417	1.1436	.0583	.7528	.8767	50	.8523
.7214	20	.6604	.8198	.8796	.9443	1.1369	.0557	.7509	.8756	40	.8494
.7243	30	.6626	.8213	.8847	.9468	1.1303	.0532	.7490	.8745	30	.8465
.7272	40	.6648	.8227	.8899	.9494	1.1237	.0506	.7470	.8733	20	.8436
.7301	50	.6670	.8241	.8952	.9519	1.1171	.0481	.7451	.8722	10	.8407
.7330	42° 00'	.6691	9.8255	.9004	9.9544	1.1106	0.0456	.7431	9.8711	48° 00'	.8378
.7359	10	.6713	.8269	.9057	.9570	1.1041	.0430	.7412	.8699	50	.8348
.7389	20	.6734	.8283	.9110	.9595	1.0977	.0405	.7392	.8688	40	.8319
.7418	30	.6756	.8297	.9163	.9621	1.0913	.0379	.7373	.8676	30	.8290
.7447	40	.6777	.8311	.9217	.9646	1.0850	.0354	.7353	.8665	20	.8261
.7476	50	.6799	.8324	.9271	.9671	1.0786	.0329	.7333	.8653	10	.8232
.7505	43° 00'	.6820	9.8338	.9325	9.9697	1.0724	0.0303	.7314	9.8641	47° 00'	.8203
.7534	10	.6841	.8351	.9380	.9722	1.0661	.0278	.7294	.8629	50	.8174
.7563	20	.6862	.8365	.9435	.9747	1.0599	.0253	.7274	.8618	40	.8145
.7592	30	.6884	.8378	.9490	.9772	1.0538	.0228	.7254	.8606	30	.8116
.7621	40	.6905	.8391	.9545	.9798	1.0477	.0202	.7234	.8594	20	.8087
.7650	50	.6926	.8405	.9601	.9823	1.0416	.0177	.7214	.8582	10	.8058
.7679	44° 00'	.6947	9.8418	.9657	9.9848	1.0355	0.0152	.7193	9.8569	46° 00'	.8029
.7709	10	.6967	.8431	.9713	.9874	1.0295	.0126	.7173	.8557	50	.7999
.7738	20	.6988	.8444	.9770	.9899	1.0235	.0101	.7153	.8545	40	.7970
.7767	30	.7009	.8457	.9827	.9924	1.0176	.0076	.7133	.8532	30	.7941
.7796	40	.7030	.8469	.9884	.9949	1.0117	.0051	.7112	.8520	20	.7912
.7825	50	.7050	.8482	.9942	9.9975	1.0058	0.0025	.7092	.8507	10	.7883
.7854	45° 00'	.7071	9.8495	1.0000	0.0000	1.0000	0.0000	.7071	9.8495	45° 00'	.7854
		Value	Log Cosine	Value	Log Cotangent	Value	Log Tangent	Value	Log Sine	Degrees	Radians

Answers to Odd-Numbered Exercises

SECTION 1-1, PAGE 3

1. $\{1, 2, 3, 6\}$.
3. (a) $A \cup B = A$.   (b) $A \cap B = B$.
    (c) $D \cup C = \{3, 7, 11, 5, 10, 15, 20, 25, \ldots\}$.
    (d) $D \cap C = \phi$.   (e) $A \cup C = \{1, 2, 3, 4, 5, 6, 7, 11\}$.
    (f) $A \cap C = \{3\}$.
5. (a) 2.   (b) 4.   (c) 8.   (d) 16.   (e) 2^n.
7. (a) $S \cap W = \{2\}$.   (b) $S \cap T = \phi$.   (c) $T \cap W = \{3\}$.
    (d) $S \cup W = \{1, 2, 3, 4, 6\}$.   (e) $T \cup W = \{1, 2, 3, 5, 7\}$.
9. (a) False.   (b) True.   (c) False.   (d) True.   (e) False.   (f) True.
11. $n(S \cup T) = a + b - c = n(S) + n(T) - n(S \cap T)$.   Notice that $a + b$ "counts" the number of elements in the intersection twice so this number must be subtracted once.

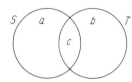

Ex. 11

13. Let S be the set that liked vanilla, T the set that liked chocolate, $n(S)$ the percentage that liked vanilla, and $n(T)$ the percentage that liked chocolate. $n(S) = 58$, $n(T) = 62$, and $n(S \cup T) = 87$. Notice that 25 percent ate only vanilla and 29 percent ate only chocolate (of this combination).

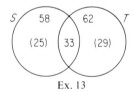

Ex. 13

15. (a) 46.   (b) 264.   (c) 152.

SECTION 1-3, PAGE 9

1. By the definition of division, $x \div 0$ is meaningless if $x \neq 0$ since there is no number times zero with product x, and if $x = 0$ there is more than one number times zero with product x.
3. (a) -13.   (b) $2/3$.   (c) $\sqrt{3}$.   (d) 0.
5. (a) 11.   (b) 1.   (c) 1.   (d) 0.   (e) $\sqrt{3}$.

SECTION 1-4, PAGE 13

1. $\{x \mid x < 12\}$.
3. $\{x \mid -3 < x < 3/2\}$.

5. $\{x \mid -1/2 < x < 7/3\}$.
7. $\{x \mid -1/5 < x < 33/87\}$; $\{x \mid x < -5/4\}$.
9. $\{x \mid -18/7 < x < -6/7\}$.
11. The set of all real numbers.
13. $\{x \mid 0 < x < 1\}$.
15. $7x + 12y \leq 20{,}000$.
17. 60 miles is the minimum mileage for truck A.

SECTION 2-1, PAGE 17

3. (a) $A(-3, -1)$, $B(2, 5)$, $C(5, 5/2)$
$$|AB| = \sqrt{(-3 - 2)^2 + (-1 - 5)^2} = \sqrt{61}$$
$$|BC| = \frac{\sqrt{61}}{2} \quad \text{and} \quad |AC| = \frac{\sqrt{305}}{2}.$$

(b) $|AB|^2 + |BC|^2 = 61 + \dfrac{61}{4} = \dfrac{305}{4} = |AC|^2$.

(c) Area $= \dfrac{1}{2}\sqrt{61} \cdot \dfrac{\sqrt{61}}{2} = \dfrac{61}{4}$.

7. $A(3, 0)$, $B(5, 6)$, $C(6, -1)$
$$|AB| = \sqrt{40}, \ |BC| = \sqrt{50}, \ |AC| = \sqrt{10}$$
$$|AB|^2 + |AC|^2 = 40 + 10 = 50 = |BC|^2$$
Area $= \dfrac{1}{2}|AB\|AC| = \dfrac{1}{2}\sqrt{40} \cdot \sqrt{10} = 10$.

SECTION 2-2, PAGE 25

1. (a) Yes. (b) $\{2, 3, 4\}$. (c) $\{7, 8, 2\}$.
3. (a) No. (b) $\{3\}$. (c) Set of real numbers.
5. (a) Yes. (b) Set of real numbers. (c) $\{t \mid t \geq 4\}$.
7. (a) Yes. (b) $\{x \mid x \geq -11/3\}$. (c) $\{y \mid y \geq 0\}$.
9. (a) Yes. (b) $\{x \mid x > 5/3\} \cup \{x \mid x \leq -1/2\}$.
   (c) $\{y \mid y \geq 0 \text{ and } y \neq 2/3\}$.
11. (a) 13. (b) 16/27. (c) $(t - 2)(t + 7)$. (d) $t + 7$.
13. (a) $x = -3$. (b) $x > -3$.

SECTION 2-3, PAGE 28

1. Yes; $f^{-1} = \{(7, 3), (8, 5), (2, 11)]$.
3. Yes; $f^{-1}(x) = x$.
5. Yes; $f^{-1}(x) = \dfrac{x - 11}{6}$.
7. No.

9. Yes; $f^{-1}(x) = \dfrac{x^2 + 3}{2}$ where $x \geq 0$.

11. Yes; $f^{-1}(x) = \dfrac{1}{x - 1}$ for $x \neq 1$ and $f^{-1}(1) = 0$.

13. (a) $f^{-1}(x) = \dfrac{ax + b}{cx - a}$.

   (b) The graph of f is symmetric to the graph of the identity function.

SECTION 2-4, PAGE 32

1. (b) Zero.   5. $f(x) = \dfrac{-2}{5}x + 6$.

7. (a) $t = -18$.   (b) $(-18, -65)$.

SECTION 2-6, PAGE 41

1. Increases on the set of all real numbers.
3. Increasing: $\{x \mid x > -3\}$. Decreasing: $\{x \mid x < -3\}$.
5. Increasing: $\{x \mid x > 1/6\}$. Decreasing: $\{x \mid x < 1/6\}$.
7. $x = -1 + \sqrt{3}$ and $x = -1 - \sqrt{3}$.
9. (a) If $h = f + g$, then $h(x) = 10x + 7$. Reals.
   (b) $h(x) = f(x)g(x) = 21x^2 + 53x - 8$. Reals.

   (c) $h(x) = \dfrac{7x - 1}{3x + 8}$. Reals except $x = -8/3$.

   (d) $h(x) = \dfrac{3x + 8}{7x - 1}$. Reals except $x = 1/7$.

   (e) $f(g(x)) = 21x + 55$. Reals.
   (f) $g(f(x)) = 21x + 5$. Reals.
11. (a) $f + g = \{(x, x^2 + 5x)\}$. Domain: Set of reals. Range: $\{x \mid x \geq -25/4\}$.
   (b) $h(x) = 3x^3 + 5x^2 + x - 1$. Domain: Set of reals.

   (c) $h(x) = \dfrac{3x - 1}{x^2 + 2x + 1}$. Domain: $\{x \mid x \neq -1\}$.

   (d) $h(x) = \dfrac{x^2 + 2x + 1}{3x - 1}$. Domain: $\{x \mid x \neq 1/3\}$.

   (e) $f(g(x)) = 3x^2 + 6x + 2$. Domain: Set of reals. Range: $\{x \mid x \geq -1\}$.
   (f) $g(f(x)) = 9x^2$. Domain: Set of reals. Range: $\{x \mid x \geq 0\}$.

SECTION 3-1, PAGE 44

1. (a) Neither.   (b) Arithmetic: $d = 7$.   (c) Geometric: $r = 3$.

   (d) Arithmetic: $d = 3$.　(e) Neither.　(f) Geometric: $r = 1/2$.
   (g) Arithmetic: $d = 8$.　(h) Geometric: $r = 2$.
3. $0, 1, 0, 1, 0, 1, 0, 1, 0, 1$; $t_{50} = 1$.

SECTION 3-2, PAGE 53

1. $t_5 = 17$; 124.　　　　　　　　　　3. $t_{30} = 148$; 8,732.

5. $t_3 = (1.6)^3$; $\dfrac{1.6^{13} - 1.6}{0.6}$.

SECTION 3-3, PAGE 55

1. Change at the smallest value of k for which $\dfrac{1}{n - k + 1} \geq \dfrac{2}{n}$.

3. $t_{10} = \dfrac{-1}{243}$, $s_{10} \approx 60.8$, $S = 60.75$.

5. $x = \dfrac{C}{\dfrac{(1 + i)^n - 1}{i}}$, \$17,500 per year.

SECTION 4-2, PAGE 65

1. $-19/3$.　　　　　　　　　3. $5/3$.
5. $1/6$.　　　　　　　　　　7. $1/16$.
9. $1/3t^{2/3}$.　　　　　　　　11. $-3/2t^{5/2}$.
13. 2.71828.

SECTION 4-3, PAGE 72

1. $3t^2$.

3. $\dfrac{1}{2} t^{-1/2}$.

5. $-\dfrac{1}{2} t^{-3/2}$.

7. (a) $\dfrac{t^2 - 1}{t^2}$.　(b) $t = 1$, $t = -1$.　(c) $\{t \mid -1 < t < 1\}$.
   (d) $\{t \mid t > 1\} \cup \{t \mid t < -1\}$.
9. (a) $f'(t) = 8t^2 + 36t + 36$.　(b) $t = -3$, $t = -3/2$.
   (c) $\{t \mid -3 < t < -3/2\}$.　(d) $\{t \mid t < -3\} \cup \{t \mid t > -3/2\}$.
11. Approximately 7.

SECTION 5-1, PAGE 75

1. $f'(x) = 36x^2 + 5 \quad f'(2) = 149.$
3. $f'(x) = 20x^3 - 26x \quad f'(2) = 108.$

5. $f'(x) = \dfrac{5}{2}x^4 \quad f'(2) = 40.$

7. (a) $x = 0.$ (b) $\phi.$ (c) $\{x \mid x \neq 0\}.$
9. (a) $f'(x)$ is never zero. (b) $\phi.$ (c) Set of real numbers.
11. (a) $x = 6, x = -1.$ (b) $-1 < x < 6.$ (c) $x < -1$ or $x > 6.$
13. $f'(x) = 9(3x + 5)^2.$
15. $f'(x) = 3$ for $x = 2/3$ or $x = 2.$
17. $x \approx 208.$

SECTION 5-2, PAGE 77

1. $f'(x) = (x^2 + 3x + 5)(2x - 3) + (x^2 - 3x + 7)(2x + 3) =$
   $4x^3 + 6x + 6.$
3. $f'(x) = 2(x^3 + 7x^2 + 3x + 11)(3x^2 + 14x + 3).$
5. $f'(x) = 3(3x^5 + 7x^2 - 2)^2(15x^4 + 14x).$
7. (a) If $h = uvwz = (uvw)z$, then $h' = (uvw)'z + (uvw)z'$. Using the formula for the derivative of the product of three functions, $h' = [uvw' + uv'w + u'vw]z + uvwz' = u'vwz + uv'wz + uvw'z + uvwz'.$
   (b) $h'(x) = (2)(3x^2 + 11)(5x - 11)(x^3 + 7) + (2x + 3)(6x)(5x - 11) \cdot (x^3 + 7) + (2x + 3)(3x^2 + 11)(5)(x^3 + 7) + (2x + 3)(3x^2 + 11) \cdot (5x - 11)(3x^2).$
   (c) Let $v = u$, $w = u$, and $z = u$ in part a.
   (d) $h'(x) = 4(3x^3 + 7x + 2)^3(9x^2 + 7).$

SECTION 5-3, PAGE 82

1. $f'(x) = -1/x^2.$

3. $f'(x) = \dfrac{x^2 + 6x + 5}{(x + 3)^2}; f'(x) = 0$ where $x = -5$ or $x = -1.$
   $f'(x) > 0$ where $x > -1$ or $x < -5.$ $f'(x) < 0$ where $-5 < x < -1,$
   except $x = -3.$

5. $f'(x) = \dfrac{x^4 + 10x^2 + 10x - 7}{(x^2 + 1)^2}.$

7. $f'(x) = \dfrac{-13}{(2x - 1)^2}.$

9. $P'(x) = \dfrac{F}{x^2} - \dfrac{P_0}{(x + 1)^2}.$

SECTION 5-4, PAGE 85

1. Assume $p = q/r$; then $h(x) = [g(x)]^{q/r}$ and $[h(x)]^r = [g(x)]^q$. Differentiating both sides, $r[h(x)]^{r-1} h'(x) = q[g(x)]^{q-1} g'(x)$. Thus $h'(x) = \frac{q}{r} \frac{[g(x)]^{q-1}}{[h(x)]^{r-1}} g'(x)$. But $[h(x)]^{r-1} = \{[g(x)]^{q/r}\}^{r-1} = [g(x)]^{q-q/r}$. Hence

$$h'(x) = \frac{q}{r} \frac{[g(x)]^{q-1}}{[g(x)]^{q-q/r}} g'(x) = \frac{q}{r} [g(x)]^{q/r-1} g'(x) = p[g(x)]^{p-1} g'(x).$$

3. $t'(x) = (x^2 + 1)^{1/2}(4x^2 + 1)$.

5. $h'(x) = \dfrac{x - 2}{(x^2 + 1)^{1/2}(2x + 1)^2}$.

7. $g'(x) = \dfrac{2x(6x^3 + 1)}{(3x^3 + 1)^{1/3}}$.

9. $f'(x) = 2[(x^2 + 1)^{1/2} + 7x][x(x^2 + 1)^{-1/2} + 7]$.

11. $f'(x) = 5x(5x + 7)^{-1/2}/2 + (5x + 7)^{1/2} = (15x + 14)/2 \sqrt{5x + 7}$.

SECTION 5-5, PAGE 88

1. $f'(x) = 30x^{29}$, $f''(x) = (30)(29)x^{28}$, $f^{(4)}(x) = (30)(29)(28)(27)x^{26}$, $f^{(30)}(x) = 30!$, $f^{(31)}(x) = 0$.

3. (a) $f'(x) = \dfrac{9x^2 - 6xf(x) - 6x^2 f(x) + 2}{3x^2 + 2x^3}$.

 (b) $y' = \dfrac{9x^4 - 8x^3 + 336x^2 + 342x}{3x^2 + 2x^3}$.

5. $q = \sqrt{\dfrac{2C_2 D}{C_3 + C_4}}$.

7. (a) $R'(t) = -875{,}000/t^2$; $M'(t) = 75 + 1600t$. (b) $t = 9$ is the best integer solution. (c) $t = 1.05$ years.

9. $f''(x) = 12f(x)f'(x)/(3[f(x)]^2 - 6xf(x) - 1)$.

SECTION 6-2, PAGE 96

1. (a) $x > 0$. (b) $x < 0$. (c) None. (d) ϕ. (e) All reals.

3. (a) $x < 0$; $x > 2$. (b) $0 < x < 2$. (c) $(1, -2)$. (d) $x > 1$. (e) $x < 1$.

5. (a) $x < \dfrac{-5 - \sqrt{73}}{6}$; $x > \dfrac{-5 + \sqrt{73}}{6}$.

 (b) $\dfrac{-5 - \sqrt{73}}{6} < x < \dfrac{-5 + \sqrt{73}}{6}$.

(c) $(-5/6, 539/54)$. (d) $x > -5/6$. (e) $x < -5/6$.

7. (a) $x < 0$; $x > 7/6$. (b) $0 < x < 7/6$. (c) $(7/12, 343/5184)$.
   (d) $x > 7/12$. (e) $x < 7/12$.

SECTION 6-3, PAGE 108

1. (a) $x < -1; x > 6$. (b) $-1 < x < 6$. (c) $(5/2, f(5/2))$.
   (d) $x > 5/2$. (e) $x < 5/2$. (f) $f(-1)$. (g) $f(6)$. (h) None.
   (i) None.
3. (a) $x < -5/3; x > 1/2$. (b) $-5/3 < x < 1/2$.
   (c) $(-7/12, f(-7/12))$. (d) $x > -7/12$. (e) $x < -7/12$.
   (f) $f(-5/3)$. (g) $f(1/2)$. (h) None. (i) None.
5. (a) $x > \sqrt{2}; x < -\sqrt{2}$. (b) $-\sqrt{2} < x < \sqrt{2}$.
   (c) None. (d) $x > 0$. (e) $x < 0$. (f) $f(-\sqrt{2})$.
   (g) $f(\sqrt{2})$. (h) None. (i) None.
7. (a) $3 < x < 49/16$. (b) $x > 49/16$. (c) None.
   (d) $\emptyset$. (e) $x > 3$. (f) $-47/8$. (g) None.
   (h) $f(49/16)$. (i) None.
9. (a) $x < -11/3; x > -11/3$. (b) $\emptyset$. (c) None. (d) $x < -11/3$.
   (e) $x > -11/3$. (f) None. (g) None. (h) None. (i) None.
11. (a) $x < -1/3; x > 29/9$. (b) $-1/3 < x < 29/9$.
    (c) $(13/9, f(13/9))$. (d) $x > 13/9$. (e) $x < 13/9$. (f) $f(-1/3)$.
    (g) $f(29/9)$. (h) None. (i) None.
13. Row to a point on the shore $\sqrt{3}$ miles from the nearest point on shore then walk to destination.

15. Radius $\dfrac{R\sqrt{6}}{3}$; height $\dfrac{2R\sqrt{3}}{3}$.

21. 7 stories.

SECTION 6-5, PAGE 113

1. $\sqrt{19/3}$.
3. 1.
5. $4/3$.
7. HINT: Derivative of sum is sum of derivatives.

9. $\dfrac{1}{4}x^4 + C$.

11. $\dfrac{5}{4}x^{12/5} + C$.

13. $\dfrac{4}{3}x^3 + \dfrac{5}{2}x^2 - 11x + C$.

15. $\dfrac{1}{12}(3x + 5)^4 + C$.

17. $\dfrac{1}{16}(2x + 1)^{16} + C$.

19. $\dfrac{2}{5}(x^2 + 4)^{5/2} + C$.

21. $\dfrac{1}{14}(3x^2 + 4)^{7/3} + C$.

23. $\dfrac{1}{6}(3x^2 + 4x - 13)^6 + C$.

SECTION 6-6, PAGE 116

1. 25π.

SECTION 6-7, PAGE 119

1. $dy = 3x^2\,dx$.
3. $dy = (x^2 + 3)^{-1/2}(2x^2 + 3)\,dx$.
5. (a) 27.324 cc. (b) 27.325297728.
7. (a) 5.0267. (b) 33.04.
9. 3.24.

SECTION 6-8, PAGE 122

1. 2.01341 (correct to nearest five places).
3. 1.030 (correct to nearest three places).

SECTION 7-1, PAGE 129

1.

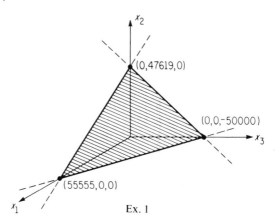

Ex. 1

3.

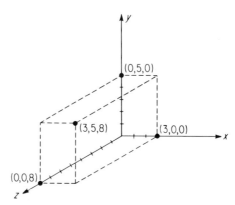

Ex. 3

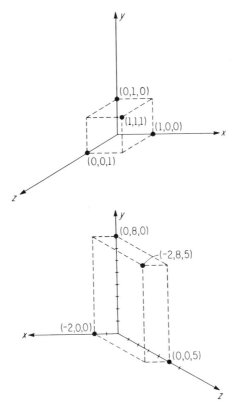

Ex. 3 (*continued*)

5. (a) $\sqrt{21}$. (b) $(3, -1, 13/2)$.
7.

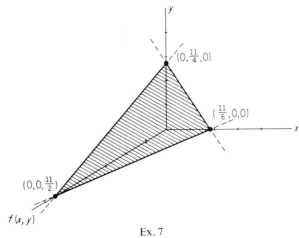

Ex. 7

9. Paraboloid of revolution about the $f(x,y)$-axis with vertex at $(0,0,-2)$.

SECTION 7-2, PAGE 132

	f_x	f_y	f_{xx}	f_{yy}	f_{xy} and f_{yx}
1.	$2x + 7$	$6y$	2	6	0
3.	$2xy^3 + 6$	$3x^2y^2 + 5$	$2y^3$	$6x^2y$	$6xy^2$
5.	$3x^2y - 6xy^2 + 7$	$x^3 - 6x^2y - 5$	$6xy - 6y^2$	$-6x^2$	$3x^2 - 12xy$

SECTION 7-3, PAGE 134

1. $\dfrac{1}{2}\left(\dfrac{2C_2D}{C_3}\right)^{1/2}\left(\dfrac{h}{C_2} + \dfrac{t}{C_3}\right).$ 3. 16 cu in.

5. (a) 16.25526.   (b) 16.256.

SECTION 7-4, PAGE 143

1. No maximum; minimum at $x = -y$.
3. No maximum or minimum.
5. Base: 10.64 in. by 10.64 in.; height: 5.32 in.
7. $p_1 = 80$; $p_2 = 90$.

SECTION 7-5, PAGE 152

1. $x = y = 500$.   3. (a) $x = y$; $\lambda = 2$. (b) $x = y = 4$.
5. Maximum at $x = y = z = 36$; maximum is $(36)^3$.

SECTION 8-1, PAGE 156

1. $g'(5) = 1/3$.   3. $g'(5) = 1/4$.
5. $g'(5) = 5/2$.   7. $g'(5) = -23/49$.
9. $g'(5) = -26/121$.   11. $g'(5) = 1/6$.
13. $g'(5) = 1/6$.

SECTION 8-2, PAGE 164

1. 0.0531.   3. $3e^{3x}$.
5. $2xe^{x^2}$.   7. $f(x) = x \ln x$, $\quad f'(x) = 1 + \ln x$.
9. $e^{1/x}(2x - 1)$.   11. $\dfrac{2 - \ln x^2}{x^2}$.

13. $-\ln x$.   15. $\dfrac{2}{x \log_e 10}$.

SECTION 8-4, PAGE 170

1. (See text for trig table.)
5. Note that $|x - y| = \pi/2$ if and only if $\tan x = -1/\tan y$.

SECTION 8-5, PAGE 172

1. $\tan x \sec x$.

3. $\csc^2 x$.

5. $\sin 2x - \dfrac{\cos x}{2\sqrt{1 - \sin x}}$.

7. $3 \sec^2 3x$.

9. $-\sin 6x$.

11. $[-\sin (\sin x)] \cos x$.

13. 0.

15. $-3 \sin x \sin 3x + \cos x \cos 3x$.

SECTION 8-6, PAGE 175

Inflection at $x =$	Maximum at $x =$	Minimum at $x =$	Concave Upward	Concave Downward
1. $\pi/4, 5\pi/4$	$3\pi/4$	$7\pi/4$	$(0, \pi/4)$ $(5\pi/4, 2\pi)$	$(\pi/4, 5\pi/4)$
3. π	2π	0	$\pi < x < 2\pi$	$0 < x < \pi$
5. $\pi/2, 3\pi/2$	$7\pi/6$	$11\pi/6$	$(0, \pi/2)$ $(3\pi/2, 2\pi)$	$\pi/2 < x < 3\pi/2$

7. Acute angle: $53° 10'$ approx.
9. 0.4794.

SECTION 9-1, PAGE 181

1. (a) 84. (b) 98. (c) $91 - 49/n$. (d) $91 + 49/n$.
   (e) For "large" n, $49/n$ is "close" to zero, and both $91 - 49/n$ and $91 + 49/n$ are "close" to 91.
3. Show that $U(P, f) = \sum_{k=1}^{n} \dfrac{4}{n}\left(2 + k\,\dfrac{4}{n}\right)^2$ and use summation properties.
5. Since the maximum value of f on each interval in the right-hand end point, the summation $U(P, f) - L(P, f)$ will telescope and leave $f(b) - f(a)$.

SECTION 9-3, PAGE 192

1. $27/2$.

3. $-49/10$.

5. $14/3$.

7. $1023/5$.

9. $259/8$.

11. $7/3$.

13. Incorrect: $f(x) = x^{-2}$ is not continuous (or defined) at $x = 0$. Therefore it cannot be integrated over an interval containing 0. There are several arithmetic errors.

15. Note that $\int_{-a}^{0} f = -\int_{0}^{a} f$. By Theorem 9-3,

$$\int_{-a}^{a} f = \int_{-a}^{0} f + \int_{0}^{a} f = -\int_{0}^{a} f + \int_{0}^{a} f = 0.$$

17. 27/6.

19. 315/4.

21. 36.

23. $2x(x^2 - x^4)^n + \int_{x}^{x^2} n(x^2 - t^2)^{n-1} 2x \, dt = 2x(x^2 - x^4)$

$$+ 2nx^3(x^2 - x^4)^{n-1} - 2nx(x^2 - x^4)^{n-1}$$

SECTION 10-1, PAGE 198

1. $2/9(3x + 1)^{3/2} + C.$

3. $\dfrac{2\sqrt{3}}{15}(x - 2)^{3/2}(3x + 4) + C.$

5. $\dfrac{1}{14}(x^2 - 2x)^7 + C.$

7. $\dfrac{1}{40}(3x + 1)^{5/3}(5x - 1) + C.$

9. $\ln(\ln x) + C.$

11. $\dfrac{x^2}{2} + \dfrac{2}{15}(x + 1)^{3/2}(3x + 8) + C.$

13. $\dfrac{1}{3 \ln 2} 2^{x^3} + C.$

15. $\dfrac{2}{3}(x + 1)^{1/2}(x - 2) + C.$

SECTION 10-2, PAGE 202

1. $\dfrac{2}{27}(3x + 1)^{1/2}(3x - 2) + C.$

3. $\dfrac{1}{21}(x - 4)^6(3x + 2) + C.$

5. $\dfrac{x^2}{4}(2 \ln x - 1) + C.$

7. $-e^{-x}[x^2 + 2x + 2] + C.$

9. $\dfrac{x^3}{27}[(3 \ln x - 1)^2 + 1] + C.$

11. $x \sin x + \cos x + C.$

13. $\dfrac{e^x}{2}[\sin x + \cos x] + C.$

15. $\dfrac{e^x}{2}[\sin x - \cos x] + C.$

SECTION 10-3, PAGE 207

1. $\dfrac{1}{4} \ln\left(\dfrac{x - 3}{x + 5}\right) + C.$

3. $\dfrac{1}{46} \ln \dfrac{(3x + 7)^{24}}{2x - 3} + C.$

5. $\ln[(x + 5)^3(x^2 + x + 1)] + C.$

7. $-\dfrac{1}{4}(2x + 5)^{-2} + C.$

SECTION 10-4, PAGE 210

1. $\dfrac{1}{34} \arctan \dfrac{x}{2} + \dfrac{1}{17} \ln \dfrac{(2x + 1)^2}{(x^2 + 4)} + C.$

3. $\dfrac{1}{3} \arctan \dfrac{x}{3} + C.$

SECTION 11-1, PAGE 213

1. -2.
5. $3/4$.
9. Does not exist.

3. No limit.
7. $1/2$.

SECTION 11-2, PAGE 216

1. 0.
5. $-\infty$.
9. 0.
13. $1/e$.

3. $+\infty$.
7. 0.
11. 0.

SECTION 11-3, PAGE 220

1. Converges to $1/2$.
3. Diverges.
5. Let $f(x) = x$.

SECTION 12-2, PAGE 226

1. $y = C(3x)^{1/3}$.
3. $\ln y = e^{-x}(x + 1) + C$.
5. $y = \dfrac{1}{1 - Cx}$.

SECTION 12-3, PAGE 230

1. $y = \left(\dfrac{1 - Cx^3}{3Cx}\right)^{1/3}$.
3. $\ln x = \dfrac{2x}{x + y} + C$.
5. $y = x \ln x + Cx$.

SECTION 12-4, PAGE 232

1. $y = \dfrac{C - x^2}{2e^x + 12}$.

3. $x^3 y + xy^2 = C$.

SECTION 12-5, PAGE 233

1. $y = \dfrac{x^3}{4} + \dfrac{C}{x}$.
5. $y = \dfrac{x^2}{3} + 2 + \dfrac{C}{x}$.

3. $y = 1 + Ce^{-x^3/3}$.

Index

Absolute maximum, 34, 135
Absolute minimum, 33, 135
Absolute value, 10
Angle of inclination, 168
Antiderivative, 112
Approximations
    differentials, 113
    Newton's method, 116
    Taylor's polynomials, 119
Arithmetic sequence, 43
Arithmetic series, 45

Bar graph, 21
Base
    of exponential function, 157
    of logarithm function, 158
    of natural logarithm function, 160
Boundary conditions, 223
Break-even point, 27

Cartesian coordinate system, 15, 123
Chain rule, 83
Closed interval, 10
Closure, 5
Common difference, 43
Common ratio, 44
Completeness property, 9
Composition of functions, 40
Concave
    downward, 93
    upward, 93
Concavity, 93
Constant function, 29
Continuous function, 64
Continuous interest, 162
Coordinate
    on a line, 5
    in a plane, 15
    in three-dimensions, 124
Coordinate axis, 15, 124

Decision variable, 21
Decreasing function, 34, 91
Definite integral, 182, 184
Dependent variable, 19

Depreciation, 48, 49
Derivative, 58, 66
Derived function, 58
Difference, 5
    of functions, 39
Differential, 113
Differential equations, 221
    exact, 230
    first order linear, 232
    homogeneous, 226
    order of, 221
    ordinary, 221
    partial, 222
    separable, 224
Differentiation, 58
    implicit, 87
    of the inverse of a function, 153
    Leibnitz's rule, 191
    notation for, 85
    theorems on, 73–83
    of the trigonometric functions, 171
Directly proportional, 31
Discontinuous, 64
Discounting, 50
Disjoint sets, 2
Distance
    on a line, 10
    in a plane, 16
    in three-dimensions, 125
Domain, 18

Economic lot size, 82
Elements of a set, 1
Empty set, 2
End-point extrema, 100
Equality of sets, 1
Even function, 25
Exact differential equation, 230
Exponential functions, 157

Field properties, 7
First coordinate, 15
    axis, 15
First-order linear differential equation, 232
Function, 19
    constant, 29

Function (*continued*)
  even, 25
  exponential, 157
  homogeneous, 226
  inverse, 26
  linear, 29
  logarithm, 158
  odd, 25
  of one variable, 23
  quadratic, 33
  trigonometric, 165
  of two variables, 23, 123
Fundamental theorem of calculus, 185
Future value, 50

General solution, 223
Geometric sequence, 44
Geometric series, 45
  infinite, 54
Graph
  bar, 21
  line, 23
  on a line, 10
  of a relation, 18
Greater than, 8
Greatest lower bound, 14

Half-open interval, 10
Higher order derivatives, 85
Homogeneous differential equation, 227
Homogeneous function, 226

Identity function, 24
Implicit differentiation, 87
Improper integral, 218
Increasing function, 34, 90
Indefinite integral, 112
Independent variable, 19
Indeterminate form, 216
Inequalities, 8, 12
Infinite limits, 213
Inflection point, 96
Initial conditions, 222
Integrating factor, 233
Integration
  by partial fractions, 202
  by parts, 198
  by substitution, 193
Intersection of sets, 2
Interval, 10
Inventory theory, 79
Inverse function, 26
Inverse relation, 26
Irrational number, 6

Lagrange function, 145
Lagrange multiplier, 145
Learning curve, 70

Least upper bound, 9
Left-hand coordinate system, 125
Leibnitz's rule, 191
Less than, 7
L'Hôpital's rules, 211, 215
Limit, 59
  definition, 59
  infinite, 213
  theorems, 60–62, 211, 215
Line graph, 23
Linear function, 29
Local maxima, 97
Local minima, 97
Logarithm function, 158
Lower bound, 14
Lower sum, 177

Mapping, 21
Maximum, 34, 135
  with constraints, 144
Mean value theorem, 110
Members of a set, 1
Midpoint
  on a line, 10
  in a plane, 17
  in three-dimensions, 126
Minimum, 34, 135
  with constraints, 144
Monotonic, 34

Natural logarithm function, 160
Newton quotient, 58
Newton's method, 116

Odd function, 25
Open interval, 10
Order, 7
Ordered pair, 15
Ordinary differential equation, 221

Parabola of revolution, 127
Partial derivatives, 130
Partial differential equation, 222
Partial fractions, 202–207
Partial sum, 45
Particular solutions, 223
Partition, 176
Present value, 50
Prime numbers, 1
Product of functions, 39
Proper subset, 2
Properties of inequalities, 12

Quadratic function, 33
Quotient, 6
  of functions, 39

Radian measure, 165
Range, 18
Rate of change, 68
Rational numbers, 6
Rational operations, 6
Rational point, 6
Real decision variable, 21
Real function, 19
Real numbers, 4, 6
Relations, 18
Relative maximum, 97
Relative minimum, 97
Riemann integral, 182, 184
Right-hand coordinate system, 125
Rolle's theorem, 110

Saddle point, 136
Second coordinate, 15
    axis, 15
Separable equations, 224
Sequence, 43
    arithmetic, 43
    finite, 43
    geometric, 44
Series, 45
    arithmetic, 45
    geometric, 45
Set, 1
    operation, 2
Sigma notation, 51
Slope, 31, 57
Solution of a differential equation, 221
Solution set, 11
Stationary point, 91
Straight-line method, 49
Strictly monotonic, 34

Subset, 2
Substitution technique, 193
Sum of functions, 39
Summation notation, 51

Taylor's formula, 121
Taylor's polynomials, 120
Telescoping property, 52
Term of a sequence, 43
Total differential, 132
Transitive property, 8
Triangular inequality, 11
Trichotomy property, 8
Trigonometric functions, 165

Unequal sets, 1
Union of sets, 2
Universal set, 2
Upper bound, 8
Upper sum, 177

Value of decision, 19
Variable, 2
    cost, 27
Venn diagram, 3

x-axis, 15
x-coordinate, 124

y-axis, 15
y-coordinate, 124
y-intercept, 31

z-axis, 124
z-coordinate, 124
zero, division by, 6